Advanced Energy
Design Guide
for
Large Hospitals

*This publication was prepared under the auspices of ASHRAE Special Project 136
and was supported with funding from DOE through NREL subcontract # AGN-1-11923.*

PROJECT COMMITTEE

Shanti Pless
Chair

Merle McBride
Vice-Chair

Mara Baum
AIA Representative

Ray Pradinuk
AIA/GBHC Representative

Walt Vernon
ASHE Representative

Jeff Boldt
ASHRAE Representative

Mick Schwedler
ASHRAE Representative

John Gill
IES Representative

Joel Loveland
IES/AIA Representative

Don Colliver
Steering Committee Ex Officio

John D'Angelo
USGBC Representative

Kim Shinn
USGBC Representative

Tim Peglow
Member-at-Large

Eric Bonnema
Analysis Support

Matt Leach
Analysis Support

Lilas Pratt
Staff Liaison

Bert Etheredge
Staff Support

STEERING COMMITTEE

Don Colliver
Chair

Bill Worthen
AIA Representative

Rita Harrold
IES Representative

Brendan Owens
USGBC Representative

Costas Balaras
ASHRAE Representative

Jeremy Williams
DOE Representative

Mick Schwedler
ASHRAE SSPC 90.1 Liaison

Adrienne Thomle
ASHRAE TC 7.6 Liaison

Lilas Pratt
ASHRAE Staff Liaison

**Any updates/errata to this publication will be posted on the
ASHRAE Web site at www.ashrae.org/publicationupdates.**

Advanced Energy Design Guide for Large Hospitals

Achieving 50% Energy Savings Toward a Net Zero Energy Building

ASHRAE
The American Institute of Architects
Illuminating Engineering Society of North America
U.S. Green Building Council
U.S. Department of Energy

ISBN 978-1-936504-23-7

© 2012 ASHRAE
1791 Tullie Circle, N.E.
Atlanta, GA 30329
www.ashrae.org

Cover design by Emily Luce, Designer.
Front cover rendering by Studio/216.
Back cover photos courtesy of John D'Angelo, Cleveland Clinic, and Joel Loveland (University of Washington)

Library of Congress Cataloging-in-Publication Data

Advanced energy design guide for large hospitals : achieving 50% energy savings toward a net zero energy building / ASHRAE ... [et al.] ; project committee, Shanti Pless, chair ... [et al.].
     p. cm.
   Includes bibliographical references.
     ISBN 978-1-936504-23-7 (softcover : alk. paper) 1. Hospitals--Energy conservation. 2. Hospital buildings--Energy conservation. 3. Sustainable buildings--Design and construction--Standards--United States. I. Pless, Shanti D. II. American Society of Heating, Refrigerating and Air-Conditioning Engineers.
   RA967.9.A436 2012
   725'.51--dc23
                              2012005084

ASHRAE STAFF

SPECIAL PUBLICATIONS

Mark Owen
   Editor/Group Manager
   of Handbook and Special Publications

Cindy Sheffield Michaels
   Managing Editor

James Madison Walker
   Associate Editor

Elisabeth Parrish
   Assistant Editor

Meaghan O'Neil
   Editorial Assistant

Michshell Phillips
   Editorial Coordinator

PUBLISHING SERVICES

David Soltis
   Group Manager of Publishing Services
   and Electronic Communications

Jayne Jackson
   Publication Traffic Administrator

PUBLISHER

W. Stephen Comstock

Contents

Sidebars—
Case Studies and
Technical Examples

Acknowledgments

The *Advanced Energy Design Guide for Large Hospitals* is the fourth in a series of publications designed to provide strategies and recommendations for achieving 50% energy savings over the minimum code requirements of ANSI/ASHRAE/IESNA Standard 90.1-2004, *Energy Standard for Buildings Except Low-Rise Residential Buildings*. The 50% AEDG series addresses building types that represent major energy users in the commercial building stock. This Guide is the result of the dedicated, collective efforts of many professionals who devoted countless hours to help hospitals use less energy.

The primary authors were the 12 members of the ASHRAE Special Project 136 Committee (SP-136) who represented the participating organizations—primarily ASHRAE, the American Institute of Architects (AIA), the U.S. Green Building Council (USGBC), the Illuminating Engineering Society of North America (IES), and the U.S. Department of Energy (DOE). The American Society for Healthcare Engineering (ASHE) was also represented. Thanks also to members of the ASHRAE Standing Standards Project Committee (SSPC) 90.1 and ASHRAE Technical Committee (TC) 9.6, Healthcare Facilities.

The project would not have been possible without DOE's financial support for project committee expenses, Guide development, National Renewable Energy Laboratory energy modeling analysis, and committee leadership. The Chair would personally like to thank Jeremiah Williams, the DOE technology development manager in the Building Technologies Program, for his support and leadership.

The chair would also like to thank all members of the project committee for their diligence, creativity, persistence, and willingness to take time to support this Guide. They worked extremely hard to pull together practical, technically sound information covering all aspects of low-energy-use hospital design. Their expertise and differing views greatly enriched this publication. The authors brought many years of experience and good practice in design, construction, commissioning, and operation of hospitals to achieve significant energy savings.

The project committee met four times and held four conference calls in ten months. Each face-to-face meeting required two nights in a hotel; thus, the chair would also like to express his appreciation to the authors' families for their patience. The chair also gratefully acknowledges the support of the project committee members' employers, including Owens Corning; HOK; Stantec; Mazzetti; KJWW Engineering Consultants; Trane, a business of Ingersoll Rand; CRS Engineering Inc.; University of Washington; Cleveland Clinic; TLC Engineering for Architecture, University of Texas MD Anderson Cancer Center; University of Kentucky; and the National Renewable Energy Laboratory.

The project committee's efforts were guided by the AEDG Steering Committee, composed of members from the partner organizations—ASHRAE, AIA, USGBC, IES—with the additional support and participation of DOE. Its members provided direction and guidance to complete the Guide within 12 months. The Steering Committee assembled an expert team of authors and defined a scope that kept the project committee's task manageable and focused. The representatives from these organizations brought a collegial and constructive spirit to the task of setting policy.

In addition to the voting members of the project committee, a number of individuals played key roles in the Guide's success. Specifically, thanks to the ASHRAE meetings staff, the American Society for Healthcare Engineering, and MD Anderson Cancer Center for serving as gracious hosts at their facilities.

Twenty people participated in two peer reviews, providing more than 1000 remarks that helped strengthen and clarify the Guide. Their thoughtful input is much appreciated and the chair hopes they see the impacts of their recommendations in the finished publication.

A huge debt of gratitude is extended to the authors of the previously published 30% and 50% AEDGs, for they paved the way and defined basic structure, content, and format, as well as reporting and review procedures. Following in their footsteps has resulted in consistency among the AEDGs and has been a tremendous time saver. Building on their success enabled the project committee to finish its work promptly.

Additional thanks to the ASHRAE staff, including Lilas Pratt and Bert Etheredge, whose direction and guidance were invaluable and whose organizational skills and dedication helped keep the project committee on track, and to Matt Walker of ASHRAE Special Publications for editing and layout. The ASHRAE staff managed an enormous number of documents, coordinated with all authors with great competence and efficiency, and helped turn the documents into a first-rate publication. This Guide could not have been developed without their contributions.

Special thanks to Donald E. Wojtkowski, Executive Director of Design, Construction, and Facilities Management at SSM Health Care St. Louis, who provided assistance and data critical to the energy modeling analysis.

Finally, the committee greatly appreciates Eric Bonnema and Matt Leach of the National Renewable Energy Laboratory for providing detailed simulation and analysis support.

Shanti Pless
Chair, Special Project 136

April 2012

Abbreviations
and Acronyms

ach	air changes per hour
AHJ	authority having jurisdiction
AIA	American Institute of Architects
ASC	ambulatory surgery center
ASTM	ASTM International
ANSI	American National Standards Institute
BIAF	backward inclined airfoil
BAS	building automation system
BIM	building information modeling
BF	ballast factor
BoD	Basis of Design
Btu	British thermal unit
C	thermal conductance, $Btu/h \cdot ft^2 \cdot °F$
c.i.	continuous insulation
Cx	commissioning
CxA	commissioning authority
CAV	constant air volume
CBECS	Commercial Buildings Energy Consumption Survey
CCT	corrected color temperature
CDD	cooling degree day
CFL	compact fluorescent lights
cfm	cubic feet per minute
CKI	Commercial Kitchens Initiative
CMH	ceramic metal halide
CMMS	computer maintenance management system
CMS	Centers for Medicare and Medicaid Service
COP	coefficient of performance, dimensionless
CRI	color rendering index
CRRC	Cool Roof Rating Council
CT	computed tomography
CUP	central utility plant
DCV	demand-controlled ventilation
DL	Advanced Energy Design Guide code for *daylighting*

DOAS	dedicated outdoor air system
DOE	Department of Energy
DX	direct expansion
E_c	efficiency, combustion, dimensionless
ECM	energy conservation measure *or* electronically commutated motors
E_t	efficiency, thermal, dimensionless
EER	energy efficiency ratio, Btu/W·h
EF	energy factor
EL	Advanced Energy Design Guide Code for *electric lighting*
EN	Advanced Energy Design Guide Code for *envelope*
ESCO	energy service company
EUI	energy use intensity
F	slab edge heat loss coefficient per foot of perimeter, Btu/h·ft·°F
FC	filled cavity
fc	foot candles
FGI	Facility Guidelines Institute
FGI Guidelines	*Guidelines for the Design and Construction of Healthcare Facilities*
FHC	family health center
GSHP	ground-source heat pump
Guide	*Advanced Energy Design Guide for Large Hospitals*
HC	heat capacity, Btu/(ft²·°F)
HDD	heating degree day
HEPA	high-efficiency particulate air
HID	high-intensity discharge
HRC	heat recovery chiller
HSPF	heating seasonal performance factor
HV	Advanced Energy Design Guide code for *HVAC systems and equipment*
HVAC	heating, ventilating, and air conditioning
IAQ	indoor air quality
IDF	intermediate distribution frame
IES	Illuminating Engineering Society of North America
IESNA	Illuminating Engineer12-026ing Society of North America (no longer used)
IGU	insulated glazing unit
in.	inch
IPLV	integrated part load value, dimensionless
kBtu	thousands of British thermal units
kW	kilowatt
LBNL	Lawrence Berkeley National Laboratory
LCCA	life-cycle cost analysis
LDR	labor, delivery, and recovery
LEC	light-emitting capacitor
LED	light-emitting diode
LEED®	Leadership in Energy and Environmental Design
LINAC	linear particle accelerator
LPD	lighting power density, W/ft²
LPW	lumens per watt
Ls	liner systems
LSG	light-to-solar gain
LWBT	leaving wet-bulb temperature
N/A	not applicable
M&V	measurement and verification
MDF	main distribution frame
MLPW	mean lumens per watt
MOB	medical office building

MRI	magnetic resonance imaging
NEMA	National Electrical Manufacturers Association
NICU	neonatal intensive care unit
NFRC	National Fenestration Rating Council
NREL	National Energy Renewable Laboratory
O&M	operation and maintenance
OA	outdoor air
OPR	Owner's Project Requirements
PACU	postanesthetic care unit
PET	positron emission tomography
PF	projection factor, dimensionless
PIR	passive infrared
PL	Advanced Energy Design Guide code for *plug loads*
PPL	plug and process loads
PNNL	Pacific Northwest National Laboratory
POE	postoccupancy evaluation
ppm	parts per million
PSC	permanent-split capacitor
PV	photovoltaic
QA	quality assurance
R	thermal resistance, $h \cdot ft^2 \cdot °F/Btu$
R - in.	R-value followed by the depth of insulation in inches
RFID	radio-frequency identification
RFP	request for proposal
rh	relative humidity
ROI	return on investment
SAT	supply air temperature
SCN	special care nurseries
SDU	split dehumidification unit
SEMP	strategic energy management planning
SFU	supply fixture unit
SHGC	solar heat gain coefficient, dimensionless
SHR	sensible heat ratio
SP	special project
SRI	Solar Reflectance Index, dimensionless
SSPC	standing standards project committee
SWH	service water heating
TAB	test, adjust, and balance
TC	technical committee
U	thermal transmittance, $Btu/h \cdot ft^2 \cdot °F$
USGBC	U.S. Green Building Council
UV	ultraviolet
UVGI	ultraviolet germicidal irradiation
VAV	variable air volume
VFD	variable-frequency drive
VT	visible transmittance
W	watts
WH	Advanced Energy Design Guide code for *service water heating*
WSHP	water-source heat pump
WWR	window-to-wall ratio

Foreword: A Message to Healthcare Leaders

The purpose of healthcare organizations is to improve the life quality of its patients and the health of the communities they serve. As healthcare services and specialized knowledge have dramatically improved, diagnostic and treatment equipment and techniques have evolved to support them. The pace of this change can only increase in the face of the demographic, technological, and regulatory/reimbursement transformations necessary to ensure the financial sustainability of the healthcare delivery process.

In many cases, modern healthcare facilities and their overall environment of care have not contributed to the public health mission and have even been inadvertent contributors to the decline in human health. Understanding the impacts of hospitals on the natural environment and on public health, and connections between the built environment and occupant health, is a relatively recent phenomenon. Although links between these factors and the financial demands on healthcare are increasingly clear, the connections are often indirect, leading some owners to prioritize architecture over operational achievement.

A well designed, constructed, operated, and maintained facility is a major contributor to the environment of care and can improve patient outcomes, safety, and comfort. Quality lighting provides clear and even illumination during diagnosis and intervention, can help prevent medication errors, and help deter criminal activity in parking areas and adjacent grounds. HVAC systems that can deliver clean air quietly and at the correct volume, temperature, humidity, and pressure to support infection control and help keep patients comfortable. Efficient water systems reduce use and maximize reuse where safe, and can help communities by reducing the need for larger, more costly treatment plants that consume more energy. Carefully selected finishes can reduce infections and improve cleanliness.

Because healthcare leadership focuses more on the architectural than operational design of healthcare facilities, many designers substitute quantity for quality, resulting in overlighted spaces or oversized equipment. Reducing lighting power density while increasing lighting quality is not only possible but can accompany a reduction to both first cost and lifecycle cost. Reducing fixture wattage through the use of solid-state lighting allows for fewer circuits to be run and for the purchase of smaller transformers. Longer mean time between failures results in a lower maintenance cost, which can equal or surpass the savings from reduced electricity use. Lower wattage can also mean a lower risk of fire, less lighting waste heat to dissipate, more spare capacity in emergency power systems for egress lighting, and higher circuit reliability. Use of solid-state lighting also allows variable dimming for daylighting and "quiet at night" applications not possible with some sources without expensive modifications.

Focusing on the fundamental environment of care throughout the lifecycle of a facility provides additional positive effects for the natural environment as well as for the public health. Lower waste heat from lighting can lead to smaller cooling plants, which can lead to lower initial and operating costs. Lower power consumption can lead to a reduction of particulate matter in the air, and of mercury and other waste contamination in groundwater at power stations.

This positive cycle of lower costs; improved patient outcomes, safety, and experience; and better stewardship of community health is not a distant possibility in the far future—it is achievable today, using readily available technology with a history of successful and reliable implementation in facilities around world. Using available technology, designers are capable of delivering quality plans for a large hospital that is up to 50% more energy efficient. Likewise, construction professionals can economically build these low-energy buildings, and hospital facilities' staffs can successfully operate and maintain them.

Healthcare facilities play an influential role in promoting public wellness by educating their staff on the importance and techniques of sustainability, which they take home and spread to their communities at large. Some healthcare institutions have leveraged sustainability efforts to provide even greater value to their communities. At least one large healthcare organization is considering selling the renewable energy credits provided by the large number of solar power panels it has installed and using the proceeds to provide medical care to the uninsured—perhaps the most direct form of community benefit.

The *Advanced Energy Design Guide for Large Hospitals* shows that existing reliable technologies and design philosophies can be used to reduce energy use in large hospitals by up to 50% of ANSI/ASHRAE/IESNA Standard 90.1-2004 recommendations. In addition, the 30% savings guide, *Advanced Energy Design Guide for Small Hospitals and Healthcare Facilities*, can be applied to freestanding ambulatory surgery centers and high-acuity medical office buildings, and the 50% savings guide, *Advanced Energy Design Guide for Small to Medium Office Buildings*, can be applied to administrative or low-acuity medical office buildings. Although these guides focus on methods of achieving and documenting up to 30% or 50% energy savings, the approaches used are not intended to limit savings to 50% or to be the only way of achieving savings.

Most important in *Advanced Energy Design Guide for Large Hospitals* is the recognition that patient outcomes, safety, and experience trump all cost- and energy-saving strategies. Regardless of their potential for savings, no strategy is adopted that would cause risk to the direct care of the patients, or to the health of staff and visitors of these facilities. The Guide emphasizes design approaches that reduce risk, and hospitals are encouraged to consider carefully the interrelated factors that contribute to an overall environment of care when making design decisions. As many large hospitals are major employers and community pillars, the need to reduce impact on the natural environmental through energy savings and sustainable operational practices cannot be ignored. Staff and community leaders expect healthcare facilities to be environmentally responsible. These philosophies also make economic sense.

In addition to reducing risk to occupant health and the natural environmental, correctly executed measures to reduce energy consumption can lead to greater staff engagement and attendance, as people like to work in attractive spaces with access to natural light and tend to take fewer sick days. Any improvement to overall environment of care will provide similar improvement to staff work environment. While the greatest measure of a quality medical center is the recommendation of satisfied patients and families, the recommendations of staff to their peers is a close second. Time and again, those healthcare facilities that build green report easier recruiting, and higher retention of staff than competing facilities. In an era of increasingly scarce human assets, this may be the most important additional benefit of a program to conserve energy.

Introduction

1

The *Advanced Energy Design Guide for Large Hospitals* (the Guide) provides user-friendly, how-to design guidance and efficiency recommendations for large hospitals. Applying the Guide's recommendations should result in facilities that consume 50% less energy than conventional hospitals (defined by the minimum requirements of ANSI/AHSRAE/IESNA Standard 90.1-2004, *Energy Standard for Buildings Except Low-Rise Residential Buildings* (ASHRAE 2004). This document contains recommendations to design a low-energy-use building. It is *not* a minimum code or standard but is rather a voluntary guidance document designed to supplement existing codes and standards. It is not intended to replace, supersede, or circumvent them. Although several design packages are provided in the document, this Guide represents *a way*, but not the *only way*, to build energy-efficient hospitals that use significantly less energy than those built to minimum code requirements.

The intended audience of this Guide includes, but is not limited to, building owners, architects, design engineers, energy modelers, general contractors, facility managers, and building operations staff. Specifically, Chapter 2 is written for a target audience of all design team members, including design professionals, construction experts, owner representatives, and other stakeholders. Chapters 3 through 5 are oriented more toward design professionals. These chapters include sound design advice and identify interdisciplinary opportunities for significant energy reduction. The focus of this Guide is to identify proven concepts that are feasible to implement, and to benchmark necessary energy performance criteria for 50% energy savings. The Guide will require healthcare leaders and design professionals to be intentional about the goals of their projects and to think differently about their processes and operations.

The energy savings projections of this Guide are based on site energy consumption rather than source energy. *Site energy* refers to the amount of energy consumed on the site and typically metered at the property line. *Source energy* takes into account the efficiency with which raw materials are converted into energy and transmitted to the site and refers to the total amount of energy originally embodied in the raw materials. For example, it is generally accepted that site electrical energy is 100% efficient, but in fact it takes approximately 3 kWh of source energy to produce and deliver 1 kWh to the customer because the production and distribution of electrical energy is roughly 33% efficient.

The Guide was developed by a project committee representing a diverse group of professionals and practitioners. Guidance and support was provided through a collaboration of ASHRAE, the American Institute of Architects (AIA), the Illuminating Engineering Society (IES), the U.S. Green Building Council (USGBC), and the U.S. Department of Energy (DOE).

Advanced Energy Design Guide for Large Hospitals
Executive Summary

Advanced Energy Design Guide for Large Hospitals is fourth in a series of guides designed to achieve 50% energy savings over the minimum code requirements of ASHRAE/IESNA Standard 90.1-2004. The Guide provides user-friendly assistance and energy savings recommendations to the building community and building owners. Included are prescriptive recommendations for the envelope; fenestration; lighting systems (including electric interior and exterior lights and daylighting); heating, ventilation, and air-conditioning (HVAC) systems; building automation and controls; outdoor air (OA) requirements; service water heating (SWH); and plug and process loads (PPL). The guide provides practical recommendations for exceeding code minimums and helping design teams and owners produce high-efficiency hospitals. In general, the guide contains recommendations for the following:

* A building envelope approximately 45% better on average than Standard 90.1-2004.
* Interior lighting power densities that result in a 25% better whole-building lighting power density than Standard 90.1-2004, along with LED surgery light recommendations that save 60% of the energy used for lighting, while significantly reducing the energy demands for cooling surgeons and warming patients.
* Exterior lighting recommendations that include a 33% reduction over Standard 90.1-2004 for parking lots and drives.
* ENERGY STAR® exclusive plug-in equipment, best-in-class plug in equipment where ENERGY STAR does not apply, best in class commercial kitchen equipment, traction elevators exclusively, and regenerative traction elevators for high use.
* Service water heating that is 13% more efficient than Standard 90.1-2004 on average.
* Aggressive reduction in reheat resulting from decoupling space conditioning loads and ventilation loads, either with a dedicated OA system and zone-level conditioning equipment or advanced variable-air-volume (VAV) with separate OA treatment, heat recovery chiller, aggressive supply air temperature reset, and zone airflow setback.
* Additional HVAC recommendations that include airflow setback in surgery suites, best-in-class equipment efficiencies, demand controlled ventilation, air-side energy recovery, air side pressure drop and coil face velocity reductions, elimination of steam boilers, and high-delta-T chilled-water loops.

As with previous Guides in the series, *Advanced Energy Design Guide for Large Hospitals* provides a simple, easy-to-use reference to help building professionals and owners identify a clear prescriptive path to 50% energy savings over Standard 90.1-2004. The combination of a set of recommendations contained on a single page, along with numerous how-to tips to help the construction team complete the project successfully, should result in increased energy efficiency in new buildings. Case studies of actual applications add to the comprehension of energy-efficiency opportunities. The ultimate goal of the Advanced Energy Design Guide partner organizations is to achieve net zero energy buildings, and the 50% savings guides represent a step in reaching this goal.

Members of the project committee are also affiliated with ASHRAE Standing Standards Project Committee 90.1 (SSPC 90.1), the ASHRAE Technical Committee on Healthcare Facilities (TC 9.6), and the American Society of Healthcare Engineers (ASHE).

In essence, this Guide provides design teams a methodology for achieving energy savings goals that are financially feasible, operationally workable, and otherwise readily achievable. Because technology to conserve and generate energy is growing rapidly, it is clear that innovation is an important ingredient to the success of reducing energy consumption in healthcare facilities. It is the hope of the authors that this publication will expose other existing best practices and lead to new concepts.

GOAL OF THIS GUIDE

The Guide strives to provide guidance and recommendations to reduce the total energy use in large hospitals by at least 50%, on a site energy basis, using ASHRAE/IESNA Standard 90.1-2004 as the basis for a minimum code-compliant building. The energy savings goal is to be achieved in each climate location rather than an aggregated national average. The 50% savings is determined based on whole-building site energy savings, which includes process and plug loads.

SCOPE

This Guide has been created for a "standard" mid-to-large-size hospital, but the approaches and strategies suggested can be applied to all sizes and classifications of large hospitals. In general, most large hospitals are at least 100,000 ft^2. Space types covered by the Guide include cafeterias, kitchens, and dining facilities; conference, lobby, lounge, and office areas; reception/waiting areas and examination and treatment rooms; clean and soiled workrooms and holding areas; nurse stations, nurseries, patient rooms, corridors and transition spaces, lockers, and restrooms; operating rooms, procedure rooms, recovery rooms, and sterilizer equipment areas; pharmacies, medication rooms, and laboratories; triage, trauma, and emergency rooms; physical therapy and radiology/imaging rooms; and storage, receiving, and mechanical/electrical/telecom rooms. This Guide will not directly address other atypical or special-use spaces.

The primary focus of this Guide is new construction, but recommendations may be equally applicable to hospitals undergoing complete renovation and, in part, to many other hospital renovation, addition, remodeling, and modernization projects (including changes to one or more systems in existing buildings).

Included in the Guide are recommendations for the design of the building opaque envelope; fenestration; lighting systems (including electrical interior and exterior lights and daylighting); heating, ventilation, and air-conditioning (HVAC) systems; building automation and controls; outdoor air (OA) requirements; service water heating (SWH); and plug and process loads (PPL), including kitchen equipment. Additional savings recommendations that are not necessary for 50% savings are discussed in the "Additional Bonus Savings" section of Chapter 5.

The recommendation tables do not include all of the components listed in ASHRAE/IES Standard 90.1. Though this Guide focuses only on the primary energy systems within a building, the underlying energy analysis assumes that all of the other components and systems comply with the minimum design criteria in ASHRAE/IES Standard 90.1, ASHRAE Standard 62.1, and ASHRAE/ASHE Standard 170.

In addition, the Guide is not intended to be a substitute for rating systems or references that address the full range of sustainability issues in hospital design, such as acoustics, productivity, indoor air quality (IAQ), water efficiency, landscaping, and transportation, except as they relate to energy use. Nor is it a comprehensive design text. The Guide assumes good design skills and expertise in hospital design.

PROJECT PROCESS FOR ACHIEVING 50% ENERGY SAVINGS

Meeting the 50% energy savings goal is challenging and requires more than doing business as usual. Below are the essentials. The sidebar "Steps for the Building Owner to Follow when Using the Advanced Energy Design Guide" shows additional steps from an owner's perspective. Many of these issues are addressed in greater detail in Chapter 2.

1. *Obtain building owner buy-in.* There must be strong buy-in from the owner/operator and leadership and staff. The more they know about and participate in the planning and design process, the better they will be able to help achieve the 50% energy savings goal after the

hospital becomes operational. The building owner must decide on the goals and provide the leadership to make the goals reality.

2. *Assemble an experienced, innovative design team.* Interest and experience in designing energy-efficient buildings, innovative thinking, and the ability to work together as a team are all critical to meeting the 50% energy savings goal. Communicate energy savings goals in the request for proposal (RFP) and give significant weight when selecting a design team to the team's ability to meet the goals. The design team implements the goals for the owner.

3. *Adopt an integrated design process.* Cost-effective, energy-efficient design requires trade-offs among potential energy-saving features. This requires an integrated approach to hospital design. The greater the energy savings are, the more complicated the trade-offs become and the more design team members must work together to determine the optimal mix of energy-saving features.

4. *Consider a daylighting consultant.* Daylighting is an important energy saving strategy to achieve the 50% energy savings goal; however, successful implementation of a daylighting strategy requires sound technical design. If the design team does not have experience with a well-balanced daylighting design, it may need to add a daylighting consultant.

5. *Consider energy modeling.* This Guide provides a few design packages to help achieve energy savings of up to 50% without energy modeling, but whole-building energy modeling programs can provide more flexibility to evaluate the energy efficiency measures on an individual project. These simulation programs have learning curves of varying difficulty, but energy modeling for hospital design is highly encouraged and is considered necessary for achieving energy savings of up to 50%. See the Building Energy Software Tools Directory (DOE 2012) at the Department of Energy, Energy Efficiency and Renewable Energy Web site for links to energy modeling programs. Part of the key to energy savings is first identifying and evaluating major loads, including those imposed by the envelope, and then reducing them. The interactions between climate, hospital buildings, and HVAC systems are complex. Energy modeling helps determine the nonintuitive trade-offs that lead to deep savings that are too complex to evaluate otherwise. Developing HVAC load calculations is neither energy modeling nor a substitute for energy modeling.

6. *Use building commissioning.* Studies verify that building systems frequently do not operate as efficiently as expected, whether due to design, installation, and/or operational factors. The 50% energy savings can be elusive to achieve in practice without thorough building commissioning to ensure that all systems—including envelope, lighting, and HVAC—perform as intended. Comprehensive commissioning increases the likelihood of achieving expected energy savings. See the section "Project Details by Phase" in Chapter 2 and the "Quality Assurance" sections of Chapter 5 of this Guide for more information.

7. *Train building users and operations staff.* The long-term operational efficiency of a building is the result of thousands of individual choices that users and operations staff make every day. Training involves both instructing operations staff in what adjustments are necessary to achieve optimum performance and informing building occupants of the consequences of their choices to use water and energy. Often, the building system users receive training from the operations staff on an exception basis after there is a system failure. Systems that put real-time information about the impact of plug loads and energy-efficient appliances on the user's desktop may be effective in modifying behavior to conserve energy use.

8. *Monitor the building.* Buildings that do not meet energy goals may have operational deficiencies that can be corrected with dramatic effect. An energy monitoring plan is useful in discovering what components of the building load are contributing to high energy use. Even simple plans that record and plot monthly utility bills may offer clues leading to operational changes and performance improvements.

Steps for the Building Owner to Follow when Using the Advanced Energy Design Guide		
Project Phase	**Actions**	**Outcomes**
Project Conception	☐ Select the AEDG(s) for your building type from *www.ashrae.org/aedg*. ☐ Learn about the business case for advanced energy design in the Foreword. ☐ Review similar projects in the case studies.	➢ Appropriate AEDG ➢ Project specific energy performance goals
Team Selection	☐ Incorporate AEDG recommendations into RFPs. ☐ Ask proposers how they used AEDG recommendations and made the business case for energy savings in past projects.	➢ Team with AEDG experience ➢ Team committed to using AEDG
Conceptual Design	☐ Require design teams to implement AEDG recommendations. ☐ Learn about integrated design in Chapter 2. ☐ Review site specific cost and benefit of the AEDG recommendations.	➢ Understanding and application of the AEDG recommendations ➢ Awareness of cost impacts of the AEDG recommendations
Design Development	☐ Include AEDG recommendations in the Owner's Project Requirements (OPR). ☐ Integrate AEDG recommendations into project tracking and status meetings.	➢ Design that incorporates AEDG recommendations
Construction	☐ Request regular updates on progress towards AEDG goals. ☐ Ensure that late project modifications to not compromise AEDG goals.	➢ Verification that AEDG recommendations are installed as designed (through commissioning process)
Operation	☐ Verify that AEDG recommended systems function as intended (through commissioning). ☐ Leverage the one-year warranty period to address outstanding issues.	➢ High-performance building incorporating AEDG recommendations ➢ Achievement of design energy goals

CONDITIONS TO PROMOTE HEALTH AND COMFORT

Throughout the project, the design team should continuously determine how energy-saving measures will impact comfort, IAQ, and acoustics. The design and construction of a high-performance hospital requires an integrated approach where these factors remain a priority and are not adversely affected when striving for energy reduction.

The ways in which indoor environmental factors, such as thermal conditions, IAQ, acoustics, and illumination, interact can be either beneficial or detrimental to both sustainability efforts and occupant health. For specific guidance regarding the interaction of indoor air quality, thermal comfort, sound and vibration, and other factors, refer to ASHRAE Guideline 10, *Interactions Affecting the Achievement of Acceptable Indoor Environments* (ASHRAE 2011).

VENTILATION AND INDOOR AIR QUALITY (IAQ) IN HOSPITALS

ASHRAE Standard 62.1 and ASHRAE/ASHE Standard 170 define minimum requirements for the design, installation, operation, and maintenance of ventilation systems. Standard 170 also provides minimum requirements for filter specifications, pressure relationships where required, and temperature ranges. It is the standard recognized by Centers for Medicare and Medicaid Services (CMS) for meeting conditions of participation. For more information, refer to *Indoor Air Quality Guide: Best Practices for Design, Construction, and Commissioning* (ASHRAE 2009b), which provides specific guidance for achieving the following key objectives:

- Manage the design and construction process to achieve good IAQ.
- Control moisture in building assemblies.
- Limit entry of outdoor contaminants.
- Control moisture and contaminants related to mechanical systems.
- Limit contaminants from indoor sources.
- Capture and exhaust contaminants from building equipment and activities.
- Reduce contaminant concentrations through ventilation, filtration, and air cleaning.
- Apply more advanced ventilation approaches.

THERMAL COMFORT

AHSRAE/ASHE Standard 170 defines required temperature standards in clinical settings. ASHRAE Standard 55 defines the combinations of indoor thermal environmental factors and personal factors that will produce conditions acceptable to a majority of the occupants in nonclinical environments.

According to ASHRAE Standard 55, six primary factors must be addressed when defining conditions for thermal comfort: metabolic rate, clothing insulation, air temperature, radiant temperature, air speed, and humidity. For example, appropriate levels of clothing, the cooling effect of air motion, and radiant cooling or heating systems can increase occupant comfort efficiently.

Also, all parties should consider allowing a wide deadband for occupied mode setpoints as a measure to reduce energy use (as compared to the minimum deadband range stated in energy codes). However, these expanded temperature ranges should not be so extreme as to compromise productivity in the workspace.

VISUAL COMFORT

To minimize visual comfort issues, integrate daylight and electric light into the design, making sure to meet Illuminating Engineering Society (IES) recommended light levels (IES 2012). Light levels that are too high or too low cause eye strain and result in lost productivity.

Control glare from direct and reflected sunlight to avoid the discomfort caused by high contrast ratio. Orient workstation terminals and audio-visual displays perpendicular to the window line to reduce discomfort from reflections.

Further recommendations on lighting visual comfort can be found in IES's *The Lighting Handbook: Reference and Application*, specifically in Chapter 2 "Vision: Eye and Brain" and Chapter 4 "Perception and Performance" (IES 2012).

ACOUSTIC COMFORT

Proper acoustic design must be a priority when considering all design decisions and must not be sacrificed in striving for energy reduction. Addressing proper acoustics during the design phase of a project, rather than attempting to fix problems after construction, will likely minimize costs. *Guidelines for the Design and Construction of Healthcare Facilities* (AIA Guidelines) (AIA 2010) defines acoustic performance in the clinical environment.

Additional recommendations on acoustic comfort can be found in the 2009 *ASHRAE Handbook—Fundamentals*, Chapter 8, "Sound and Vibration" (ASHRAE 2009a).

ENERGY MODELING ANALYSIS

A hospital prototype energy model was developed and analyzed using hourly building simulations to provide a baseline to quantify the energy savings for this Guide. The building energy model has an area of 427,000 ft^2, which was carefully assembled to represent typical construction for healthcare facilities of that size and class. Information was drawn from a number of sources, including the Commercial Buildings Energy Consumption Survey (CBECS), Dodge Construction Data, and various hospital templates from around the country. Space types included in each prototype design are shown in Table 1-1. The Guide covers additional spaces in the recommendations beyond those included in the prototype modeling.

Two sets of hour-by-hour simulations were run for each prototype using EnergyPlus Energy Simulation Software (DOE 2011). The first set meets the minimum requirements of ASHRAE/IESNA Standard 90.1-2004, and the second uses the recommendations in this Guide. Each prototype was simulated in eight climate zones adopted by the International Energy Code Council (IECC) and ASHRAE in development of the prevailing energy codes and standards. The climate zones were further divided into moist and dry regions, represented by 16 climate locations. All materials and equipment used in the simulations are commercially available from two or more manufacturers.

Table 1-1 Prototype Design Modeled Space Types

Space Types	
Anesthesia gas storage	Office
Cafeteria	Operating room
Clean workroom/holding	Patient room
Conference room	Pharmacy
Corridor/transition	Physical therapy
Dining facilities	Procedure room
Examination/treatment room	Radiology/imaging
Food preparation center (kitchens)	Reception/waiting
Laboratory	Recovery room
Lobby area	Restroom
Locker	Soiled workroom/holding
Lounge	Sterilizer equipment room
Mechanical/electrical/telecom room	Storage/receiving
Medical supply/medication room	Trauma/emergency room
Nurse station	Triage
Nursery	

Energy savings for the recommendations vary depending on climate zone and HVAC system type but are at least 50% in all cases when compared to ASHRAE 90.1-2004, ranging from 50% to 59% savings. Analysis also determined energy savings ranging from approximately 49% to 58% when compared to ASHRAE Standard 90.1-2007 (ASHRAE 2007) and from approximately 34% to 45% when compared to Standard 90.1-2010 (ASHRAE 2010c). A savings range of approximately 56% to 64% is estimated when compared to Standard 90.1-1999 (ASHRAE 1999), the baseline standard of the 30% AEDG series. Energy saving analysis approach, methodologies, and complete results of the prototype building simulations are documented in a Bonnema et al. (2010).

HOW TO USE THIS GUIDE

- Review Chapter 2 to understand how integrated design is used to maximize energy efficiency.
- Review Chapter 3 to understand the integrated design strategies, including architectural design features and energy conservation measures by climate zone. This chapter provides integrated design strategies to help design professionals make good decisions in the early stages of project design. This is especially important when the project has building or site characteristics that do not match the baseline building in shape, orientation, and glazing.
- Review Chapter 4 for climate-specific design strategies and select specific energy saving measures by climate zone. This chapter provides prescriptive packages that do not require modeling for energy savings. These measures also may be used to earn credits for LEED® and other building rating systems, pending formal adoption.
- Use Chapter 5 to apply the energy saving measures in Chapter 4. This chapter includes suggestions for best design practices; how to avoid problems; and how to achieve additional savings with energy-efficient appliances, plug-in equipment, and other energy saving measures.
- Refer to the Appendices for additional information:
    Appendix A—Envelope Thermal Performance Factors
    Appendix B—International Climatic Zone Definitions
- Note that this Guide is presented in inch-pound (I-P) units only; it is up to the individual user to convert values to the International System (SI) as required. The Guide is also oriented toward projects in the northern hemisphere. Projects located in the southern hemisphere should reverse north/south orientations accordingly.

REFERENCES AND RESOURCES

AIA. 2010. *Guidelines for the Design and Construction of Healthcare Facilities.* Dallas, TX: Facility Guidelines Institute.

ASHRAE. 1999. ANSI/ASHRAE/IESNA Standard 90.1-1999, *Energy Standard for Buildings Except Low-Rise Residential Buildings.* Atlanta: ASHRAE.

ASHRAE. 2004. ANSI/ASHRAE/IESNA Standard 90.1-2004, *Energy Standard for Buildings Except Low-Rise Residential Buildings.* Atlanta: ASHRAE.

ASHRAE. 2007. ANSI/ASHRAE/IESNA Standard 90.1-2007, *Energy Standard for Buildings Except Low-Rise Residential Buildings.* Atlanta: ASHRAE.

ASHRAE. 2008. ANSI/ASHRAE/ASHE Standard 170-2008, *Ventilation of Health Care Facilities.* Atlanta: ASHRAE.

ASHRAE. 2009a. *ASHRAE Handbook—Fundamentals.* Atlanta: ASHRAE.

ASHRAE. 2009b. Indoor Air Quality Guide: Best Practices for Design, Construction, and Commissioning. Atlanta: ASHRAE.

ASHRAE. 2010a. ANSI/ASHRAE Standard 55-2010, *Thermal Environmental Conditions for Human Occupancy.* Atlanta: ASHRAE.

ASHRAE. 2010b. ANSI/ASHRAE Standard 62.1-2010, *Ventilation for Acceptable Indoor Air Quality.* Atlanta: ASHRAE.

ASHRAE. 2010c. ANSI/ASHRAE/IES Standard 90.1-2010, *Energy Standard for Buildings Except Low-Rise Residential Buildings.* Atlanta: ASHRAE.

ASHRAE. 2011. ASHRAE Guideline 10-2011, *Interactions Affecting the Achievement of Acceptable Indoor Environments.* Atlanta: ASHRAE.

Bonnema, E., D. Studer, A. Parker, S. Pless, and P. Torcellini. 2010. Large Hospital 50% Energy Savings: Technical Support Document. NREL Report No. TP-550-47867, National Renewable Energy Laboratory, Washington, DC.

DOE. 2011. EnergyPlus Energy Simulation Software, Version 7.0. Washington, DC: U.S. Department of Energy.

DOE. 2012. Building Energy Software Tools Directory. U.S. Department of Energy, Washington, DC. http://www.eere.energy.gov/buildings/tools_directory.

IES. 2012. *The Lighting Handbook: Reference and Application*, 10th edition. New York: Illuminating Engineering Society.

Integrated Design

2

INTRODUCTION

Buildings consume approximately 40% of all of the energy used in the United States (USGBC 2012). Healthcare buildings are the second largest consumer of energy per unit of floor area of all building types (EIA 2008). For too many years, the architecture and engineering community has designed buildings to meet minimal energy performance goals. In order to change this practice, energy performance must be considered in the earliest stages of the design process.

Early prioritization of energy performance leads to strategies with the lowest cost to the project overall. Since energy performance questions span all aspects of building planning, design, construction, and project operations, early engagement enables early integrated team building, problem definition, and goal setting. This is true for most types of construction, but particularly true for highly complex, expensive, and lengthy projects, such as large hospitals.

Large hospitals are complicated to design, construct and operate. Integrated design has provided significant advancements in energy and operational efficiency at minimal to no additional capital cost. Since 80% of the building's lifecyle costs occur during the operational phase, these opportunities offer tremendous payback. The prioritization of energy efficiency starts with the earliest business and operations planning phases in the context of strategic energy management planning (SEMP), often several years before the traditional design process starts, and continues through construction to long-term building operations. In order to manage a process designed around long-term operations goals for energy efficiency, the integration of planning, design, construction, and operations team members is absolutely critical. Managing long-term goals requires new lanes of responsibility and new ways of reconciling building performance decisions outside of commonly exclusive, discipline-specific, independent budget categories.

Integrated design is inclusive of construction and operations. It is a framework for incorporating the early and continuous input of engineers, building contractors, and operators into the working process of a collaborative group of key design decision makers. This chapter summarizes the overarching principles of integrated design for energy efficiency. The two following guidance documents for structuring integrated project teams offer more in-depth treatment of the topic.

- *Integrated Project Delivery: A Guide* (AIA 2007)
- *ANSI/MTS 1.0 Whole Systems Integrated Process Guide (WSIP)-2007 for Sustainable Buildings & Communities* (MTS 2007)

The design team considers the following, looking synergies between them and for opportunities to improve energy and cost efficiencies:

- Reducing loads
- Designing the most appropriate hybrid passive and active building environmental control systems
- Using climate resources (site)
- Responding to patterns of use (the building program)
- Developing architectural systems as primary systems of environmental control
- Designing the highest-performing building mechanical and electrical systems

The result is a more comfortable and productive built environment that yields more energy and operational efficiencies than a building that complies only nominally with an energy code

Decisions about building orientation on the site, building envelope, and building geometry should be strongly influenced by a diversity of expertise and points of view. As an example, the design of a window is greatly affected by assumptions and questions about specific building mechanical and electrical system alternatives. Factors such as available space for a ground-source heat pump (GSHP) bore field will affect the amount of cooling load that can be provided by this system, and thereby affect the amount of load that is acceptable to be gained through the envelope. Similarly, decisions regarding building mechanical systems, such as whether to decouple them, impact the allowable maximum peak loads on the envelope. The design team must consider that the critical task of limiting direct sunlight to avoid overheating is most easily accomplished via building orientation and related fenestration systems. Lastly, all of these decisions are influenced by operations and maintenance protocols.

In a nonintegrated design process, a building's overall energy performance typically receives cursory attention at a predesign or schematic design level. For the integrated design process to be successful at providing energy savings in the range of at least 50%, all parties should engage in detailed dialog early in the design process, using a team approach and taking time to understand how each portion of the work affects the project as a whole.

PRINCIPLES OF INTEGRATED DESIGN FOR ENERGY EFFICIENCY

WHAT IS INTEGRATED DESIGN?

Integrated design is a highly collaborative approach to project management that spans all phases of building planning, design, construction, and operations.

In a traditional project delivery system, owner, designers, consultants, and builders work strictly within their respective disciplines, and success is often narrowly framed in terms of profit and being on-budget for a particular task, rather than in terms of the overall success of the final product. In integrated design, all parties involved work in sustained collaboration to ensure optimal and efficient planning, design, construction, and operation from beginning to end. This approach is intended to save money and to provide higher-performing buildings that a more conventional method. Table 2-1 compares an integrated process to a more traditional model.

The efficiency and quality of design and construction flow from the following criteria, all of which build toward reciprocal respect and trust:

- Early involvement of all primary planning, design, construction, and building operations team members.
- Initially agreed-upon, objective, and documented common goals; metrics for gaging the successful achievement of these goals; and evaluation methods to be used to produce the metrics that will guide the team's progress towards meeting the goals.
- Open communication about meeting the agreed upon metrics and goals, with periodic tests of performance.
- Assessment of metrics and goals for a minimum of 3–5 years postoccupancy.

Table 2-1   Project Delivery Method Comparison (AIA 2007)

Traditional Project Delivery		Integrated Project Delivery
Fragmented; assembled on just-as-needed or minimum-necessary basis; strongly hierarchical; controlled	**Teams**	An integrated team composed of key project stakeholders; assembled early in the process; open; collaborative
Linear, distinct, segregated; knowledge gathered just-as-needed; information hoarded; silos of knowledge and expertise	**Process**	Concurrent and multilevel; early contributions of knowledge and expertise; information openly shared; stakeholder trust and respect
Individually managed; transferred to the greatest extent possible	**Risk**	Collectively managed, appropriately shared
Individually pursued; minimum effort for maximum return; (usually) first-cost based	**Compensation/Reward**	Team success tied to project success; value based
Paper based, two-dimensional; analog	**Communications/ Technology**	Digitally based, virtual; building information modeling (three, four, and five dimensional)
Encourage unilateral effort; allocate and transfer risk; no sharing	**Agreements**	Encourage, foster, promote and support multilateral open sharing and collaboration; risk sharing

A key distinguishing element of integrated design is the formation of the project team as early in the project as possible, with team members that are committed to the success of the final product. Mutually agreed-upon metrics of performance, success criteria, and corresponding compensation align all project members with the fundamental goals of overall project success. This inclusiveness and buy-in then facilitates open collaboration and trust between the participants, which is paramount to the success of the integrated design process.

Integrated design hinges on participants working as an integrated team—either as participants who will be involved in the entire project from beginning to end or as key supporting participants who are included for advice pertaining to their specific areas of expertise as needed throughout the project's development. The integrated design method deliberately moves toward a more open and transparent agreement, focusing on mutual benefits and rewards by encouraging parties to converge on the project goals rather than individual goals. Project goals must be defined and recorded early in the project and should be

- defined by collaborative agreement between all key participants;

- reasonably concise, so that few disagreements can arise due to individual interpretation;

- defined by congruent rewards based on individual risk (and, in an integrated project delivery process, include points that illustrate how all parties will benefit more due to the overall success of the project); and

- written with clauses that describe how problems are to be resolved and that they be resolved nonjudgmentally.

Through high-performance planning, design, construction, and operations, the resulting building's value is greatly increased. Integrated design allows ownership to take greater control of project delivery and the design and construction team to take greater control of actual performance.

WHY USE INTEGRATED DESIGN TO MAXIMIZE ENERGY EFFICIENCY?

Integrated design is meant to remove barriers between designers, builders, and owners to encourage early contributions of wisdom and experience and provides many benefits to the owner, including the following:

- *Savings* from reduced project costs resulting from smaller systems or the elimination of systems. These savings can be reinvested in other energy-focused project features, extending the project budget.
- *Decreased energy use* means savings in fuel and may result in decreased maintenance for the owner. The lower operating expense and project costs can be reinvested in the owner's core business activities.
- *Healthier and more productive environments*—people inside a space that uses key features of energy-efficient buildings, such as natural light and ventilation, feel healthier and are commonly more productive.
- *Environmental stewardship* in the form of pollution reduction from reduced energy needs, and the overall reduced demand on natural resources, contributes to improved community health and well being.

HOW TO ASSEMBLE AN INTEGRATED DESIGN PROJECT

PROJECT DETAILS BY PHASE

Assembling the Team

The conventional method of assembling a team, with a linear process of design, construction, and operation, does not work as well for large hospitals because of the inherent complexity of the project. Integrated design is about choosing the right people, developing trust, and solving problems. When choosing the design team, consider giving greater weight to members' openness to the integrated design process and their commitment to continued quality performance improvement. In the integrated design process, everyone shares an equal responsibility for the project as a whole. Design, construction, and operations teams need to determine the right approach for themselves, but it must be one the supports the holistic purpose of integrated design. Potential efficiencies may include the following:

- Reduce the heating, cooling, ventilating, and lighting loads to potential passive and active environmental control systems.
- Design hybrid active mechanical and electrical systems to provide the needed environmental control not available through use of passive systems—i.e., electric lighting during non-daylight hours
- Design the best building environmental control and feedback systems to enable the optimum sequencing of building operations from passive modes to active mechanical modes, and to provide building occupants with feedback regarding their use of individual building zones of control.

Certain decisions that impact the building's performance are made earlier in integrated design than they are in a conventional design, such as the selection of mechanical and electrical systems but not necessarily the size of those systems. The designer needs to work with existing hospital staff skill sets when designing systems.

Project Kickoff

The project kickoff meeting is critically important to success, as it is used to establish the Owner's Project Requirements (OPR). This exercise allows the owner's personnel and stakeholders to define what a successful project means for them. The requirements can cover construction costs, longevity, operating costs, specific characteristics, spaces required, functional aspects, specific maintenance or system preferences, frequency of use, aspirational goals, and any other critical issues. Functional requirements would typically include indoor environmental quality aspirations, such design criteria for available power density to support business processes, thermal comfort for occupants, acoustic performance of the space, lighting levels to support the necessary work tasks, and sufficient ventilation for indoor air quality (IAQ). It is strongly recommended that the traditional OPR arising from the commissioning process be further augmented to include the following information:

- Targeted absolute energy use intensities (EUIs)
- Energy and/or energy/green building rating targets—e.g., ENERGY STAR® (EPA 2011), bEQ (ASHRAE 2012), Leadership in Energy and Environmental Design (LEED®) (USGBC 2011), or Green Globes (GBI 2011)
- Payback period/return on investment thresholds used by the owner with regard to intelligent investment in construction upgrades
- Clear prioritization of the requirements as "necessary for basic function," "necessary for intended function," and "desired upgrades"
- Clear prioritization of the topics within each of the categories in the preceding bullet point to guide future fund allocation decisions
- Clear delineation of the hierarchy related to decision making among the owner's constituent parties (who may request changes, who approves expenditures, etc.)
- Any preagreed-upon funding set-asides meant to achieve specific goals (such as those due to departmental contributions or a named donor)
- Any constraints imposed by the site, code, or planning agreements with the city, preexisting standards (if any), corporate sustainability policy statements, etc.

This OPR information is necessary so that all parties on the team are equally aware of the owner's priorities and can recommend systems that initially meet the stated criteria instead of spending time chasing alternates that cannot succeed and therefore will not receive ownership buy-in later in the process. This lowers risk for all parties with regard to rework and provides a written document to refer to when budgetary pressures arise later in the design cycle. It is fully acknowledged that the OPR may evolve over time to accommodate owner preferences that are only made apparent as the design progresses. Nevertheless, it is good practice to have a consolidated location for listing all original and added intent.

Predesign

A successful predesign process incorporates a series of free-flowing brainstorming sessions that allow the integrated design team to review the OPR in the context of the site to look for opportunities and risks. A key conceptual exercise usually covers a series of holistic site investigations and building configuration studies to look at which alternate best addresses the following issues:

- Status of site conditions (preexisting shading or wind-shadows from adjacent buildings or landscaping, outdoor air quality, outdoor ambient noise environment, site surface material).
- Availability of natural resources (sun, wind, geothermal energy, climate, bodies of water) for daylighting and minimization of cooling loads from the climates' hot exterior temperatures and solar heat gain. This defines the roles and active participation in the integrated design team of an early energy modeler and a daylighting consultant.
- Site documentation with regard to utility availability.
- Status of surrounding buildings and review of code/planning regulations that may create obstructions to natural resources in the future or otherwise limit the design (such as the effects of the proposed building on its neighbors or other city planning concerns).
- Hardscaping or landscaping potential to reduce heat island effect or provide natural shading.

Building Information Modeling

Building information modeling (BIM) can save time, cost, and energy by facilitating energy and daylight modeling and by supporting an integrated design, construction, and operations process.

BIM software packages have evolved in recent years to incorporate design-friendly tools for conceptual- and schematic-level daylighting and energy analysis. All major BIM packages now have a conceptual-level energy plug-in. Design teams should be aware of the capabilities and limitations of these early design-phase energy analysis tools. They don't take the place of more detailed energy and daylight models, but they can pave the way for improvements to massing, orientation, and other important decisions that are typically made early in a project (Stumpf and Brucker 2008). The BIM design model can be set up to serve as a starting place for a more detailed energy model, depending on what software is chosen. BIM models can also be set up for use with a variety of different daylighting or shading analysis software packages. However, given the different software structures, goals, and outcomes of the early-phase analysis and detailed energy and daylight models, the same programs typically wouldn't be used for both types of models.

Use of BIM in construction documents and construction administration does not alone lead to more energy-efficient buildings, but it can assist in the construction of a tighter building envelope and reduce conflicts in the design and construction of highly integrated systems. All of the energy-efficient mechanical systems discussed in this Guide require considerable coordination with architectural, plumbing, structural, and other building components and systems. Use of BIM during design and construction can support this effort (Eastman et al. 2011).

(continued next page)

Example BIM Output
Reprinted with permission of HOK

BIM can also help improve occupant comfort and save time, money, and energy when used in facility management. It offers an opportunity to help manage future system performance through a combination of routine commissioning and the support of more intelligent system modifications and alterations. The type and quantity of information BIM provides the owner offers enormous potential for energy savings when fully developed. Finding ways to develop system component efficiencies for partial load modeling, paired with advanced building automation systems (BAS) can provide owners a powerful tool.

For example, imagine a BAS that picks up a high-temperature alarm at a variable-air-volume (VAV) box. The BAS is programmed to cycle a valve in order to try and correct the issue without manual intervention. If that does not clear the alarm, the BAS automatically opens a corrective maintenance ticket in the computer maintenance management system (CMMS). The CMMS inventory database identifies the VAV box in question as one serving a patient room and queries the BAS to determine if the room is occupied in order to set the appropriate priority on the work ticket. It then queries its own maintenance database for any existing maintenance history for this component. Finally, it queries the BIM database for the aforementioned data. Before a patient even notices an issue, a service technician is dispatched with an emergency work order to fix the VAV box located 14 ft off the floor above ceiling tile 101-C in suite B5. Because the technician was given the manufacturers name, box type, and service history, he or she has the correct tools and materials to make the repairs on the first trip to the site.

When combined with CMMS software and a well-maintained BAS, BIM can allow the facility management program to be more proactive and cost effective in terms of both maintenance and energy costs.

Example BIM Output
Reprinted with permission of HOK

The goal of the design meetings is to quickly pass through a number of schemes, including system choices and their implications for building configuration, occupant comfort, and energy efficiency, in order to assess their pros and cons. One cannot expect to link precise energy efficiency levels or hard costs to each model in real time, or to determine the final systems, but on the basis of past experience, the integrated design team can rank each scheme qualitatively against the OPR. The exercise usually results in the entire team coming to some fundamental realization of the large-scale site constraints and identifying the three top architectural alternate configurations that might best meet the most fundamental of the OPR.

Schematic Design

Schematic design is meant to give the integrated design team time to further develop the ideas that are still feasible given the OPR and the constraints of the site. In this phase, team members usually formalize how the various program occupancies fit in the building. Typical approaches generally locate building occupants toward the perimeter of the building to improve their connection to the outdoors, thus leaving the core of the building for frequently unoccupied zones (conference rooms, copier rooms, storage areas, stairs, and restrooms) and high-heat-load areas, such as server rooms, where energy can be recovered.

Very quickly this leads to identifying where in the façade windows can be located to enhance the indoor environment for occupants. At this point, the prediction of solar extent is recommended to assess the exposure of intended glazing locations and the resulting penetration of solar rays into the occupied perimeter zone. It is strongly recommended at this early phase that the design team also perform a back-check on glazing areas and thermal performance against the ASHRAE/IESNA Standard 90.1 prescriptive requirements or the recommendations of this Guide for the relevant climate zone. Such a check allows the integrated design team to avoid becoming too attached to a heavily glazed scheme that may potentially fail to meet energy efficiency goals. Early discovery of this allows funds that might have been spent on increased glazing area to be more appropriately allocated to improve the glazing performance or the overall building services performance to further reduce energy use. Similarly, a more detailed weather/climate/natural resource analysis usually quantifies true frequency of occurrence potential for the following:

- Natural ventilation for cooling
- Daylighting
- Heat recovery
- Use of radiant surfaces

All of this additional analysis begins to inform the design team with regard to which mechanical and electrical systems could be installed in order to provide a comfortable indoor environment. As a start, nominal mechanical and electrical plant room sizes, riser locations, and ceiling cross-sectional depths should be generated for the most traditional services approach, as this serves as a base case for first cost and life-cycle cost comparisons in subsequent phases. Additionally, occupancy schedules need to be developed in order to perform energy modeling and to carry over into control sequences and commissioning.

Once a base-case building is created, its cost is estimated and compared to the OPR to ensure that even the most standard of the available designs meets first-cost and program requirements. If this is the case, it is often useful to perform a preliminary energy analysis by zone to determine approximate annual operating costs. This usually involves analyzing energy for one representative room per floor-plate zone (north, south, east, west, and interior) and projecting from that result an energy usage on a per-square-foot basis that can be extrapolated across all of the areas of similar characteristics. During schematic design, this level of calculation is usually good enough to confirm trends in energy savings associated with key design decisions.

The last necessary piece of work for the schematic design phase is to identify bundles of energy conservation measures (ECMs) that represent specific efficiency scenarios and are compared to the base case. This is the point at which it is necessary to document a thorough discussion of trade-offs, as choices have cascading effects on other systems. Typical exploratory interdisciplinary discussions during this phase include the following:

- Selection of structural material and its relative use as thermal mass or thermal insulation
- Selection of general internal finish type and color so as to improve their potential to absorb internal heat gains and improve the luminosity of spaces from their reflected light
- Selection of façade type and orientation and each face's relative proportion and performance of glazing and opaque wall insulation
- Selection of glazing visible transmittance (VT) versus solar heat gain coefficient to allow daylighting without overheating
- Configuration of roofing shape/slope/direction and applicability of cool-roofing materials, clerestory skylights, and/or installation of photovoltaic or solar hot-water panels
- Selection of electric lighting approach and zoning compatibility to accommodate ambient versus task lighting, occupancy sensors, daylight harvesting, and time-of-day controls
- Commitment to ENERGY STAR equipment for plug-load usage reduction
- Review of plug-load use intensity by the hospital
- Review of alternative HVAC and comfort cooling systems and technologies covered in Section 5

As a conclusion to the discussions, the design team usually identifies a certain number of ECMs that they wish to pursue as optimizations imposed onto the base case. At that point, a fuller, more complex energy model is created to test the relative operating cost savings that are achieved for having invested first costs to install the upgrade. A matrix of options is usually developed to allow the integrated design team to assess each ECM against a common set of criteria, usually including at least the following:

- Additional first-cost investment
- Anticipated capital cost increase or reduction
- Anticipated annual energy cost savings
- Anticipated annual maintenance cost savings
- Simple payback period
- Return on investment (ROI)
- Reduction of $kBtu/ft^2/yr$
- Carbon emissions savings
- Additional percentage savings as compared to ASHRAE/IES Standard 90.1-2010 (ASHRAE 2010)
- Potential to achieve "Designed to Earn the ENERGY STAR—Commercial New Construction" designation (EPA 2011)
- Potential additional USGBC LEED points for Energy and Atmosphere Credit 1 (USGBC 2011)
- Range of indoor temperatures achieved throughout the year
- Range of lighting levels achieved throughout the year

There will likely be other project-specific OPRs that should be incorporated into the matrix. The key point is that it is important for all parties to understand the whole view of any ECM application so that a balanced decision can be made, inclusive of all impacts on the desired goals of the project. The goal is to pick a selection of ECMs to pursue on a single scheme during the design development phase. The alignment of design intent within the integrated design team, including ownership and energy utility interests, is crucial before significant design work and final calculations begin in the next phase of project development.

Design Development

The design development phase involves applying the final package of ECMs onto the unique architectural scheme for the project. The final energy models are usually used for submission

Be Green without Spending the Green
Excerpted from "Green on a Budget" (Nicklas 2008)

Although many green building options have lower construction and operational costs than conventional approaches, the designers that pursue higher degrees of sustainability are challenged by initial costs. To achieve the highest level of sustainability within budget, begin the design by implementing strategies, systems, materials, and products that have a lower initial cost.

Projects have many design trade-offs, which still will meet or exceed the owner's objectives without impacting quality. If designers begin the project with the belief that sustainability is an important component of the design, they will view potential trade-offs in different ways. The result likely will be the implementation of more sustainable concepts, while staying within the overall project budget. By making smart trade-offs, firms can integrate sustainable design strategies and still keep projects an average of 5% under budget.

Start with basic objectives such as saving energy and water, helping the environment, improving indoor environment quality, and using resources efficiently. Judge the solutions based on impact. Considering the budget, determine what strategy or groups of strategies will make the most positive impact.

Form Follows Function

A basic concept taught to every architectural student is that form follows function. When this concept is practiced, the result is almost always cost and resource savings. Unfortunately, designers often ignore this creed. Poor examples are everywhere. There are ramifications when functional benefits can only be rationalized after the architects created design elements based primarily on aesthetics.

Complementary Strategies

Think whole building, not individual measures. Typically, a single green approach, by itself, will be more expensive than conventional approaches. But, in combination with other green elements, the overall impact may be significant enough to lower first costs and improve sustainability.

Dual Function Approaches

Whether designing building or site components, the more functions that can be served by one design element, the more resourceful and cost efficient the design.

to code authorities to show compliance with ASHRAE/IES Standard 90.1 and may be used for submissions for LEED. The development of the scheme includes further design, calculation, and documentation of all building envelope, lighting, and mechanical/plumbing services that are regulated by code, and owner-agreed limits on plug-load densities. Additionally, there is often a financial investment/life-cycle cost analysis (LCCA) of the ECM components in conjunction with the cost estimates, which are more detailed at this phase. The LCCA gives the entire team greater confidence in the value of the investment in all ECM upgrades at a point in the project where there are often pressures to engage in value engineering and other cost-cutting exercises. During this phase, the focus is primarily on documentation and implementation of design intent, and most disciplines with energy-using devices will write a Basis of Design (BoD) report that explains the full design and control intent. This BoD is then compared by the commissioning authority (CxA) to the OPR during a peer-review process to ensure that the owner's goals are likely to be met by the current state of design.

This phase usually provides a more detailed cost confirmation to ensure that the ECMs as applied have not adversely affected the construction budget. It should be noted that there are often value engineering discussions that occur during this phase, and items might be removed from the OPR or downgraded from "necessary" requirements in order to allow the project to move forward. If an ECM is removed or downgraded in this value-engineering phase, the unintended consequences of this decision must be explored; e.g., lowering the glazing visible transmittance (VT) to reduce solar heat gain may eliminate daylighting as an ECM, which will require investigation of additional ECMs to meet the stated energy-savings goals.

Because controls are essential to achieve energy efficiency at the levels proposed by this Guide, it is recommended that the design team produce a preliminary document describing the controls design intent for each category of HVAC and lighting equipment, including zoning approaches, required feedback, and energy-use monitoring, anticipated normal and emergency sequences of operations, and corrective algorithms to quickly return the system to an energy-efficient operation after it has been disrupted from stable operation. It is recommended that these sequences be reviewed by the CxA to ensure their feasibility in practical application.

Construction Documents

The construction documents (CDs) phase is the final detailing of all systems, inclusive of sustainability features, energy target goals, and ECMs. The mechanical, electrical, and plumbing systems incorporate system drawings, specifications, BoD reports, controls drawings, controls points lists, and sequences of operation. The CxA usually reviews all of the documents and the updated BoD in order to confirm for the owner that the currently stated goals are on track to be met.

At this point in the design life, it is important for the construction team to confirm detailed constructability related to coordination, to review cost optimization and waste-reduction techniques or sizing methods to be incorporated in the final drawings, and to confirm that they will provide the necessary documentation and acquisition of materials to meet the performance requirements for each of the energy-conservation measures. Additionally, the construction team should review the controls strategies and have clarification embedded into the specifications if there is an ambiguity about design intent.

It is essential to have a fully documented controls package inclusive of points list, controls drawings, and sequences of operation for every controlled system in the building. This includes traditional and hybrid-passive HVAC systems, integrated daylighting and electric lighting systems, and any plug-load setback or shutdown systems. The integration of a controls contractor at this point in the process is recommended to ensure that the intended sequences are capable of being programmed given the control system architectures available on the market. The designer, controls contractor, and CxA should review the intent in a collaborative method to ensure the success of the stable control of all components as an integrated system and to identify any high-risk areas associated with implementation in the field.

Bid Phase

On many integrated design teams, the construction team is already on board before the end of construction documents. If that is not the case, however, general contractors and major subcontractors are brought in at this phase. It is necessary for the entire integrated project design team to educate bidders on design intent and to stress the team's commitment to the ECMs that have been proposed. As the team grows exponentially during the construction phase, it is an absolute necessity that all incoming parties be brought into the collaborative mind set and indoctrinated with the projects principles, approaches, and commitment to low-energy design.

Construction

During the construction phase, the CxA and the design professionals on the integrated project design team review submittals to ensure compliance of the proposed materials with the required performance as stated within the CDs. The integrated design team ensures that items are installed to meet all regulatory requirements and are in compliance with the manufacturers' warranty and performance requirements. All parties are responsible for reviewing the installation, reporting any deficiencies in installed work, and requiring remedial efforts to correct. Any deviation from the CDs must be documented with proof that the substitution will not adversely affect energy efficiency.

Near the end of the construction process, after all equipment is installed and the building is closed, equipment manufacturers perform testing procedures during start-up and confirm that the equipment is correctly operational. A testing, adjusting, and balancing (TAB) contractor manipulates the settings on the equipment to achieve the correct water flows and airflows as required in the CDs. The CxA writes prefunctional checklists on the basis of the equipment submittals that were reviewed during the construction phase. The CxA turns these checklists over to the construction team to complete based on the manufacturers' start-up reports and other collected information, such as warranty and wiring information.

The contracting team and the manufacturers' representatives are responsible for producing a set of operation and maintenance (O&M) manuals and performing the specific hours of training for the owner's personnel. It is strongly recommended that the key technical facility operators of the building be brought on board at least a month before the prefunctional checklists are started so that they can familiarize themselves with the design intent and then accompany the contractor during the prefunctional checklist and functional testing protocols in order to familiarize themselves with the physical equipment.

Commissioning

The commissioning (Cx) process is the last performance testing applied to most new building projects. Once the prefunctional checklists are complete, the CxA visits the site and performs a random sampling to back-check a percentage of results to confirm that the reported findings are true and repeatable. Once this is confirmed, the CxA releases the functional test procedures, which were written in response to the contractor's detailed sequence of operations as submitted. The CxA supervises the controls contractor running the equipment through its paces to prove adequate automatic reaction of the system in response to artificially applied inputs that simulate a variety of extreme, transition, emergency, and normal conditions. When this functional testing is complete to the satisfaction of the CxA, a report is written for the owner, and handover can occur with confidence on the part of the owner that he or she has a fully functional building that meets the remaining requirements of the OPR.

The following activities and the associated personnel should be considered:

- Site-based Cx requires input from at least the following parties: the general contractor; the mechanical, electrical, controls, and TAB subcontractors; the CxA; the owner's representative; and the mechanical, electrical, and lighting designers.
- Prefunctional test procedures usually require evaluation of motors and wiring by the electrical subcontractor and the manufacturer's representative and evaluation of component performance by the manufacturer's representative and the mechanical, TAB, and controls subcontractors. The CxA generally samples to back-check the values reported in the prefunctional checklist results.
- Functional tests involve the CxA and the controls and TAB subcontractors at a minimum.

Additionally, the CxA usually assists with supervision of the formal training of the owner's personnel in order to coach them on the appropriate corrective actions to take in the event that the system starts to drift away from its commissioned state. It is often useful, if possible, to run and monitor key aspects of the building for a one-month period just before handover and to verify energy-related performance and the final setpoint configurations in the handover O&M documents. This allows the owner to return the systems to the commissioned state (assuming good maintenance protocols) at a future point and have a set of comparative results.

In addition to the usual tests of control sequences, it is also important to document that the building is ready from an IAQ point of view, as it is necessary to remove the construction-related odors and off-gassing chemicals from the air volume of the space prior to permanent occupancy.

This can be accomplished through physical testing in which concentrations of typical pollutants are measured and compared to health standards. It can also be proven (with agreement of all team members) through the careful documentation of preoccupancy purge procedures, which usually involve multiple hours of 100% ventilation air supply.

Because of the need for strong continuity of operations procedures, it is recommended that emergency test scenarios to simulate loss of power, loss of water, or loss of other critical functions be developed to include restoration of service and return to normal operations. Quality assurance, including Cx, is discussed in more detail in Chapter 5.

Operation and Maintenance (O&M)

Operation and maintenance of equipment and systems after handover is crucial to achieving the planned energy savings goals for the life of the building. Very often, the first year after occupancy reveals a truer nature of the real occupancy patterns within the building than those included in the predictive energy model. Experience shows that many high-performance buildings never achieve their anticipated performance due to the complexity of the systems and the difficulty of operating them in the most effective ways. Education of the facility operation staff during design and hand-off must be a central element of the development process.

One way to ensure effective operation is to contract with the CxA to return at the 12–18 month mark after handover to review the status of operations at that point in time and recommend slight adjustments to setpoints or modifications to the controls sequences in order to optimize the operation of the equipment with a view toward minimizing energy use. Occasionally, a second measurement and verification exercise is performed at this time to benchmark the energy use of each piece of equipment, usually in a season different from that of the original measurement and verification exercise if there are extreme seasonal differences in the given climate.

Project delivery with incentives tagged to building performance is another way to ensure that the building meets its intended energy performance goals. The National Renewable Energy Laboratory (NREL) has pioneered a design-build-perform mode of project delivery that seeks to ensure that a building actually performs as its designers intend and that uses financial incentives for all parties to ensure such performance.

Maintenance is the second owner-controlled aspect of operational efficiency. The O&M manuals contain volumes of information about regular preventative maintenance, annualized maintenance activities, and periodic overhauls that should be performed to keep the equipment running at top performance. Just a few examples of how lack of attention to these matters can greatly reduce efficiency include: dirty filters increasing pressure drops, broken sensors causing poor feedback for the controls system, broken actuators disrupting demand-controlled ventilation (DCV) and/or air-side economizer cycles, and poor water quality fouling heat exchangers and inner surfaces of piping. Additionally, beyond the energy-efficiency issues, poor maintenance can lead to reduced performance. Examples include poor IAQ arising from microbial growth occurring due to bad condensate drain pan maintenance, reduced indoor lighting levels due to depreciation of lamp output or dirt accumulation on lighting fixtures, and discomfort arising from lack of modulating control of supply air due to out-of-calibration sensors within the space.

Of crucial importance to effective operation is a system of meters and controls that allows the operator to understand the ongoing performance of the building and to make appropriate adjustments to better tune the systems and achieve the desired performance levels. Hospital energy systems are complex, particularly the power distribution systems, and they interact with each other in ways that are not always obvious, especially to the untrained facility operator. Careful attention to the placement of metering in strategic, highly leveragable points of the various systems must be a critical design component, one that is tested during the commissioning process and carefully demonstrated to the facility operation staff on building handover.

Ongoing Occupant Engagement

Clevenger and Haymaker (2006) show that energy performance is as often as much about occupant behavior as it is about technical design. The experience of the authors is that facility operations staff are forced to set their systems in what they loosely describe as "least complaint mode." That is, due to their staffing levels, they prefer to set the system parameters to minimize callbacks rather than to maximize energy savings. This phenomenon derives from occupant behavior and intolerance for varied climate comfort as well as from differences in perception between relatively sedate patients wearing only a thin gauze gown and harried healthcare staff actively moving around, lifting patients, and delivering care.

The psychology behind occupant comfort is complex, and the overriding goal of patient comfort cannot be compromised. Nonetheless, there is ample opportunity to align healthcare staff and facility operations staff so that consistently improved energy performance can be realized. Experience from the California Energy Crisis of 2001 shows clearly that building occupants and facility staff can achieve significant energy demand reductions on a sustained basis when properly motivated (Goldman et al. 2002). One significant opportunity is to ensure occupant control over their environment. Many facility systems in healthcare deny control to the occupant in order to ensure maximum system safety, but again, Galasiu and Newsham (2009) clearly show that giving occupants greater control over their environment and providing them incentives through education and other methods, can lead to easy and dramatic reductions in energy use.

In buildings designed for low energy use, it is always important to remember that occupant behavior is crucial to achieving anticipated performance. When people understand the goals of the building and their roles, they can substantially reduce energy use. It can be beneficial for the design and construction team to host a lunchtime talk for the initial occupants and describe the building's design intent and sustainability features. This is the ideal venue in which to introduce an occupant education guide and to allow the local leadership to state support for the energy-efficiency initiative in the building. It is important to forewarn occupants that although the building was commissioned, low-energy buildings sometimes take a season or two to settle on their final, optimized control strategies, so all occupants are invited to submit comments on performance as additional inputs for improving the operations. This type of personal engagement not only encourages positive-impact behaviors with the initial occupants, but these first adopters can act as efficiency coaches for all future staff members. For optimum results, occupant engagement programs should be deployed on an ongoing basis.

FINANCIAL CONSIDERATIONS

Budget Sharing

One often heard but fundamentally unnecessary question is "Whose budget pays for improved energy efficiency?" The answer is always "The owner's budget!" When a team commits itself to delivering low-energy, holistic solutions, it is virtually impossible to separate by trade or discipline the cost of energy efficiency measures "purchased" during the course of the project through its respective design decisions. A classic example is the cost of shading: there are increased structural and façade costs, but these may be offset by reduced capital costs for window glazing and air conditioning. These trade-offs are absolutely necessary to explore in consideration of the particular goals and context of the building. As long as the overall building construction budget remains consistent with the OPR, it doesn't matter where the money was spent if the whole building performs.

What this tells us, however, is that discipline-based construction budget allocations might be inappropriate for the integrated design paradigm and should be reviewed early in the project. Similarly, it might be argued that traditional fee percentages may also unintentionally preventing the disciplines most capable of proposing and proving energy-reduction techniques from applying their analytical technologies and abilities to the solutions. For example, a fee based on the cost of the mechanical systems rewards more expensive (often higher capacity) systems, which is not generally the result of an integrated design.

Lastly, the EUI "budget" itself must also be equitably shared. The building envelope does not consume energy but significantly affects the energy use of mechanical and lighting systems. Therefore, it is important for design teams to carefully review the relative proportion of energy use by discretionary design choice and collectively tackle those systems/features that represent the greediest energy users. A classic example of an energy-wasting feature is the use of all-glass façades with the expectation that highly efficient HVAC systems will somehow accommodate for the extravagant and inefficient design; thankfully, the energy codes are now written to avoid this practice. Another more subtle example is the issue of plug loads in highly efficient buildings. As the intentional reduction of lighting and mechanical energy use is applied, the plug loads grow in a relative manner to upward of 30%. This should immediately tell all parties that plug loads need to be addressed, either with automatic shutdown controls or with substantial reduction in required, desired, or assumed load on the part of the owner and design team. If the team knows that it is accountable for sharing the responsibility for the end energy-use burden, it sets the tone for sharing the energy-savings burden as well.

ECM Investment Financial Analysis

Many energy-saving measures that exceed code minimum provisions require higher initial investments. Building owners and designers often justify such first-cost premiums through various forms of financial analysis demonstrating the long-run value of the investment. The Sustainability Roadmap for Hospitals Web site (AHA 2012) contains a worksheet developed in conjunction with various healthcare chief financial officers to facilitate the calculation of simple instances of these kinds of measures. Various federal agencies define particular methodologies they require, including some of the inputs (see, e.g., 10 C.F.R. 436). Commonly used methods for such financial analysis include the following:

- *Simple payback period* is a calculation method that divides first costs by the annual energy cost savings to determine how long it will take to break even on the investment. Because of its relative simplicity, this is probably the most common method of analysis, but also the most limited in its accuracy.
- *Discounted payback* is similar to simple payback but adds a discount factor to the annual cash flows in order to take into account the time value of money.
- *Return on investment* (ROI) is a calculation of the energy savings over a predefined number of years minus the first costs divided by the first costs. It essentially answers the question "What is my rate of return on the investment?" and allows a somewhat parallel comparison to the rate of return used in the financial markets.
- *Life-cycle cost*, in its simplest form, aggregates all of the costs (first costs, maintenance costs, energy costs, replacement costs) and all of the savings (energy cost savings, tax savings due to depreciation, end-of-life salvage value) anticipated for the life of the piece of equipment or possibly the building. Discounting the value of these inputs to take into account the time value of money results in a net present value.
- *Net present value* measures in current dollars the multiyear value of a particular financial investment, taking into account the first costs; the expected life of the device; the replacement costs; the annual operating costs; and even, for taxable entities, the tax deductions available due to depreciation, all discounted by the appropriate factor. Properly performed, this is the most accurate way to measure the investment.
- *Internal rate of return* measures the rate of return that makes the net present value of all cash flows for the investment equal to zero. This method is most accurate when compared to a known cost of capital (investments with initial rate of return greater than the known cost of capital should be undertaken). This method can also be used to rank various alternative investments.
- *Impact to bottom line* measures the annual expense likely to be borne by the organization over the life of the investment. It spreads the first costs of the investment over an appropriate number of years through depreciation. Some healthcare financial experts argue that this is the correct way to think about the impact of a proposed energy investment.

None of these methods of analysis can ultimately determine whether an organization can, should, or would pursue a particular investment; ultimately, any capital investment will compete for available capital from the organization according to its pressures and priorities.

Finally, it is important to note that the discussion above has assumed the purchase of the energy investment by the organization that is independent of financing methods. A wide and increasing number and variety of methods is available to finance projects, in addition to changing incentive programs for particular technologies. Choosing the right mix of energy reduction investments should include financial analysis, capital availability assessment, available incentives, and intended financing vehicles.

REFERENCES AND RESOURCES

AHA. 2012. Business Case Cost-Benefit Worksheet. Sustainability Roadmap for Hospitals, the American Society for Healthcare Engineering, American Hospital Association, Chicago, IL. http://www.sustainabilityroadmap.org/strategies/businesscase.shtml.

AIA. 2007. *Integrated Project Delivery: A Guide*. Washington, DC: American Institute of Architects (AIA National and AIA California Council). http://www.aia.org/contractdocs/AIAS077630.

ASHRAE. 2010. ANSI/ASHRAE/IES Standard 90.1-2010, *Energy Standard for Buildings Except Low-Rise Residential Buildings*. Atlanta: ASHRAE.

ASHRAE. 2012. Building Energy Quotient (eQ). www.buildingeq.com. Atlanta: ASHRAE.

Clevenger, C.M., and J. Haymaker. 2006. The impact of the building occupant on energy modeling simulations. Stanford University, Stanford, CA. Accessed September 30, 2011, from http://peec.stanford.edu/people/profiles/Caroline_Clevenger.php.

Eastman, C.M., P. Teicholz, R. Sacks, and K. Liston. 2011. *BIM Handbook: A Guide to Building Information Modeling for Owners, Managers, Designers, Engineers and Contractors*. Hoboken, NJ: John Wiley and Sons.

EIA. 2008. Consumption and Efficiency. 2003 CBECS Detailed Tables. http://www.eia.gov/emeu/cbecs/cbecs2003/detailed_tables_2003/detailed_tables_2003.html#consumexpen03. Washington, DC: U.S. Energy Information Administration.

EPA. 2011. ENERGY STAR. www.energystar.gov.Washington, DC: U.S. Environmental Protection Agency.

Galasiu, A.D., and G.R. Newsham, G.R. 2009. Energy savings due to occupancy sensors and personal controls: A pilot field study. National Research Council Canada, Ontario, Ottowa. Accessed September 30, 2011 from http://www.nrc-cnrc.gc.ca/obj/irc/doc/pubs/nrcc51264.pdf.

GBI. 2011. Green Globes. www.greenglobes.com. Portland, OR: Green Building Initiative.

Goldman, C.A., J.H. Eto, and G.L. Barbose. 2002. California customer load reductions during the electricity crisis: Did they help to keep the lights on? Lawrence Berkeley National Laboratory, Berkeley, CA. Accessed on September 30, 2011, from http://eetd.lbl.gov/ea/ems/reports/49733.pdf.

MTS. 2007. *ANSI/MTS 1.0 Whole Systems Integrated Process Guide (WSIP)-2007 for Sustainable Buildings & Communities*. Washington, DC: Institute for Market Transformation to Sustainability.

Nicklas, M. 2008. Green on a budget. *High Performing Buildings* (Fall 2008):6–16.

Stumpf, A., and B. Brucker. 2008. BIM enables early design energy analysis. U.S. Army Corps of Engineers, Engineer Research and Development Center, Construction Engineering Research Laboratory. http://www.cecer.army.mil/td/tips/docs/BIM-EnergyAnalysis.pdf.

USGBC. 2011. Leadership in Energy and Environmental Design (LEED) Green Building Rating System. www.usgbc.org/Display Page.aspx?CategoryID=19. Washington, DC: U.S. Green Building Council.

USGBC. 2012. About USGBC. http://www.usgbc.org/DisplayPage.aspx?CMSPageID=124. Washington, DC: U.S. Green Building Council.

WHO. 2009. *WHO Guideline 2009—Natural Ventilation for Infection Control in Health-Care Settings*. World Health Organization, Geneva, Switzerland.

CLEVELAND CLINIC A CASE STUDY

In 2011, Cleveland Clinic opened two new family health centers (FHC) and ambulatory surgery centers (ASC) in Northeast Ohio. The two campuses are nearly identical in size, services, and cost to construct but have different energy performances. As they were designed and built concurrently, the difference in performance is rooted in the decisions made by the design teams as they attempted to maximize the environment of care performance in accordance with Cleveland Clinic design standards.

Both campuses provide primary and specialty care, outpatient surgery, and a full-service emergency department, and are designed to reduce energy consumption and incorporate a number of efficiency measures and design features by following the U.S. Green Building Council Guidelines for LEED-NC while still maintaining a commitment to creating healthy environments for the delivery of world-class care.

INTERIOR LIGHTING

Campus 1

Circulation and public waiting areas, predominantly around the perimeter, were configured to maximize daylighting and to provide light and views, and special attention was taken to limit the use of electric lighting and to provide a highly efficient lighting system. The result is a combined building lighting power density (LPD) of approximately 0.61 W/ft^2 and an overall decrease in lighting energy consumption of 46% over ASHRAE/ASHE Standard 90.1-2004 requirements. Specific measures used include the following:

- A combination of T5 and light-emitting diode (LED) fixtures are used in the building.
- Luminaires are controlled by an automated lighting control system which is also used for all outdoor lighting, public spaces, and support areas that are not occupied on a 24-hour basis.
- Occupancy sensors are installed in public restrooms.
- Lighting in office areas consists primarily of fluorescent fixtures with multilevel switching or dimming ballasts.
- Lighting in exam rooms, treatment rooms, and similar patient care areas consists of lensed fixtures with automatic multilevel switching control at the entrance door.
- Lighting in corridors and public waiting areas is achieved with recessed LED lighting.
- All corridors/public waiting areas are controlled by the network lighting control system.
- Perimeter corridor areas with glass walls include photocell sensors for daylight harvesting.
- Exit signs with light-emitting capacitor (LEC) lamp technology are installed. The LEC exit sign draws 0.25 W per exit sign compared to 12 W LED technology.

Campus 2

The interior lighting was designed with a lighting power density of 1.06 W/ft^2 for the entire building, and the campus achieved a 19% reduction in energy usage over Standard 90.1-2004 requirements. Measures employed include the following:

- Energy-efficient ballasts and T8 fixtures were used.
- Occupancy sensors were used in all areas where it would not be disruptive to patients or staff.
- Daylight harvesting was used in staff areas with southern, eastern, and western exposures.
- The building automation system (BAS) is used to turn off unnecessary lights during unoccupied building periods.

Cleveland Clinic Northeast Ohio Campus
Photos courtesy of Cleveland Clinic

Recessed LED Lighting in Mechanical Hallway (left) and Heliport Landing Area (right)
Photos courtesy of Cleveland Clinic

EXTERIOR LIGHTING

Campus 1

The site lighting levels are in compliance with IESNA, Cleveland Clinic standards, LEED dark sky, and LEED light trespass requirement, and the overall exterior lighting power density is 60% better than code requirements. The exterior parking area lighting includes the following:

- High-intensity discharge (HID) (metal halide) pole-mounted luminaires and HID (metal halide) bollards are used at pedestrian walkways and entrances.
- LED lamp sources are used for building signage.
- Heliport landing lights, beacons, obstruction lights and wind sock use LED light sources.
- Canopies use recessed LED downlights.
- All exterior lighting and signs are controlled by the network lighting control system.

Campus 2

The exterior lighting power was reduced by 82% over Standard 90.1-2004 requirements. To achieve this, LED lights were used in place of more traditional exterior lights, allowing for a reduction in the total number of poles required to light the parking lot, as well as providing greater energy efficiency and longer life.

HVAC

Campus 1

Energy modeling was used to predict annual energy performance and guide the design of mechanical systems to minimize energy consumption throughout the life of the facility. Specific systems used include the following:

- The FHC and noncritical areas of the ASC are heated, cooled, and ventilated by variable-air-volume packaged rooftop units. Dedicated outdoor air system (DOAS) units are connected to the packaged rooftop units at both the FHC and the ASC to provide fresh, filtered outdoor air to the building whenever a helicopter is detected and/or the emergency generator is in operation.
- The operating rooms and all related critical areas within the surgery suites are served by a single, custom-grade roof-mounted air-handling unit (AHU). A DOAS unit complete with carbon and high-efficiency filters provides fresh outdoor air to the AHU at all times.
- The main distribution frame (MDF), uninterruptable power supply (UPS), and information technology (IT) rooms in the ASC building are conditioned by either floor-mounted or ceiling-suspended computer room air-conditioning units that are connected to remote roof-mounted air-cooled condensers.

Electrical rooms and other temperature-sensitive rooms within the facility are served by a variable refrigerant flow system that incorporates the following:

- Fan-coil units are mounted directly within the space and are interconnected to a common air-cooled condensing unit on the roof.
- The main air-distribution ductwork extends to numerous VAV boxes with hot-water reheat coils on every floor. Each floor is subdivided into zones based on use and exposure.
- Every VAV box and reheat coil in the building is controlled by a wall-mounted thermostat. The reheat coils at the VAV boxes are sized to meet the minimum code ventilation requirements while providing tempered air to the occupied space.
- Hot-water radiant panels are located in all public areas that have large exterior glass walls. The wall-mounted thermostat that serves the VAV boxes in these areas also controls the hot-water control valve for the radiant panels.

The heating hot-water plant consists of two gas-fired, flexible water-tube boilers. Features include the following:

- Each boiler is sized to meet 70% of the load.
- A base mounted, variable-speed heating hot-water-pump package distributes hot water throughout the facility. The pump package consists of two horizontal end suction pumps, with each pump also sized for 70% of the load.
- Two natural-gas-fired storage-type water heaters provide domestic hot water for the facility, with each heater sized to meet 50% of the design load.

Campus 2

The campus is controlled by a fully automatic direct digital BAS. All HVAC equipment and lighting are controlled and monitored through the BAS and have adjustable setpoints. Specific systems used include the following:

Campus 1: Domestic Water Heaters (left) and High-Efficiency Water Tube Boilers (right)
Photos courtesy of Cleveland Clinic

 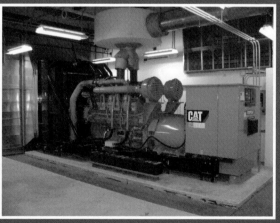

Campus 1: Pumps with Variable Frequency Drives (VFD) (left) and Emergency Generators (right)
Photos courtesy of Cleveland Clinic

- The FHC is served by two evaporatively cooled VAV rooftop units. The heating in these units is provided from the building heating hot-water system.
- The ASC is served by three VAV AHUs, each with equally sized, dual supply fans and dual return-air fans. The AHUs have coils fed from the building chilled-water and heating hot-water systems. A DOAS is provided for the operating room wing of the ASC. The DOAS uses a Type 3 desiccant to absorb moisture without the need for a regenerative section.
- VAV systems are used throughout the building to provide cooling with hot water reheat coils. Individual space sensors and thermostats maintain each room at 74°F cooling and 72°F heating.
- Exterior spaces are heated by hot-water fin-tube heaters controlled from the same sensors/thermostats as the VAV box in order to avoid simultaneously heating and cooling the same space.
- The building chilled water is provided by four 70 ton high-efficiency modular chillers that allow for excellent turndown ratios to meet building demand.
- Data rooms have computer-room-type air-conditioning units with associated outdoor-air-cooled condensing units.
- The electrical substation rooms are provided with mechanical cooling on noneconomizer days. When air economizing temperatures are able to be used, the room is cooled with outdoor air.

The building heating hot-water system is served by four gas-fired high-efficiency condensing boilers with efficiencies up to 92%. The chilled water and heating hot-water pumps are provided with VFD and premium-efficiency motors to reduce energy use. One module of the chiller and boiler was provided for redundancy in the event of a module failure.

Systems Comparison		
Element	**Campus 1**	**Campus 2**
Size	190,000 ft^2	190,000 ft^2
Energy savings over Standard 90.1-2004 minimum requirements	25% improvement	16% improvement
Anticipated LEED	42 points - Gold	38 points - Silver
Envelope		
Walls	R-10 (FHC), R-22 (ASC)	R-13
Roof	R-20, reflective	R-30, reflective
Glazing	U = 0.4, SHGC = 0.23	U = 0.35, SHGC = 0.215
Lighting		
Exterior	HID site, LED building	LED
Interior LPD	0.61 W/ft^2	1.06 W/ft^2
Lamps	LED downlights, T5 area lights	T8
EXIT signage	LEC	LED
HVAC		
FHC	Evaporatively cooled RTU with economizer with hot-water reheat	Evaporatively cooled RTU with economizer with hot-water reheat
ASC	Custom AHU with DOAS, forced-draft flex-tube heating boiler	AHU with high-efficiency modular chiller and condensing boilers
Pumps and motors	Premium efficiency	Premium efficiency

Energy Efficiency Strategies for Integrated Design

3

INTRODUCTION

Integrated design strategies begin to remove barriers between disciplines and are necessary to achieve energy efficiency of up to 50% over ASHRAE/IESNA Standard 90.1-2004 requirements (ASHRAE 2004). Chapter 3 focuses on key interdisciplinary opportunities and design strategies for achieving significant whole-building energy savings. Discussion is at a strategic level. More details on how to implement a particular component can be found in the how-to tips in Chapter 5.

The recommendation tables in Chapter 4 provide a prescriptive path for selecting components and reaching the 50% savings target, based on a conservative prototype model. Because it is unlikely that this model will be used for the shape or architectural design for every project, Chapter 3 returns control to an integrated team of design professionals responsible for making good decisions for a unique project on a specific site, especially a project whose characteristics do not match the baseline building in orientation and glazing.

Figure 3-1 shows the relative contribution of energy savings associated with each large-scale design component, building up to a 50% energy reduction over a Standard 90.1-2004 baseline building. None of the energy modeling achieved 50% energy savings through mechanical and lighting equipment optimization alone. Key architectural decisions associated with the configuration of the façade influence the heating, ventilating, and air conditioning (HVAC) and lighting components that drive energy use. Therefore, the performance of the envelope and its impact on loads and lighting is essential to reaching the energy use intensity (EUI) goal.

SETTING ENERGY TARGETS

To achieve a hospital that uses 50% less energy takes careful goal setting. One recognized approach is by setting a target of 50% less than a baseline hypothetical building built to an existing standard. Another best practice approach that provides a better defined target the goal, is to determine an absolute whole building energy use (EUI). Designers and owners should strive to set their own whole building EUI targets to provide focused and measurable 50% savings goals. These EUI targets can be used to select design teams as part of a procurement strategy, to set early design goals, to track design development progress, and to verify performance during operations. EUI targets can be generated from multiple data sources, including:

- 50% of the calculated energy use of a minimally prescriptive Standard 90.1-2004 compliant building. This level typically represents the high end of allowable energy use.
- U.S. Environmental Protection Agency's ENERGY STAR® Portfolio Manager (EPA 2011).
- U.S. Energy Information Administration's Commercial Buildings Energy Consumption Survey (CBECS) (EIA 2011).
- California Energy Commission's California Commercial End-Use Survey (CEUS) (CEC 2008).
- Other local hospitals in the area or in neighboring areas.
- Case studies of high-performance hospitals with similar programs and climate zones (see sidebars and case studies throughout this chapter).
- The recommended EUIs presented in Table 3-1 are based on a typical set configuration for hospitals. It is a good target, but may not apply if your hospital has specific high-use energy loads or other special circumstances.

In general, the energy targets in this Guide are applicable to most large hospitals with typical programs and use profiles. For the purpose of using these targets, a hospital is defined as having the following common space types:

- Cafeterias, kitchens, and dining facilities
- Administrative, conference, lobby, lounge, and office areas
- Reception/waiting areas and examination and treatment rooms
- Clean and soiled workrooms and holding areas
- Nurse stations, nurseries, patient rooms, hallways, lockers, and restrooms
- Operating rooms, procedure rooms, recovery rooms, and sterilizer equipment areas
- Pharmacies, medication rooms, laboratories

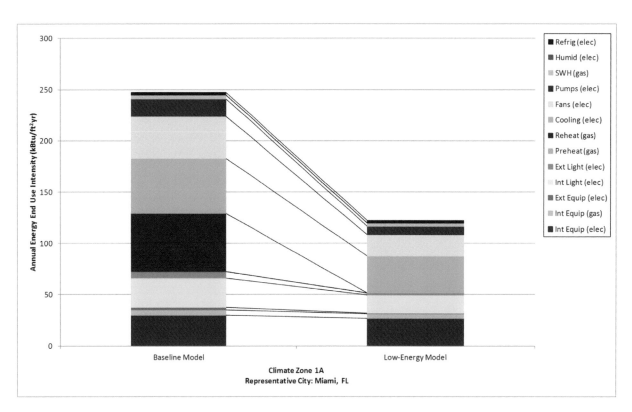

Figure 3-1   Comparison of Baseline to Prescriptive 50% AEDG Solution Showing Breakdown of Energy Savings Components

- Triage, trauma, and emergency rooms
- Physical therapy and imaging/radiology rooms
- Storage, receiving, laundry, and mechanical/electrical/telecomm rooms

The energy targets for large hospitals in this Guide are based on a 427,000 ft^2 prototype large-hospital design and apply to all sizes and classifications of new-construction hospital buildings. The models meet minimum ventilation requirements and maintain ASHRAE comfort standards year round. However, there are situations where the assumptions in the models may not apply to a specific building. Caution should be used when applying these targets, especially if your hospital

- has atypical or specialty spaces with extraordinary heat or pollution generation.
- has a low percentage of diagnostic/treatment and inpatient unit space. A hospital with a greater percentage of clinical or office space would have a lower energy target.
- is located where it does not experience typical weather within its climate zone (Figure 3-2).
- has use patterns that do not align with the specific modeled plug load and control assumptions.
- has equipment that is not properly operating or is not well maintained.
- staff has not been trained to make energy-use choices that are consistent with the modeled assumptions.

Table 3-1 Large-Hospital Energy Use Targets to Achieve 50% Energy Savings

Climate Zone	Plug/Process Loads, kBtu/ft^2·yr	Lighting, kBtu/ft^2·yr	HVAC, Btu/ft^2·yr	Total, kBtu/ft^2·yr
1A			68	124
2A			68	124
2B			63	119
3A			62	118
3B:CA			55	111
3B			55	111
3C			55	111
4A			65	121
4B	38	18	50	106
4C			55	111
5A			67	123
5B			51	107
6A			69	125
6B			55	111
7			69	125
8			84	140

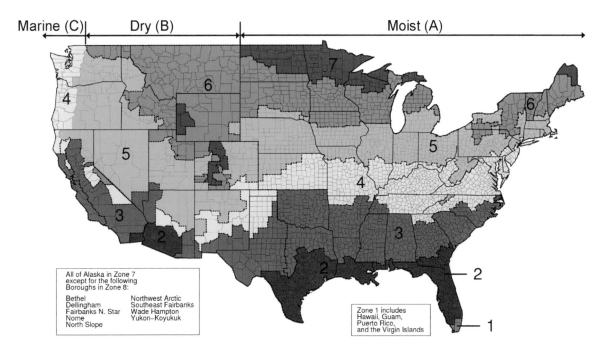

Figure 3-2 United States Climate Zone Map
Source: Briggs et al. (2002c)

The whole-building annual energy models indicate that following the prescriptive recommendations in Chapter 4 allows a building to meet or exceed the energy targets using any of the three recommended HVAC system types. For additional details about the assumptions used in generating these energy targets, see the technical support document for this Guide (Bonnema et al. 2010).

The energy targets give designers flexibility, while still reaching the 50% energy savings goal. For example, the numbers given in Table 3-1 are annual whole-building and subsystem energy consumption targets. However, if a specific recommendation is not feasible in a specific project, this Guide can still be used to achieve 50% savings. For instance, in the case where one of the three recommended HVAC system types is not feasible, the selected alternative system type must be capable of meeting the HVAC target in the table to reach the 50% savings goal. If that is not possible, then measures to reduce lighting or plug loads may compensate for HVAC energy that exceeds the target. Ultimate flexibility is provided to a project team by allowing a project to meet the whole-building 50% savings targets without restricting the team to certain subsystems or prescriptive requirements.

Table 3-1 represents energy targets for 50% savings over Standard 90.1-2004 requirements, based on end use (lighting, HVAC, plug/process loads) by the 16 defined climate zones. For more information on setting EUI targets in your building, please see "Setting Absolute Energy Use Targets for High Performance Buildings" (Leach et al. 2011).

OVERVIEW OF DESIGN INFLUENCES

Many design decisions influence the energy use of a building (as expressed in whole-building area-weighted EUI, or $kBtu/ft^2 \cdot yr$). A large hospital's primary inpatient units (IPUs) or wards and diagnostic and treatment spaces (D&T) are often exceedingly high energy users due to constant operation of ventilation, heating, cooling, and lighting equipment. Consideration of these systems dominates decision making when designing a building with 50% energy savings over Standard 90.1 requirements. Configuration of the building massing, and the pursuit of daylight as the primary source of illumination, are also major influences on design.

Hospitals generally contain many administrative and low-acuity spaces. Use the ASHRAE *Advanced Energy Design Guide for Small to Medium Office Buildings: Achieving 50% Energy Savings Toward a Net Zero Energy Building* (ASHRAE 2011) as a guide to energy efficiency improvements for these space types. Alternately, many nonhospital buildings contain spaces similar to those found in a typical diagnostic and treatment block. Buildings of this type should use this Guide.

One step to reducing total energy use is for the planning, design, construction, and ownership team to assess the relationship between ventilation loads and annual and peak heating and cooling loads. This Guide recommends decoupling and decentralizing these traditionally coupled and centralized systems in the majority of spaces within the hospital. Several options recommended in Chapter 4 accomplish this general HVAC system goal. Peak cooling loads are commonly dominated by solar heat gain. Good exterior window shading practices with exterior mounted and automated horizontal louver systems can best optimize solar shading to reduce unwanted solar heat gain and maximize diffuse daylight penetration for electric lighting energy savings. The design team must also verify that the building infrastructure and equipment is sized based on appropriate estimates of the proposed building load, including optimized internal heat gains (e.g., high-efficiency lighting fixtures, ENERGY STAR labeled products, etc.) and the diversity and pattern of occupancy at the time of design.

Another step to reducing total energy use and optimizing building performance is to attend to the building massing and envelope design. This involves prioritizing daylighting zones and mapping the building floor plans and sections to allow for daylight penetration to the majority of all regularly occupied spaces, and the selection of building glazing and insulation to increase daylight availability, reduce the need for electric lighting during daylight hours, and reduce heat transfer through surfaces, thereby reducing conduction and solar heat gain.

In addition to energy benefits, the gathering research identifying the impact of daylighting, or its absence, on medical outcomes, patient well being, and caregiver performance is sufficient to warrant an aggressive approach to setting daylighting requirements for new healthcare projects. The authors of this document strongly recommend that daylighting be a prime determinant of building form, that the building program identify daylighting requirements both by room type and as a percentage of gross floor area within 15 ft of a windowed wall, and that the building budget account for the capital cost of the increased perimeter wall and window area required to achieve these requirements.

As shown in Figure 3-3, decisions about key elements of the building envelope are interrelated and heavily influence heating and cooling strategies. While internal heat gains are all additive (i.e., cause need for cooling), gains related to interaction with the outdoor climate, such as through ventilation or the building envelope, can be either heat gains or losses and are, therefore, heavily dependent on climate zone.

Another step to reducing total energy load is to reduce electrical energy consumption associated with lighting and plug and process loads.

The remainder of this chapter discusses the important concepts associated with minimizing energy loads from sources of heat gain in the summer and sources of heat loss in the winter, and summarizes the low-energy cooling, heating, and lighting strategies most frequently applied by climate type. Multidisciplinary guidance is provided in cases where design choices are mixed and matched to achieve an optimal solution that meets both site constraints and architectural vision.

BUILDING AND SITE

Many building architectural design features impact the energy performance of a building. Major features include building location (climate); patterns of use (program); shape, size, number of

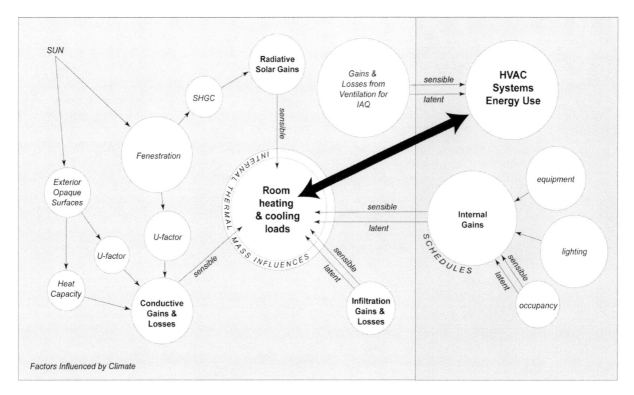

Figure 3-3   Heating and Cooling Influence

stories, and orientation of the building massing; the resultant active mechanical and electrical systems for ventilating, heating, cooling, and lighting; and controls that integrate the passive and active systems and provide users and operators feedback on the building's actual performance relative to its expected performance. The following sections present each of these issues in detail.

CLIMATE

Climate Characterizations by Location

Several major climatic variables, including temperature, wind, solar energy, and moisture, impact the energy performance of buildings. These variables continuously change and can be characterized by annual or seasonal metrics.

- An indicator of the intensity and length of the heating season is represented by heating degree days (HDDs), as shown in Figure 3-4 (DOI 1970).
- An indicator of the intensity and length of the cooling season is represented by cooling degree days (CDDs), as shown in Figure 3-5 (DOI 1970).
- An indicator of the consistent intensity of the sun's energy is represented by annual solar radiation, as shown in Figure 3-6 (DOI 1970).
- An indicator of the worst case for removal of airborne moisture (i.e., humidity) is represented by the design dew-point temperature, as shown in Figure 3-7.
- An indicator of the ability of the air to engage in evaporative cooling is represented by the design wet-bulb temperature, as shown in Figure 3-8.

In combination, these variables show that distinct patterns emerge with regard to climate types, each of which has particular energy impacts on building design and operation. The U.S. has been divided into eight primary climate zones for the specification of design criteria in the

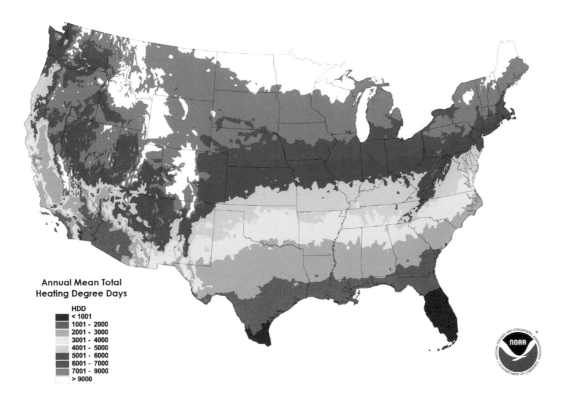

Figure 3-4   Heating Degree Days
Source: NOAA (2005)

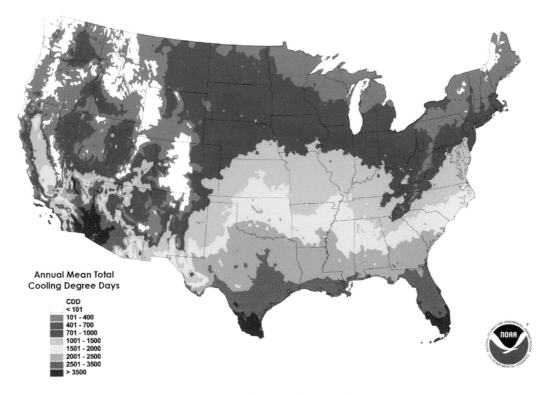

Figure 3-5   Cooling Degree Days
Source: NOAA (2005)

Global Horizontal Solar Radiation - Annual

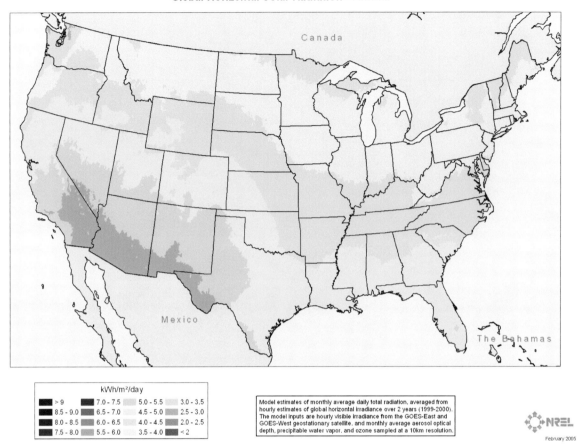

Figure 3-6   Annual Solar Radiation
Source: NREL (2005)

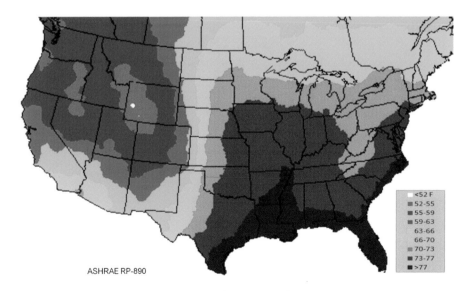

Figure 3-7   Design Dew-Point Temperatures
Source: Colliver et al. (1997)

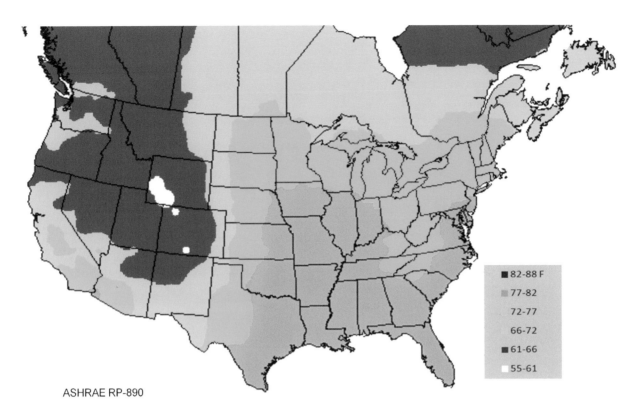

ASHRAE RP-890

Figure 3-8   Design Wet-Bulb Temperatures
Source: Colliver et al. (1997)

major energy codes such as International Energy Conservation Code (ICC 2009), ASHRAE/ IES Standard 90.1, and ASHRAE/USGBC/IES Standard 189.1 (2011c). Figure 3-9 shows these climate zones as compared to CDDs and HDDs (Briggs et al. 2002a, 2002b, 2002c).

The characterization of climate zones is based on seasonal climate characteristics, not on the peak or design values. Each climate zone is clustered by HDD65 for heating and CDD50 for cooling; these are further subdivided by moisture levels as moist or humid (A), dry (B), and marine (C) to characterize their seasonal values. Sixteen cities have been identified as sufficient to represent all of the climate zones, as shown in Table 3-2 (CFR 1992). No single design strategy applies to all of these climate combinations. Each set of climate combinations needs to be analyzed separately.

It is important for the design team to determine the unique characteristics of the climate closest to the site. Annual hourly climate data is usually used for energy modeling and is available from federal government sources (EERE 2010). In addition to the acquisition of local data, it is necessary to assess any local topography or adjacent properties that would cause reduction in access to sunlight and passive solar heating.

Climatic Influences

It is not reasonable to present every design strategy for each climate, but some fundamental principles apply. The sensible and latent loads due to people are universal across all climate zones, since the occupant densities and hours of occupation are assumed to be climate independent. Typically, the lighting power levels are the same, but the energy use for lighting changes with location due to the available daylighting. Selection of the HVAC system is an important decision primarily because each system type has inherent efficiencies.

While there are benefits to the use of renewable energies (photovoltaics, solar, wind), these technologies are not design strategies required to achieve 50% energy savings. See the

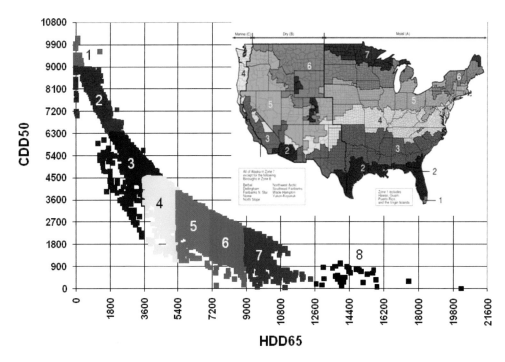

Figure 3-9   United States Climate Zone Map

Table 3-2   Cities Characterized by Climate Combinations

Climate	Hot	Mild	Cold	Very Cold	Extremely Cold
Marine		San Francisco—3C Seattle—4C			
Humid	Miami—1A Houston—2A Atlanta—3A	Baltimore—4A	Chicago—5A Minneapolis—6A		
Dry	Phoenix—2B Los Angeles—3B (coastal) Las Vegas—3B (others)	Albuquerque—4B	Denver—5B Helena—6B	Duluth—7	Fairbanks—8

"Renewable Energy" section in the "Additional Bonus Savings" section of Chapter 5 for more information on these technologies.

Climate Dependence

Energy use for combined IPU and D&T spaces in the large hospital baseline building varies little—less than 20%—from the mildest (zone 4C, Seattle) to the most extreme climate (zone 8, Fairbanks). While this variability is low, the disaggregated end-use load varies widely in the baseline building, with roughly 100% more heating in Fairbanks than in Miami and Houston. The large amounts of heating, even in hot-to-mild climates, is due to reheat from dehumidification and from overcooling that occurs in the large zones of air-based constant-air-volume (CAV) and variable-air-volume (VAV) thermal control systems. More Btus of energy are used for heating in Miami and Houston than are used for cooling. These energy-use characteristics indicate that the common energy-code-compliant large hospital is influenced less by climate and more by energy demands brought about by the interaction of the ventilation systems with the thermal control systems. As these systems are decoupled, and internal equipment energy use is reduced through better programs for energy-efficient operations and the purchase of more energy-efficient equipment, more climate variability is introduced.

Comparisons of the energy used for ventilating, heating, cooling, interior electric lighting, exterior lights, plug loads, fans, pumps, and heat recovery in a large hospital with decoupled HVAC, distributed fan-coil units, and water-source heat pumps are shown in Figures 3-10 and 3-11. A review of baseline performance shows distinct trends. In climates below 3000 HDD65, the cooling energy increases with temperature but is still dominated by heating. In climates above 5000 HDD65, heating energy use dominates cooling energy use. In all climates, energy use is essentially constant for internal and external equipment, HVAC fan and pump loads, interior lights, and exterior lights.

By decoupling ventilation from thermal control in the proposed large hospital AEDG models and adding an aggressive regimen for heat recovery from internal loads (such as plug loads and fans), heating loads are nearly eliminated, even in the coldest climate zones (Figures 3-13 and 3-14). Additional information on decoupling ventilation from thermal control is provided in Chapter 5 (HV2–5, 9).

As with other internal loads, heat from electric lighting adds to the cooling load and reduces the heating load. To reduce electric lighting loads, daylight can be used as the primary source of illumination during the day. Envelope design, floor plan, and building section configuration should figure into strategies for controlling sun penetration and diffusing daylight. The interaction between thermal and lighting effects varies greatly from one HVAC system to the next. For example, with decoupled displacement, direct sun penetration must be eliminated to maintain the proper piston effect of the air buoyancy and avoid diverting supply air from occupants. On the other hand, with traditional overhead-ducted combined heating, cooling and ventilating systems, reducing lighting energy through daylight harvesting, especially in patient rooms, can lead to an increase in reheat energy to replace the heat lost from the electric room lighting.

Fundamentally, what can be seen in Figures 3-10 and 3-11 is as follows:

- Heating, the dominant load in every climate, has nearly been eliminated, even in Fairbanks, due to the internal load dominance of the large hospital's overall energy use profile and an aggressive approach to heat recovery.
- Fan energy was greatly reduced by decoupling ventilation systems from heating and cooling, and distributing heating and cooling with water-based systems.
- Cooling loads have greatly decreased, but now they are a significant presence in every climate, larger in zones with less than 3000 HDD, but still significant even in cold climates.
- Lighting energy has been reduced across climate zones due to aggressive reductions in circuited lighting power, implementation of an aggressive lighting controls regimen, and the introduction of daylighting in a majority of spaces in every climate.
- Plug and major circuited equipment loads are constant inputs and, therefore, are consistent in the EUI budget.

BUILDING CONFIGURATION

Building Shape

The basic shape of the building has a fundamental impact on the daylighting potential, the building's transfer characteristics, and its overall energy use.

The prescriptive recommendations in this Guide are based on a standard hospital form with a deep, rectangular two-story base composed of D&T floors mixed with administrative functions (see Figure 3-12). On top of the D&T space is a five-story tower of IPUs. These floors all have mostly unobstructed ribbon or punched-opening glazing on all four sides.

The model provides little daylight to the majority of functions in the D&T space. Another option is to daylight most spaces within the IPU and D&T space by using a more perforated form with more than 50% of consistently occupied spaces zoned to within 20 ft of a windowed

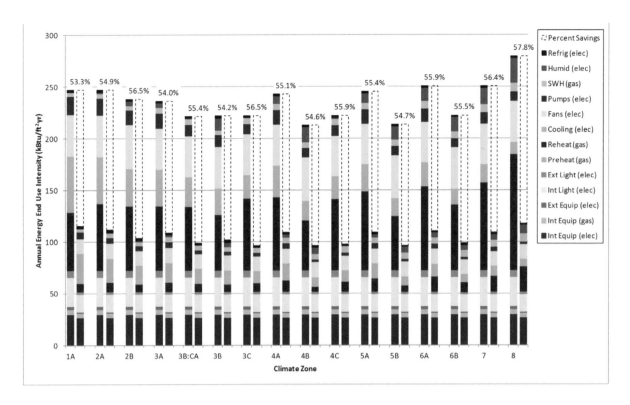

Figure 3-10   Large Hospital with Decoupled Ventilation, Heating, and Cooling Systems that Primarily Use Distributed Fan-Coil Units

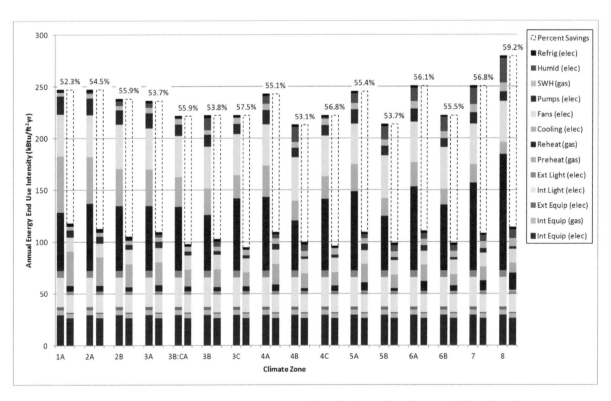

Figure 3-11   Large Hospital with Decoupled Ventilation, Heating, and Cooling Systems that Primarily Use Water-Source Heat Pumps

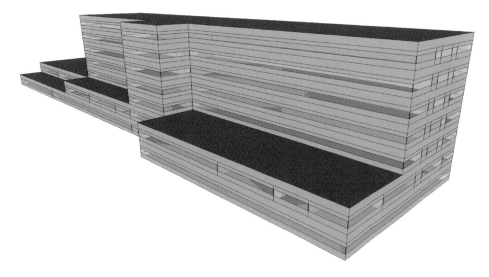

Figure 3-12 Massing Model Image of Standard Hospital Geometry
Source: NREL Technical Support Document

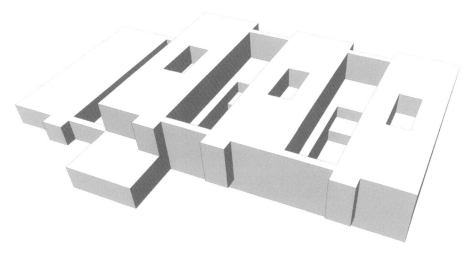

Figure 3-13 Massing Model of the Target 100! Perforated Scheme
Source: University of Washington Integrated Design Lab

wall. Figure 3-13 shows the Target 100! (Burpee and Loveland 2009) perforated form, which is often referred to as the contemporary Scandinavian model.

The IPU zone is traditionally the zone with the most aggressive and well-documented daylighting goals. Therefore the IPU's building mass generally has the greatest amount of surface area for transmission of light and heat. This zone is made up of patient rooms, corridors, nursing and semiprivate caregiver stations, and service spaces for patient support and storage. Traditionally, the IPUs are stacked in multistory configurations that are 14–15 ft, floor-to-floor, and with the patient rooms in a "race track" form around the core spaces, this tower is commonly approximately 90 ft across. This traditional IPU tower nursing unit configuration provides the opportunity for a daylighted perimeter of patient rooms, depending on the exact configuration of the patient suite, with particular care taken to locate the toilet room on the corridor wall or within a shared interstitial zone. With some attention to the design of the toilet room and the amount, position, and shading of the glazing, these perimeter zones up to about

Impacts of Building Shape and Configuration

Contemporary hospitals of the mid- to late-twentieth century have adopted a wide or deep floor plate for diagnostic and treatment (D&T) spaces, with a central inpatient unit (IPU) tower centered on the vertical transportation. Since the 1990s, many northern European hospital have adopted a new, more horizontal, and thinner courtyard configuration for D&T spaces and IPUs, deeply penetrated with daylight. This prototype, in operation since the late 1990s, offers views, daylight, and potential for natural ventilation to more than 50% of the regularly occupied spaces in these hospitals. Three hospitals from Norway, shown below, describe this new shape and configuration.

Rikshospitalet Hospital

Completed in 2001, Rikshospitalet showcases a shift in typology from a predominantly vertical to a horizontal distribution. The IPUs and D&T areas in this hospital are horizontally opposed, and circulation between the two occurs on sky bridges that span an interior street. The shift in form allows for plan-enclosed courtyards in the diagnostic and treatment area of the hospital, which allows for daylight and views into spaces such as surgery and imaging. The windows in these traditionally dark spaces are controlled with three levels of shading that can be operated by the occupants as necessary. Every opportunity for daylight is employed; recovery rooms that are not on the perimeter have operable skylights that provide for both natural illumination and natural ventilation. For staff, nursing stations all have access to a perimeter window.

(continued next page)

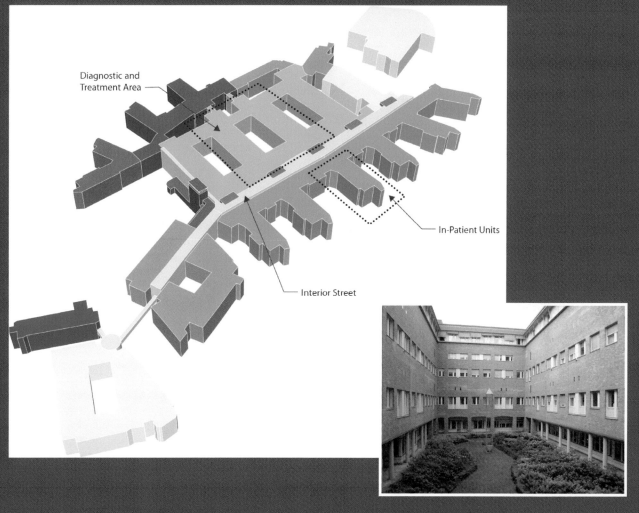

Diagnostic and Treatment Area

In-Patient Units

Interior Street

Rikshospitalet Building Configuration
Source: University of Washington Integrated Design Lab

Akershus University Hospital

Akershus was completed in the Fall of 2008 and is a more recent example of the contemporary pavilion-style hospital. Here, the diagnostic and treatment areas are organized around plan-enclosed courtyards, which affords opportunity for greater access to daylight and views in these spaces. The IPUs are organized along one double-loaded corridor, with distributed nursing stations tucked into alcoves nested with the patient-room bathrooms. These nursing stations have access to daylight through either clerestory windows, which borrow light from above the bathrooms, or on the top floor via skylights.

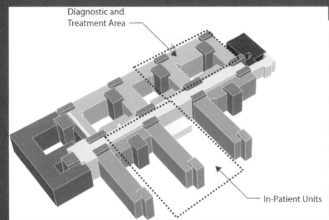

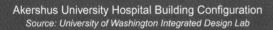

Akershus University Hospital Building Configuration
Source: University of Washington Integrated Design Lab

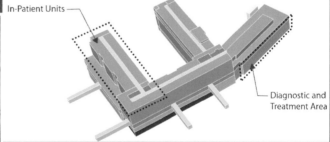

St. Olav's Gastro Center Building Configuration
Source: University of Washington Integrated Design Lab

St. Olav's Hospital

St. Olav's, completed in two phases in 2005 and 2009, is an example of a contemporary hospital designed with community placemaking in mind. Here, the horizontal concept is pushed even further, with buildings spread apart (unbundled) into separate distinct centers of care that act as individual hospitals, while maintaining connectivity between the campus at the second level via sky bridges and underground through service functions. This variability of building form gives the medical center a less institutional appearance than what is commonly experienced in such a large medical facility.

The various buildings are great examples of providing outdoor space and views within an urban setting. The buildings have thin floorplates that wrap around large central courtyards. Patient rooms open directly onto decks or terraces. Generous windows daylight the patient rooms and provide light in the surgery suites. Daylight is controlled on all of the façades with automated exterior louver blinds that move with the sun. Microadjustments of the exterior shades allow for personal control.

20 ft from the window wall can be well daylighted. This traditionally leaves the corridors and caregiver areas without access to daylight.

Reconfiguring the building to provide daylight to caregiver spaces, as well as to patient rooms, is an overarching energy performance challenge for this zone. Daylight is provided in various models by (1) reconfiguring the patient tower into a finger plan of double-loaded corridors, with core caregiver functions moved to the junction of the ward corridor and a corridor connecting several nursing units on the same floor level or (2) by inserting an atrium into the core of the traditional race track. Lastly, the tower can be reconfigured into a larger race track, where the entire building takes on a "U" or "O" shape and where the sides of the plan are double-loaded corridors with caregiver spaces allocated to the corridor knuckles and interspersed along the corridor.

The D&T zone is traditionally the zone with the least daylight access. D&T spaces tend to have very large floor plates and suffer from the unfortunate geometric rule that makes perimeters grow more slowly than areas (quadrupling the area of a square only doubles the length of its sides). Large D&T spaced with as little as 20% of their floor area within 15 ft of the daylighted perimeter are common, with much of that perimeter often dominated by circulation corridors.

The insertion of plan-enclosed courtyards—a strategy that achieves both density and daylight in buildings of most types—is the best way to substantially increase daylighting within large floor plate D&T blocks. They allow the retention of a simple overall plan shape; allow departments to ebb and flow around their corners, front, and back; and allow treatment and service spaces to be shared at the back-of-house of departments. (Atriums and other core lighting strategies may also be introduced into more compact building forms to achieve a similar effect).

Less compact forms increase a building's daylighting potential, but they also may magnify the influence of outdoor climate fluctuations. Greater surface-to-volume ratios increase conductive and convective heat transfer through the opaque building envelope, and, of greatest concern, the potential for massive radiant solar heat gains via unshaded glazing. Therefore, it is critical to assess the daylighting characteristics of the building form in combination with the shading of all glazing surfaces and the heat transfer characteristics of the building envelope in order to optimize overall building energy and daylighting performance (see DL2 in Chapter 5).

Shaping the D&T space into a thinner floor plate for daylighting increases the total amount of building skin and, therefore, the total amount of glazing, even when the percent glass-to-floor area remains the same as with traditional D&T spaces. Windows that provide daylight and allow for greater solar gains to enter the building can be a beneficial attribute during the heating season or during periods of reheat from overcooling due to dehumidification. This passive heating must be carefully balanced with increases in cooling energy required during seasonal warm and hot periods.

The building shape and glazing need to be designed so that the solar loading is properly managed for heat gain, glare, and views to the outside. The building and window configuration and solar management strategy change with variation in local climate characteristics, i.e., as the solar availability, position, and intensity differ from predominantly clear to predominantly cloudy regions (see Figures 3-14 and 3-15) and from hot to temperate or cold regional temperature regimes. Additionally, the shape of the building determines how wind impinges on the outdoor surfaces to assist natural ventilation, where allowed by code, or can create outdoor microclimates that can be assets or liabilities to the design intent.

Building Orientation

The orientation of the IPU directly impacts its energy performance and affects the impact of daylight on patient healing. This is due primarily to the orientation of the fenestration and the glazing's exposure to light and solar heat gain. Robust amounts of daylight are needed in the IPU. Both patients and staff are chronically stressed. Exposure to the shorter wavelengths of visible "blue" light stimulates nonvision-related mechanisms in our eyes. This response to light, unrelated to vision, helps humans maintain their natural circadian rhythms; enables

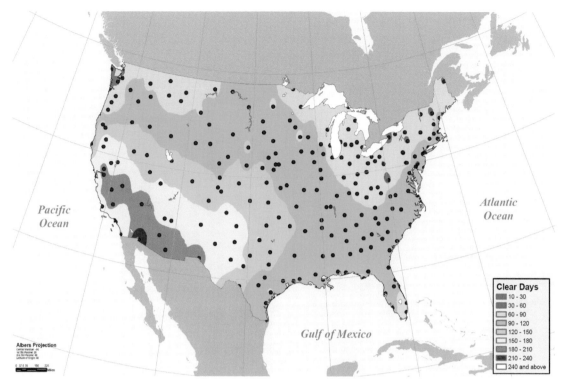

Figure 3-14   Design Sky Conditions, Annual Days of Clear Skies
Data source: The Weidt Group (2005)

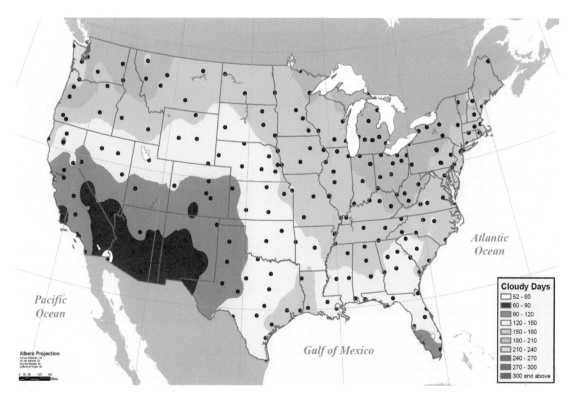

Figure 3-15   Design Sky Conditions, Annual Days of Overcast Skies 1997
Data source: The Weidt Group (2005)

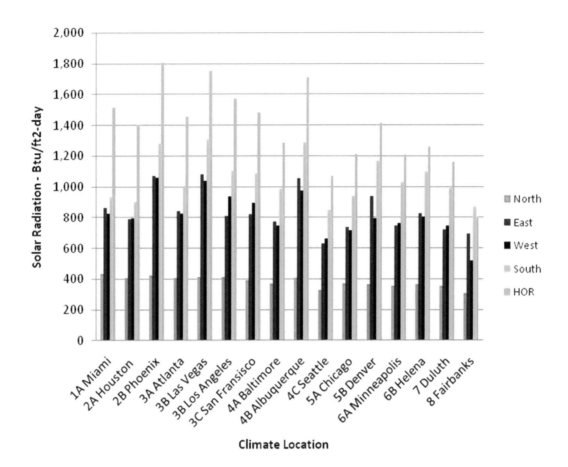

Figure 3-16   Annual Solar Radiation by Orientation
Data source: Marion and Wilcox (2008)

improved wake and sleep cycles; and, thus, reduces chronic stress and illness (Scientific American 2011).

Daylight must be carefully balanced with solar heat gain. Solar heat gain is commonly overcome in inefficient buildings through use of a large cooling infrastructure, but it cannot be overcome in an energy-efficient hospital, where peak cooling loads are kept below 15 Btu/h·ft². The annual solar radiation impinging on a surface varies by orientation and latitude, as shown in Figure 3-16 (Marion and Wilcox 2008). A balance must be developed between orienting IPU and D&T windows to capture daylight for energy efficiency and health benefits, and orienting windows to be most easily shaded, so as to redirect solar heat gain away from the building interior during cooling periods.

In the Northern hemisphere, the north solar heat gain flux is the lowest for any location and is an asset for reducing the cooling load. Daylighting with north light is commonly preferred due to few glare control requirements from direct sun penetration (reflections from adjacent buildings may require closer study for glare control). While the north glazing requires little shade and provides consistent light, the lowest amounts of visible light are available to the north. Daylighting spaces with north light glazing areas must be substantially increased to obtain the similar health benefits and electric lighting reductions that are available to the south, east, or west.

East- and west-exposed spaces in sunny climates have the greatest annualized availability of daylight of any vertical surface but also provide the greatest challenge to shading. The illumination of the sun on east and west surfaces is essentially the same, with the exception of local diurnal cloudiness variability, local vertical obstructions that may shade these surfaces unequally, and the timing of the diurnal pattern of daylight. The west exposure needs to be critically evaluated since it commonly contributes most to the peak or design cooling load.

South-facing orientations in the northern hemisphere have the greatest peak solar intensity and the least variation in sun angle of any vertical surface. Therefore, the south light is usually seen as the greatest amenity for cost-effective daylighting and shading.

Illumination or skylighting through the roof can be a great daylighting asset, but the horizontal solar flux is the largest on these horizontal surfaces in the summer when cooling loads are quite likely to be problematic. Therefore, considering the potential solar heat gain is critical if flat skylights on the roof are being considered.

Great care must be applied when designing external shading and internal glare control for any orientation, as attention must be paid to the need for diffuse daylight in patient and staff spaces, heat gain during cooling periods, glare, and the possibility of passive solar heating in cold climates during heating periods.

Permanent exterior projection from the building façade and motorized exterior blinds can greatly contribute to reducing solar gains if properly designed. Permanent projections, such as horizontal overhangs and vertical fins, provide reliable shading from solar heat gain only if carefully designed and tested so that they meet agreed-upon thermal performance criteria. These shades commonly have a large negative effect on the daylight availability to adjacent interior spaces. As these shading devices are designed and tested to meet thermal performance criteria, they must be equally tested in their ability to meet objective daylighting goals and performance criteria. Motorized exterior shades can greatly assist in meeting daylighting criteria, because they retract from the window when the sun moves away or during cloudy periods and, at the same time, provide needed shading performance.

Building orientation, the placement and proportioning of fenestration, and the design of shading and daylight control building façade systems have a critical effect on the ability of a design to provide useful daylight to perimeter zones and to maintain energy-efficient operation for cooling and heating. A good daylighting solution requires the simultaneous examination of the building configuration and internal space planning so as to maximize the amount of normally occupied space that has access to daylight for ambient illumination. This analysis must also include an assessment of the space's ability to maintain heat gain criteria for minimizing cooling energy and maximizing the potential for solar heating during cold periods An experienced daylighting consultant should be contracted from the earliest stages of design to assist the integrated design team in setting daylight design goals, performance criteria, and performance metrics, and implementing the methods for testing performance.

Number of Stories

Typically, as the number of stories of a building increases, some aspects of design become more complicated. For instance, requirements for structural performance and durability/design life may affect choice of envelope components, the viability of exposed thermal mass, and the amount of area that may be used for fenestration. All of these may affect energy performance.

Taller buildings have elevators with large energy-consuming motors but intermittent energy use. Large hospitals require frequent vertical trips and should consider the use of variable-frequency drives (VFDs) on the motors and controls to stage the travel of elevators and reduce redundant trips in response to a call button.

Tall IPUs tend to be thinner and have greater daylighting access due to a higher ratio of perimeter wall area to floor area. The commonly shorter and deeper floorplate commonly traps a large block of space as purely internal and without connection to the outdoors. If an increased amount of space with access to natural daylight or ventilation is preferred, the designer of shorter and deeper buildings can introduce daylight via the expansive roof area, thus providing toplight via skylights, clerestories, monitors, sawtooths, and atriums (See DL13 to DL15 in the "Additional Bonus Savings" section of Chapter 5). Horizontal glazing captures the brightest portion of the overcast sky and is therefore a great daylighting asset, but it may have problems with high-angle sun that is difficult to shade. Exterior louvers, translucent glazing, vertical glazing, and other means should be considered to distribute toplight evenly into an interior space.

Building Floor Plate Configuration

The first item to address in building design is the built area. For first-cost reasons, there is a drive to minimize built square footage, and the entire team should review the actual requested occupancies to determine if space can be shared for uses otherwise listed separately. For instance, shared conference or lounge spaces can reduce the redundancy of built space while encouraging interdepartmental cooperation. Another area often under scrutiny for both first cost and operating costs savings is the transient gross square footage associated with circulation space and lobbies. It is recommended that the team use space-planning exercises to review whether there are ways to reduce these types of spaces in size by merging them with other functions, or limiting or controlling the scope of their energy use under low-occupancy conditions.

The second major item for the team to address is the architectural configuration of the building. Façade square footage represents a source of conductive heat loss or heat gain as the outdoor air (OA) temperatures fluctuate; therefore, the larger the amount of façade area, the greater this impact. Additionally, most façades for hospitals contain windows for the benefit of the patients and staff. Glazing is a poorer insulator than most opaque constructions and should be reviewed with regard to its placement and size. Generally speaking, daylighting and natural ventilation are possible within about 25 ft of a façade, a value that may govern the depth of footprints for which greater connectivity to the outdoors is desired.

Beyond the impact on the interior floor plate, the shape of the building also informs where and how the building self shades and begins to inform where glazing can be most effectively placed. Generally speaking, in the northern hemisphere, glazing that points toward the north captures sky-reflected daylight with minimal solar heat content, making it the ideal source of even light. Eastern and western glazing is impacted by low-angle sun throughout the year, which can cause glare and thermal discomfort if not mitigated properly. Lastly, in the northern hemisphere, southern façades with glazing benefit from overhangs to reduce solar load during the summer season.

ENERGY CONSERVATION MEASURES

The major energy conservation measures (ECMs) for large hospitals are related to envelope, lighting, HVAC, and controls. Daylighting is a key strategy that touches each of these categories but is addressed in depth in the lighting section. This section of this chapter touches on each of these four categories to understand the relative design influence on total EUI. Energy conservation measures are used, either individually or in bundles, to help reveal which strategies or sets of strategies will result in the greatest energy savings as compared with a baseline building as defined by ASHRAE/ASHE Standard 90.1. Individual components of the building design are highly integrated and impact the energy savings of other components, so bundles of strategies give the clearest picture of whole-building energy use.

To begin an ECM analysis, first create an energy model for the baseline building. The energy model can reveal the relative proportion of energy savings contributed by each design component. In general, most energy modeling programs output end-use data (i.e., by the component actually consuming the electricity or fuel, such as heating or plug loads) instead of linking the relative influence of design decisions directly to the output. Figure 3-17 shows a classic output of a whole-building energy model for different climate zones, defined by total cooling, heating, interior lighting, exterior lighting, and HVAC system fan components. Identifying which end uses consume the largest percentages of building energy reveals areas in which to begin focusing efficiency efforts, though all end uses need to be targeted in order to achieve 50% savings. Those end uses related to HVAC are in cumulative the most significant, indicating that those systems require the most attention.

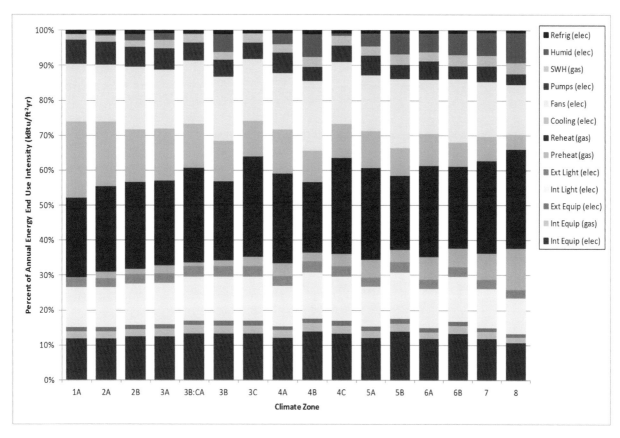

Figure 3-17   Percentage of Total Energy Usage by End-Use System

IMPACTS OF SPACE TYPES ON ENERGY USE AND ECMS

Large hospitals typically house multiple space types with very different needs and requirements that significantly impact energy use. This Guide breaks these down into three space type categories: IPUs, D&T facilities, and nonclinical spaces. The latter include offices, conference rooms, dining facilities, public lobbies, and other spaces that may support the hospital functions but are not directly used to provide care. The only way to successfully target a 50% energy reduction is to address each of these three space types individually and apply an overall understanding of how they interact. If recommendations for all three space types were combined into one discussion and set of recommendations, then all spaces would need to follow the broadest requirement, resulting in considerably more energy use for some spaces than might otherwise be desirable. As a corollary, the more these three functions can be cleanly separated, the more potential energy savings a project has the potential to see. For example, if offices can be mechanically isolated in a physically separate part of the building, or even in a separate building, then those spaces can be naturally ventilated more easily.

Diagnostic and Treatment Facilities (D&T)

D&T facilities are often the most energy-intensive space type within a large hospital. They include functions such as the emergency room, operating room suites, imaging, and other services related to the diagnosis and treatment of medical conditions. D&T facilities can serve both inpatients and/or outpatients. If, after treatment, patients require continuous medical observation or care, then they are relocated to an IPU. D&T facilities often face a number of conditions that directly impact energy use, leading to a historically high EUI:

- Infection control challenges, including immunocompromised patients and patients with undiagnosed, highly communicable diseases.
- Interior zones almost always need year-round cooling, while exterior zones have seasonal swings from heating to cooling and back again. When served by a single HVAC system, this can increase the amount of reheat required in the exterior zones during heating season (since the air coming from the shared HVAC system must be cool enough to condition the interior zones).
- Code requirements for mechanical ventilation, space pressurizations, and high ventilation rates for all spaces, especially operating room suites.
- Plug loads associated with heavy medical equipment such as MRI, CT, and PET scanning machines.
- High light levels needed for clinical functions, often with specialized lighting requirements (e.g., green light used in operating rooms).
- Typically at least some of the D&T zone is in around-the-clock operation. All of the D&T zone usually has the potential for extended and unpredictable schedules on an as-needed basis.
- High floor-to-ceiling heights can lead to increased ventilation demand.
- Conventional American medical planning practices can lead to a very deep floor plate with little or no access to daylight.

Inpatient Units (IPUs)

IPUs are composed of patient bedrooms and the spaces that support them. They are often "bed towers" usually above or adjacent to D&T spaces. They typically have less equipment and less energy-intensive spaces than D&T facilities, though they still require considerable control and have a high EUI. Some D&T components may be found in IPUs. The following issues unique to IPUs contribute to energy consumption:

- Infection control challenges, including some patients who are extremely immunocompromised and others who have highly communicable diseases, lead to relatively high air change rates throughout the spaces and increased ventilation and/or strict pressurization requirements in some spaces, such as negative- and positive-pressure isolation rooms.
- As with D&T spaces, differences in internal loads cause the need for simultaneous heating and cooling. In conventional VAV systems, this leads to a significant amount of reheat.
- Moderate plug loads associated with computers and, in some cases, more energy intensive medical equipment.
- The trend toward single-patient rooms leads to a large amount of space and, therefore, more required energy use per patient. This is not a factor in achieving energy reductions below ASHRAE/IESNA Standard 90.1, as square footage is constant between the base model and design model; however, it is a significant contributor to a building's overall energy use per year.
- High light levels needed for clinical functions, typically with special exam lights in patient rooms.
- By definition, these units operate around the clock and year round.
- Patient rooms are required by code to have windows with views to the outside. The most conventional medical planning approach is to place patient rooms along the building perimeter with staff and support spaces on the interior with little or no access to daylight and views.

Most of the recommendations for IPUs are similar to those for D&T facilities, though the inherent differences in program requirements, daylight, air changes, and other requirements provide a handful of unique energy-efficiency issues.

Nonclinical Spaces

Nonclinical spaces support the IPUs and D&T facilities and may include staff offices, lobbies, cafeterias, lounges, medical records, among others. Energy-efficiency strategies for most of these spaces more closely resemble those of other building types than those of IPUs and D&T areas. In some cases, they share requirements with the clinical spaces if they are on similar systems or serve the same populations. From an energy-efficiency standpoint, nonclinical spaces should be as isolated as possible so that they are not burdened with unnecessarily energy-intensive requirements. Some recommendations are listed here. Refer to the 50% *Advanced Energy Design Guide for Small to Medium Office Buildings* (ASHRAE 2011) for a more detailed discussion of these space types.

The remainder of this chapter introduces the recommendations discussed in this Guide at a conceptual level and identifies appropriate ECMs. The recommendations that follow include good, standard, energy-efficient design practices applicable to most building types, but they also address many issues specific to healthcare facilities. The Guide recommends systems and design strategies that comply with mainstream regulations and requirements, but they may not necessarily address discrepancies between state or local codes. The recommendations also focus on strategies that both save energy and enhance health and healing.

BUILDING ENVELOPE

The envelope is characterized by the opaque components and fenestration. Improvements should be considered for reduced thermal transmittance (i.e., U-factors), use of thermal mass, and control of solar heat gains.

Recommended upgrades to the opaque elements, such as the roofs/ceilings, walls, and foundations, include increased insulation to lower U-factors, and/or additional thermal mass for roofs and walls. Adding cool roofs with high reflectivity in most climates is often found to be a direct benefit to reducing energy associated with cooling. Many parts of D&T facilities and some spaces within IPUs require cooling year round due to high internal loads.

Fenestration has a major impact on architectural appearance, energy savings potential, and—perhaps most importantly—the improved health and well being of building occupants. A significant body of research supports the positive effect that views to the outdoors, especially to nature, have on health and healing (Heerwagen 2009). Electrical lighting energy savings is also an important benefit of daylighting. Considerable attention should be given to fenestration design to ensure proper balance of the goals for heating, cooling, daylighting, and views. Envelope design should include glazing only where necessary to provide an appropriate level and quality of daylight and views. However, areas of high glazing, if implemented to improve access to daylight, should be qualitatively weighed against the potential increased HVAC energy use due to larger window area or increased solar heat gain coefficient. The more that glazing is introduced into a façade, the higher its performance needs to be in order to achieve required energy savings. This Guide recommends 40% floor-to-ceiling, window-to-wall ratios (WWRs) and specific vertical fenestration performance values, discussed in Chapter 5, as an appropriate balance of window area and glazing performance.

Careful attention should also be paid to glare, a form of visual discomfort usually caused by the difference in relative brightness between interior surfaces, including computer screens, and the outdoors as viewed through the window. Glare is especially challenging in direct low-to-medium-angle sunlight. Use of exterior shading, such as overhangs on the south façade, can help control both solar heat gains and glare.

Additionally, placement and integrity of continuous air and vapor retarders is key to preventing the uncontrolled formation of condensation within wall cavities, a condition that can lead to increased energy use in order to keep materials dry enough to reduce the risk of microbial growth and/or "sick building syndrome." This is also an energy issue with respect to infiltration/exfiltration. It is strongly recommended that a façade consultant, or a person with similar expertise, be involved in detailing vapor retarder placement in low-energy buildings, specifically because there will be significantly less cooling capacity (and therefore less dehumidification) available in base building systems to compensate for poor wall cavity construction. Careful façade detailing for sealing, especially at joints and fenestration interfaces, also helps reduce the amount of air leakage and infiltration in the building—another potentially uncontrollable, continuous, real-time load on the HVAC system that can be mitigated with minimal attention during design and construction.

In summary, the following approaches are often beneficial:

- Enhanced building opaque envelope insulation for exterior walls and roofs
- Use of thermal mass in opaque envelope to allow for the storage of energy, often reducing cooling
- Inclusion of a cool roof in most climates
- High-performance window glazing
- Exterior shading on east, west, and south-facing windows
- Limited use of flat-roof skylights (consider north-facing clerestories/monitors)
- Vestibules at openings to the outdoors
- Use of a continuous air barrier to reduce condensation risk, reduce infiltration, and improve envelope pressure testing

Overall the requirements of the opaque envelope between the D&T, IPU, and nonclinical spaces are relatively similar, though the percent of glazing and shading strategies vary to some extent by space type, orientation, and climate zone, as discussed earlier in this chapter.

LIGHTING

The lighting system is composed of two strategies: daylighting and electric lighting. Electric lighting is further divided into interior lighting and exterior lighting. Interior electric lighting is a major consumer of energy, typically contributing up to 10%–15% of overall hospital energy use, so reducing electric lighting energy demand is an important strategy for reaching the 50% energy savings target. Daylighting can save electric lighting energy if a sufficient level of daylight is available to meet interior illuminance requirements. Exterior lighting uses less energy than interior lighting but also presents some excellent opportunities for energy reduction.

Daylighting

Providing daylight is fundamental for a healthcare facility, as it contributes to an energy-efficient, healthy, and productive environment. Studies have demonstrated that exposure to daylight is important to the health of patients and staff and should be considered a key part of the facility design, regardless of the energy savings benefit. However, daylight can be difficult to control, as it varies during the course of the day and by time of year, weather conditions, and the site's geographic location. Daylighting is both an art and a science, and a broad range of technologies and techniques can be used to provide glare-free and balanced light, sufficient illumination, and good visual comfort.

Daylighting strategies dictate the building's shape and form, and their successful integration into the design from structural, mechanical, electrical, and architectural standpoints is critical to implementation. In order to be effective, the building design must consider the geographic and climatic conditions particular to the project's site. For example, eastern and western exposures are difficult to shade, so an effective building form for daylighting is one that minimizes the amount of fenestration at these exposures and maximizes fenestration at north and south exposures.

As discussed earlier in this chapter, the prevalent medical planning paradigm in the United States typically does not provide daylight or views to most staff and support spaces within the in-patient, diagnostic, and treatment units. This can be considered primarily a cultural issue, not a technological one, as many other parts of the world daylight most of their healthcare facilities. This cultural issue poses a significant challenge. A slender floor plate, or a deep floor plate perforated with courtyards or light wells, is significantly more effective in delivering daylight to interior spaces than the deep block plan prevalent in U.S. hospital design. The form-driven daylighting option provided in the prescriptive recommendations of this Guide specifies that 75% of the occupied space, excluding patient rooms, lies within 20 ft of the perimeter, enabling those spaces to have daylight and views.

Well-designed daylighting can improve energy performance and reduce building costs. Effective daylighting uses natural light to offset electric lighting loads; electric lighting is dimmed or turned off in response to the amount of natural light in the space. There may also be beneficial synergies between daylighting and the sizing of mechanical and electrical systems; by reducing energy loads, equipment can be downsized.

With proper building design, daylighting can translate into energy savings, thus reducing operating and investment costs as a result of the following:

- Reduced electricity use and peak electrical demand for lighting
- Reduced cooling energy and peak cooling loads
- Reduced maintenance costs associated with lamp replacement
- Reduced equipment and mechanical-room size

To achieve these benefits, the following considerations must be incorporated into the design:

- Fenestration is responsive to the site-specific solar exposure and patterns.
- High-performance glazing is used to meet lighting design criteria, block solar radiation, and minimize thermal transmission gains (summer) and losses (winter).
- Effective shading devices are used and are designed to minimize solar radiation gains during peak cooling times.
- Electric lights are automatically dimmed or turned off through use of daylight-responsive photosensors.

The case for daylighting reaches far beyond energy performance. The health and performance benefits afforded may be the primary motivator for daylighting healthcare buildings. While the impacts are difficult to quantify, the potential for improvement is significant enough that daylighting should be considered during the design process. The daylighting strategies recommended in this Guide have successfully been implemented in hospitals around the world.

As discussed earlier, patient rooms are required to have windows with views to the outside, which in turn allows them to be daylighted. Daylight is important because patients are especially sensitive to their surrounding environment, and the room is the primary or only place they may spend time for days, weeks, or even months. Access to daylight and views to nature can be critical to optimum healing and to the overall patient experience. It can also have a positive affect on staff and family members in high stress situations. The façade should be designed to allow high levels of light, but only a limited amount of direct light, especially on the patient's face. High levels of light (even on overcast days) can be bright enough to cause glare for a patient lying on his or her back. Glare in patient rooms can cause patients, staff, or others to draw the blinds, which eliminates the potential health impact of the daylight and views as well as the energy reduction benefit gained by turning off electric lighting. Studies have shown that once blinds are drawn, they are rarely reopened. Façades should be designed with the intent of providing bright but comfortable spaces during as many hours of the year as possible. External shading devices, such as horizontal shades on the south and automatic louvers on the east and west (or on all façades), can help considerably.

The form-driven daylighting option discussed in this Guide requires that 75% of the occupied space, not including patient rooms, lie within 20 ft of the perimeter, providing those spaces with daylight and views to outside. These spaces should follow best practices for office and other nonclinical spaces where appropriate, especially with respect to direct sun, glare, veiling reflections and the use of computers. In the IPU, a reduction of solar gain through the use of external shading devices may provide energy savings from reduced fan power requirements for

Inboard vs. Outboard Patient Toilet Rooms

Most inpatient units (IPUs) are designed around a patient-room module that positions the patient toilet room in one of three ways: adjacent to the interior corridor (inboard), adjacent to the exterior wall (outboard), or nested with the toilet for the adjacent patient room. Inboard and outboard layouts can use either a same-handed or opposite-handed approach.

Many factors contribute to the design decision; each facility should evaluate carefully based on patient population, acuity level, values, and operational practices. Major considerations typically include the following:

- Nurses' ability to view patients from the corridor
- Direct access from the patient bed to the patient toilet via a handrail along the wall
- Efficient use of space and efficient provision of care within the patient and toilet rooms
- Views from the patient bed to the outdoors

(continued next page)

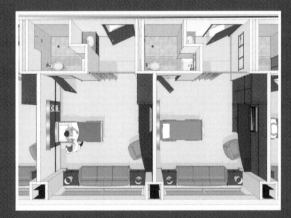

Inboard (Same Handed)

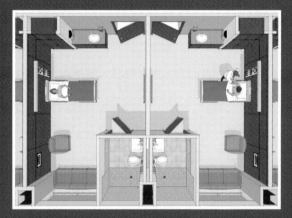

Outboard (Opposite Handed)

Example Patient Room Layouts
Copyright HOK. Reprinted with permission

spaces without a high minimum air change rate requirement. The required air change rates in many D&T spaces, on the other hand, are so high that they are not necessarily affected by a reduced cooling load due to reduced electric lighting. The same amount of fan energy would be required to move air, but potential savings may exist in space heating or cooling. While some energy may be expended on HVAC operation in conjunction with daylighting, it is generally less than for other building types.

Daylighting should be a significant ECM in nonclinical spaces, from both energy reduction and health and wellbeing standpoints. Lounges, dining facilities, waiting rooms, lobbies, and similar spaces provide an important place of respite for patients, staff, and families—this may be especially important for staff and others who have to spend much of their time in non-daylighted spaces. Furthermore, these spaces do not typically support clinical tasks or other functions that require more than task lighting for reading and writing, so daylight can often provide appropriate levels of ambient light. Although some reading and computer use may occur in these spaces, they generally have a higher tolerance for direct light, reflections, sun movement, and other conditions that can cause glare or discomfort in more sensitive spaces.

Nested conditions are less favorable in some facilities because they can require more square footage and do not allow for same-handed rooms. An outboard toilet is often favored by staff because it can provide the most expansive view from the corridor to the patient's bed. However, this condition reduces the amount of exterior wall available for the window, which limits opportunities for daylight and views and potentially reduces the area within the patient room intended for use by family members. Inboard or nested options, on the other hand, offer the full length of patient-room exterior wall. For some projects, canting the conventional inboard option provides nurses with an adequate view from the corridor while optimizing the family zone, the patient view to the outdoors, and the adjacency of the patient bed to the toilet room.

From an energy-efficiency perspective, a smaller window may be preferred. However, views to the outdoors, and especially views to nature, have been proven to improve health outcomes (Ulrich 2008). The best balance is to provide a window that shows expansive views but not to extend the glazing to the floor and ceiling, staying within the window-wall-ratio recommendations of this guide.

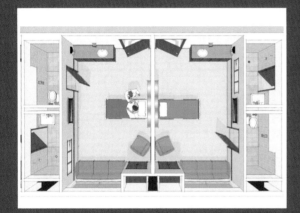

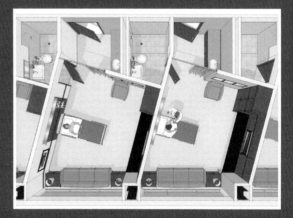

Inboard (Same Handed) Outboard (Opposite Handed)

Example Patient Room Layouts
Copyright HOK. Reprinted with permission

Occupants in these space types may have a wider range of thermal comfort than those in clinical spaces, but sun shades should still be used on the south and possibly other façades to reduce solar heat gain and glare.

Daylighting is also an important ECM for offices, though needs to be handled differently than for public spaces. More than in other space types in hospitals, daylighting increases energy performance and impacts building size and costs by downsizing fans, ductwork, and cooling equipment because overall cooling loads are reduced, allowing for trade-offs between the efforts made for daylighting and the sizing of the air-handling and cooling systems. The case for daylighting reaches far beyond energy performance alone. Indoor environmental quality benefits the office workers' physical and mental health and has a significant impact on their performance and productivity. These impacts are difficult to quantify, but the potential for improvement and economical savings is immense and needs to be taken into consideration as serious decision-making criteria in the process of office design. These benefits may far outweigh the energy savings and become the significant drivers for daylighting buildings altogether.

Electric Lighting

When daylight is unavailable, electric lighting must be used. Most hospitals operate on a constant schedule, year round, and require electric lighting throughout. The interior space types typically found in healthcare facilities are discussed in Chapter 5, along with specific how-to recommendations for lighting. Each building space distribution is unique, however, which creates different potential opportunities for energy savings.

To achieve maximum lighting energy savings, lighting power should be optimized, and most spaces should be provided with occupancy sensors and/or daylight-responsive dimming to reduce or shut off the lights when they are not needed. Additionally, lighting left on twenty-four hours a day to provide emergency egress should be designed to limit power use to no more than 10% of total lighting energy consumption.

The first opportunity for energy savings is to optimize the connected lighting power. Examining the power used for lighting is a good way to measure the effectiveness of the lighting design to ensure that necessary illumination is provided without overlighting. The metric used is lighting power density (LPD), a unit of lighting power divided by space area and measured in watts per square foot (W/ft^2). Simple reductions are possible by using high-performance light sources, such as solid-state light-emitting diodes (LED) and linear fluorescent lights with electronic ballasts. These technologies can reduce the lighting power by approximately 20% over the ASHRAE/IESNA Standard 90.1 requirements.

Ensuring that lights are on only when the space is occupied is another important way to control lighting energy use. ASHRAE/IESNA Standard 90.1 includes minimal requirements for occupancy controls. By adding manual ON or auto ON to 50% occupancy sensors to exam rooms, administrative offices, staff work and supply rooms, lounges, restrooms, and waiting areas, the lighting system will use 15% to 20% less lighting energy. In well-daylighted spaces, automatic sensors that turn the lights off, not on, commonly called "vacancy" sensors, can save lighting power.

The primary lighting goals for D&T facilities are to provide the quality and quantity of light required for a given task in the most energy efficient way possible, thereby reducing LPD. Some spaces within D&T facilities, such as operating rooms or imaging rooms, have very specific and at times high-acuity light level requirements. D&T facilities often are used significantly less at night, so individual spaces and lamps should be carefully planned to step down or shut off during off hours. Manual overrides are important for emergencies or other times when a space requires unexpected use. Night lighting intended to be left on twenty-four hours a day should be designed to limit power use to 10% of the total LPD.

IPUs are unique in that most if not all of the spaces are intended to be occupied twenty-four hours a day, seven days a year. They should be occupied differently at night, however, while patients are sleeping or trying to sleep. Support of circadian rhythms is extremely important for both patients and staff. Patients should be exposed to bright and changing light levels during the day and to little or no light at night. This may be in conflict with the needs of the night-shift staff, however, who need to stay awake and also require adequate light levels to observe patients and perform other duties. Light levels in patient rooms should be off at night to the extent possible. Night lighting in an amber or red color safely helps guide patients, visitors, or staff around the room, and the amber spectrum of lights does not affect sleep cycles. Patients should always have control over the light levels in the room.

Patient rest can also be disrupted by light pouring into bedrooms from the hallway, either from the opening and closing of bedroom doors or through glazing on walls or doors. Corridor lights that automatically step down overnight help reduce disruptive light and save energy. The brightest spaces should be staff work areas that don't have direct visual access to patient rooms. Work areas that need to be brightly lighted but are within view of patient rooms should have focused task lighting that limits light trespass into patient room.

The primary goals for office lighting are to optimize the open office spaces for daylight integration and to provide appropriate lighting levels in the private and open office spaces, while not creating a dull environment. Creating a vibrant lighting environment is extremely important when attempting to minimize energy use, especially in the building's common areas (lobby, corridors, break rooms, and conference rooms). To achieve maximum lighting energy savings, LPDs need to be reduced, and most spaces need to be provided with occupancy sensors and/or daylight-responsive dimming to reduce or shut off the lights when they are not needed. Additionally, night lighting, left on twenty-four hours a day to provide emergency egress, needs to be designed to limit power use to 10% of the total LPD.

Exterior lighting energy savings are achieved by providing optimal light levels, reducing lighting power with high-performance sources, and using automatic controls. Lighting power reduction recommendations are included in Chapter 5. Good exterior lighting considers local site characteristics, such as the building's surroundings. Tailoring the light level in a manner appropriate to the surroundings can avoid overlighting and result in more optimal energy use.

PLUG AND PROCESS LOADS

At the start of the project, the entire design team should examine all assumptions related to occupant-affiliated electrical loads, or plug loads. Some plug-load equipment may be selected by different disciplines within the design team, and other items may be selected outside the design process. If possible, hospital staff should also be involved in identifying plug-load equipment and controls.

Plug-load equipment gives off waste heat, which can increase cooling. Controlling these loads may also reduce the required size of cooling equipment. In many hospitals, developers and owners set arbitrary plug-load equipment power densities in watts per square feet as their required available capacity. But more is not always better when it comes to plug loads, especially if the air conditioning is sized to suit. Oversized HVAC equipment trying to work at low part load can result in excessive energy use and temperature instability in the spaces. Identifying the actual expected plug-load equipment power needs allows closer sizing of HVAC equipment, reducing cost and improving energy performance.

HVAC

The mission of healthcare facilities is to provide an environment of care for healing patients. HVAC systems must support this primary mission and be dependable day to day, hour to hour. The challenge is how to provide reliable systems that meet all of the various healthcare-specific criteria and use less energy. HVAC designers looking at new and innovative ways to save energy in healthcare facilities should consider the following:

- Innovative applications of proven technology
- Dependable equipment
- Appropriate redundancy
- Simple and reliable control sequences
- System complexity that is aligned with facility maintenance capabilities

Unique recommendations are included for each HVAC system type in the tables in Chapter 4. In the case of large healthcare facilities, equipment must meet the requirements of either the most current version of ASHRAE/IES Standard 90.1 or the local code requirements, whichever is more stringent.

HVAC design criteria for healthcare facilities vary as much as the medical services provided. The criteria for a hospital operating twenty-four hours a day, seven days a week, with patients who are incapable of self-preservation, are very different than those for a medical office building that operates similarly to a commercial office building.

For in-patient and surgical facilities, the federal government's Centers for Medicare and Medicaid Services (CMS) define regulations if reimbursement is involved. The state health departments are also involved in inspection and compliance. Most states reference the Facility Guidelines Institute's (FGI) *Guidelines for Design and Construction of Health Care Facilities*

Cost Control Strategies and Best Practices

Healthcare organizations, as well as others that invest in physical properties, seek to find the best use of capital for investment. Investments that do not directly lead to revenue generation face intense scrutiny. However, a focus on revenue generation alone while ignoring operating costs can lead to an underinvestment in facilities. The lack of investment can create an increase in ongoing operating costs through higher utility expenses and emergency repairs to equipment, and even ultimately affect revenue due to declining patient experiences. Nonetheless, many healthcare organizations have successfully deployed strategies to manage these capital investments and have received healthy financial returns as a result.

An investment in a highly efficient and well-designed facility should be economically successful. A key to achieving success is integrating the business case and the design case from the outset of the project. Design decisions made throughout should include consideration of the financial parameters of the project. Costs saved through an integrated design delivery by eliminating wasteful overdesign of systems, nonvalue-adding features and materials, and unproductive design and construction processes can more than offset any premium of cost for higher-performance systems and equipment.

Relating Efficiency Strategies to the Healthcare Mission

Many strategies that contribute to energy efficiency can also improve patient care, patient outcomes, and patient experience. The financial benefit of these can be hard to quantify but should be evaluated as a part of the project decision-making process. Justify all efficiency measures through meeting the mission. Some examples include the following:

* A well designed, constructed, operated, and maintained facility is a major contributor to the environment of care.
* An energy-efficient facility can improve the overall health of the community. For example, lower power consumption can lead to reduced particulate matter contaminating the air and to reduced mercury and other wastes contaminating groundwater at electricity generating plants. These side effects of a hospital's energy use cause thousands of premature deaths, asthma cases, and other health problems. The Healthcare Clean Energy Exchange offers an impact calculator to determine these statistics for specific facilities (http://www.eichealth.org).
* Employees take the energy efficiency practices they learn at work and use them at home. An Occupant Engagement Program can enhance energy efficiency both within the facility and in the surrounding community.

Relate energy-efficiency strategies to improving patient outcomes. Some examples include the following:

* Quality lighting that provides high color rendering and consistent presentation improves staff visual acuity during diagnosis, provides appropriate levels of contrast during intervention, and has been shown to reduce errors and improve staff alertness.
* Quality HVAC systems that deliver clean air at the correct volume, temperature, humidity, and pressure relationships can support infection control, improve health outcomes, and contribute to increased patient safety and comfort.

Reducing lighting power density for energy efficiency can provide cost savings in other areas. Some examples include the following:

* Reducing the fixture wattage through the use of solid-state lighting allows for the use of fewer circuits and a smaller transformer than with incandescent or fluorescent lighting.
* Longer mean time between failure results in maintenance cost savings that can easily be equivalent to the savings in electricity usage.
* Lower wattage can also mean a lower risk of fire, less required capacity on emergency power systems for egress lighting, and higher circuit reliability.
* Use of solid state lighting also allows variable dimming for daylighting and "quiet at night" applications not possible with some other light sources without expensive modifications.
* Lower lighting waste heat can lead to smaller cooling plants and, therefore, lower initial and operating costs for the hospital, especially in warmer climate zones.

Providing access to daylighting and views in caregiver environments (nurses' stations, cafeterias, corridors, etc.) through the use of courtyards and/or thinner floor plates often translates into a better-quality space, reduced medical errors, and more satisfied caregivers, which can result in improved patient care and healthier staff with less turnover.

Integrated Design

- Align the energy goals, site selection, building program and capital budget at the beginning of the project.
- Integrated design delivery has been shown to reduce errors and rework in project construction and reduce overall project duration, reducing budget contingencies and creating savings in construction finance costs.
- Efficient building planning and well-coordinated system selection and placement (structural, mechanical, electrical, etc.) reduce building volume, leading to less energy use and lower capital construction costs.
- Plan for future integration of renewable energy by designing to be renewable ready. For example, provide a large, unobstructed roof area, either south facing or flat, for future photovoltaic (PV) mounting and providing electrical conduit chases to possible future renewable sites.

Life-Cycle Cost Analysis

Include initial cost (material and construction costs), operating cost, replacement cost, and maintenance cost over the life of the building when cost justifying low-energy systems. Use cost estimates of proposed energy efficiency strategies to assess life-cycle costs of system bundles. Integrate cost estimators and design engineers into the decision-making process no later than schematic design. For example, additional first costs of ground-coupled systems can partially be offset by both energy savings and reduced maintenance costs of well fields, as compared to traditional cooling towers or heat-rejection condensers. Similarly, additional first cost of light-emitting diode (LED) fixtures can partially be offset by both energy savings and reduced relamping and maintenance costs, as compared to traditional exterior lighting fixtures. Healthcare reform will increasingly require hospitals to cut operating costs; these strategies support that goal.

Cost Trade-Offs

Carefully consider cost trade-offs throughout the design process, especially during value engineering exercises. Energy efficiency strategies are often on the chopping block, despite their significant long-term added value in comparison with desirable but unnecessary amenities such as floor-to-ceiling glass, expensive imported finishes, etc. Include installation and labor costs with material costs when evaluating total system costs. The building strategies that are used to attain the high levels of energy efficiency attributed to this publication require high levels of cross-system integration. This integration precludes common single-system value engineering. Value engineering puts in play large detrimental secondary energy efficiency affects. Also consider modular, prebuilt systems; they may have a higher material cost but reduce installation costs and construction time. Systems built in a factory are typically tighter and more uniform, reducing paths for infiltration and improving energy efficiency.

Value Added

Create additional value beyond energy savings by considering efficiency strategies that have multiple benefits, such as contributing to building operations during power outages or natural disasters. For example, PV systems can be integrated into an uninterruptable power supply, and daylighting and operable windows can provide light and air.

Alternative Financing

- Leverage all possible incentives and rebates for efficiency upgrades and renewable energy systems. Sources can include nonprofits, utilities, state energy agencies, and more (Leach et al. 2011).
- Team up with third-party financing to eliminate first costs for systems that exceed capital budget limitations and to leverage for-profit tax incentives not available to most hospitals.
- Consider the sale of environmental attributes (e.g., renewable energy credits, carbon offsets) to improve project financial performance. Consider implications of this strategy carefully.
- Use investment accounts from retained earnings. Many healthcare organizations have found that energy reduction investments often yield higher returns than other possible investments, with a much lower level of risk.
- Partner with an energy service company (ESCO) to install and maintain energy efficiency or renewable energy systems.

(the FGI guidelines), while others have generated their own criteria. A partial list of healthcare facility references for HVAC designers is as follows:

- *HVAC Design Manual for Hospitals and Clinics* (ASHRAE 2003)
- ANSI/ASHRAE Standard 62.1, *Ventilation for Acceptable Indoor Air Quality* (ASHRAE 2010b)
- ANSI/ASHRAE/ASHE Standard 170, *Ventilation of Heath Care Facilities* (ASHRAE 2008a) (FGI adopts Standard 170, including all approved addenda.)
- ANSI/ASHRAE/IES Standard 90.1, *Energy Standard for Buildings Except Low-Rise Residential Buildings* (ASHRAE 2010c)
- *ASHRAE Handbook—Fundamentals* ("Load Calculations" and "Duct Design" chapters) (ASHRAE 2009a)
- *ASHRAE Handbook—HVAC Systems and Equipment* (ASHRAE 2008b)
- *ASHRAE Handbook—HVAC Applications* ("Health Care Facilities" chapter) (ASHRAE 2011b)

BUILDING MECHANICAL SYSTEMS

This section discusses high-level mechanical system issues, while Chapter 5 provides specific HVAC, service water heating, and plug load recommendations and bonus tips. High-level issues need to be addressed by the entire project team, particularly, careful coordination of the functional space layout, building envelope and daylighting, and space for the mechanical system layout.

High-level strategies include reducing heating loads (OA, reheat, and service water heating) through the use of energy recovery and control strategies and systems that separate (or decouple) humidity and temperature treatment of OA; using controls to monitor space use during both occupied and unoccupied periods; and reducing ventilation and the energy used to treat ventilation air when possible. In addition, proper system choice—in coordination with system application to particular areas—helps increase efficiency by reducing air and water distribution energy. Finally, selecting systems that are understood and properly operated by facility managers is imperative to highly efficient systems.

Three different building mechanical systems (detailed in Chapter 5) are included in the Guide:

- HV2: Water-source heat pumps (WSHPs) with dedicated outdoor air (DOA)
- HV4: Mixed-air VAV system with separate OA treatment
- HV5: Fan coils with DOA

There are a handful of key differences in HVAC design among the different hospital space types. Distributed small WSHPs and fan coils are not recommended for critical care areas of the facility due to the limited filtration capability of this type of equipment, as well as concerns related to noise, difficulty of ensuring cleanliness (including local drain pans), and need for maintenance access within the critical care areas. Critical care areas should be served by VAV systems; these include but are not limited to surgery and trauma rooms (and other rooms where invasive procedures are performed; post-anesthesia-care-unit rooms; delivery rooms; intensive care; substerile service areas associated with critical care; and triage. (In California, CAV systems may be required in some or all of these spaces.) All other spaces can be served by any of the HVAC systems discussed in this Guide.

Unoccupied Mode

Depending on the use intensity of the inpatient unit, it may be possible to significantly step back the air changes if a patient room is not occupied. Hospitals with high occupancy rates will not see a benefit to this strategy, but many other spaces may benefit. The lighting and ventilation can both be tied to room scheduling software. They can also be turned down manually, though this is less reliable and adds an additional burden to staff.

Some new facilities intentionally position "soft" spaces, such as offices or conference rooms, adjacent to departments that will likely grow in the future. If this is the case, then the nonclinical spaces may need to be planned with similar HVAC strategies as clinical spaces, especially if the transition is expected to happen relatively quickly and without any HVAC renovation.

Aggressively Address Reheat

Reheat is often the largest single energy consuming process in large healthcare facilities because of the requirements for high air change rates and the need to both cool spaces and to maintain acceptable humidity (typically below 60% relative humidity) at lower space temperatures than most other building types. Minimizing reheat is essential to meeting the 50% energy reduction goal.

Air-Side Recovery Devices. Building owners are becoming more educated and asking insightful questions such as, "Instead of rejecting heat from cooling towers and purchasing energy to make heat using boilers, why can't heat be moved from one place to another and reused?" This is exactly what air-side energy recovery devices, recommended in many applications, do: they move energy from the exhaust airstream to the outdoor airstream. In the same manner, recovering heat from the cooling equipment—for example, from the condenser water stream—to preheat service water or to perform reheat is often a fast payback option. This may lead to selecting different equipment and designing the system in a different manner to reduce the annual energy use. Before purchasing new energy, consider the heat sources already available, and determine if they can be used, moved, or amplified to satisfy loads.

System Type Selection. One way to minimize reheat is through selection of system types that inherently reduce reheat. CAV reheat systems use the most reheat energy, and they are not an option in this Guide. VAV reheat systems reduce reheat energy, especially in unoccupied periods when air change per hour (ach) requirements generally do not apply, but reheat is still often the largest component in energy models of these systems. Systems that employ dedicated OA units with enthalpy transfer to minimize OA loads, and terminal heating and cooling equipment have the lowest need for reheat. These are described in Chapter 5.

Supply Air Temperature Reset. Supply air temperature reset was one of the larger energy reduction requirements in the Standard 90.1-2010 energy models performed by Pacific Northwest National Laboratory for the ASHRAE Standard 90.1 committee. Reset was especially beneficial in the hospital model and is therefore included in this Guide as a strategy. Raising the supply air temperature by 5°F, when appropriate, can reduce reheat by approximately 50% because zones typically don't reheat more than about 10°F on average.

Typical VAV reheat systems in hospitals maintain approximately 54°F supply air temperature downstream of the supply fan (52°F at the cooling coil plus 2–3°F of fan heat). This temperature is common because hospital workers tend to be more heavily clothed than workers in office environments, and the typical space temperature is around 72°F. ASHRAE/ASHE Standard 170 limits maximum humidity to 60% in many healthcare zones. Assuming a 90% sensible heat ratio results in a maximum air temperature of 55°F leaving the cooling coil. Since the designer can't control the settings of all thermostats, it is common to set coil discharge 2–3°F below the theoretical maximum.

Often it is possible to raise the supply air temperature. This occurs when both of the following are true:

1. The building is not at peak cooling load
2. The outdoor dew point is below about 54°F

In order to be able to take advantage of these large savings, the designer must select air terminal units for internal zones large enough to meet their peak cooling loads with air warmer than the design temperature. It is also necessary to sense the outdoor dew-point temperature to avoid losing humidity control. Humidity and dew-point sensors have historically been inaccurate instruments with substantial drift, so it is important to choose a quality instrument and to verify its calibration frequently.

Supplying Low Dew Point at Higher Air Temperatures. In the past, HVAC system options were limited for applications requiring low humidity levels to either subcooling the air to reduce supply air dew point, or using desiccant systems that require significant heat for regeneration of the desiccant. New technologies are available that can achieve low dew-point temperatures without reducing the supply air temperature (See HV18 in Chapter 5). In areas where low humidity levels are required, these technologies can help reduce reheat significantly.

Low Occupancy Mode. As stated above, ventilation airflow is a significant factor in the requirement for reheat. During times of nondesign occupancy and when allowed by code, ventilation should be reduced. Ventilation reset may be accomplished using different methods that suit specific areas, including the following:

- Occupancy sensors: private offices, as well as patient rooms and operating suites if allowed by the authority having jurisdiction (AHJ)
- Time of day sensors: Nonhealth-related spaces with known occupancy patterns
- CO_2 sensors (as a surrogate for the number of people) in open office areas

Unoccupied Mode. When zones are unoccupied, air terminal units should have their flow reduced as much as possible while still conforming to all applicable codes and standards and while maintaining the desired space conditions (which may be allowed a larger deadband than in occupied mode).

Heat Recovery Options. Once reheat has been minimized, methods should be sought to obtain the heat by using the least energy possible. Options include condenser water heat recovery (See HV38 in Chapter 5), condensing hot-water boilers (See WH3 in Chapter 5), and solar thermal systems (See RE2 in Chapter 5).

Plug Loads/Passive Reheat. The heat released by the interior lights, plug loads, and fans add to the cooling load and diminish the heating load, which highlights the importance in addressing these loads in conjunction with the envelope constructions. Where plug loads can reduce the amount of reheat necessary, they are a source of passive reheat.

Usability of Systems (Operations)

Simplify Systems. Throughout the design and construction process the people who will operate the system should be engaged, consulted, and listened to. Some of today's systems can work very efficiently as long as the proper control points are included, commissioned correctly, well calibrated, and operational. Additionally, control systems can become complex and require education of building operators.

With this in mind, there may be times when simpler systems reduce building energy in the long term, just because the systems operate properly for more hours than a more complex system.

A balance between simplicity, efficiency, and operability must be established so that the long-term, efficient operation becomes a reality.

Efficiently Dehumidify Air. HVAC systems manage air contaminants through filtration, dilution, air pressure differences between rooms, and, in some situations, airflow patterns within rooms. *Guidelines for the Design and Construction of Healthcare Facilities* (AIA 2010), which incorporate ASHRAE/ASHE Standard 170, the ASHRAE Handbook, and most of the other publications for room design criteria, use air exchange rates as a method to ensure appropriate levels of dilution. These documents list total and outside ach requirements for typical room types found in healthcare facilities.

The HVAC system is also responsible for maintaining acceptable temperature and relative humidity levels. It is common that the dilution air exchange rates require more air than is needed to maintain the space temperature. To complicate the situation, the air also needs to be dehumidified by overcooling it and causing condensation to occur at the central cooling coil. CAV reheat

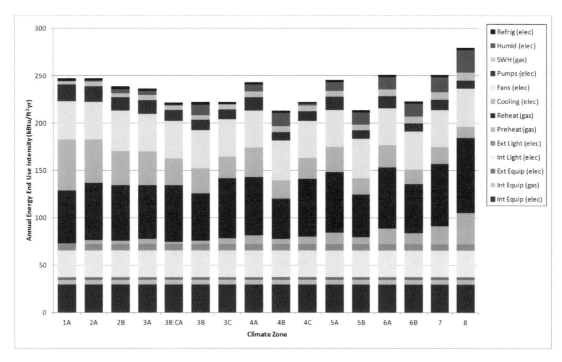

Figure 3-18   Reheat Energy (in Red) Compared to other Energy Uses in Healthcare Facilities

systems have traditionally been a common approach in these facilities because of their ability to independently control both temperature and humidity. They handle these issues easily and are simple to understand and maintain. Given the high degree of reliability and dependability required in a hospital, and the fact that energy use has historically been a small percentage of the operating budget of healthcare facilities, they were a logical choice. Unfortunately, CAV reheat systems use more energy than the system types recommended in this Guide.

Historically, because of the high air change rates and humidity control required in many of the space types found in healthcare facilities, the amount of reheat energy used by these systems is a significant portion of the total energy use. The baseline energy modeling for this Guide shows that reheat represents 20%–30% of the total energy use of the building in all climate zones (see Figure 3-18).

Minimize Distribution Energy and Costs

The *ASHRAE GreenGuide* (2010d) provides general guidance on reducing air-distribution energy and costs. Fan airflow may be harder to reduce in hospitals, since codes and standards prescribe minimum airflow rates. However, pressure drop can be dictated by the design team and reduced by maximizing ductwork and air-handler sizing, minimizing duct turns, and selecting components with low air pressure drop.

High-Level Acoustics—Indoor and Outdoor

Good sound and vibration design and the resultant sound levels are often unheralded contributors to patient comfort and health. Mitigated sound and vibration contribute to patients' ability to rest and recover and result in improved outcomes and experiences. While noise is not always an obvious problem, current research into the effect of noise on human productivity has shown it to be an important parameter affecting a worker's performance. In addition, relatively low levels of indoor noise can also adversely affect workers' well being. Outdoors, high environmental noise levels lower the general quality of life and degrades the environment. The 2010 FGI

The ASHRAE GreenGuide Recommendations on Reducing Distribution Energy and Cost
Excerpted from the *ASHRAE GreenGuide* (ASHRAE 2010d)

If air conditioning (heating/cooling) could be produced exactly where it is needed throughout a building, overall system efficiency would increase, because there would be no additional energy used to move (distribute) conditioned air or water. For acoustic, aesthetic, logistic, and a variety of other reasons, this ideal seldom is realized. Therefore, fans and pumps area used to move energy in the form of water and air. Throughout this process the goal is to minimize system energy consumption.

To reduce pressure drop the pipe or duct size should be maximized, and valve and coil resistance minimized. Coil sizes should be maximized within the space allowed to reduce pressure drop on both the water side and air side. The ideal selection will require striking an economic balance between first cost and projected energy savings.

In recent years, the 60% increase in required minimum chiller efficiency [...] has led to a reexamination of (past) assumptions used in designing hydronic media flow paths and in selecting (pumps) with an eye to reducing energy consumption [...] starting with:

[...] a chilled water temperature difference of 12°F to 20°F [...]
[...] a condenser water temperature difference of 12°F to 18°F [...]

Guidelines also limit noise from external sources, which is a major new issue for healthcare facilities (ASHRAE 2010d, pp. 185)

In healthcare situations, noise adversely effects patient outcomes. Many hospitals are located in close proximity to residential areas, and the acoustics of outdoor hospital equipment should be considered. Finally, noise is created by the systems that use energy and, when that energy is used wastefully, system efficiency is affected.

Central Plant Systems

Due to their size, hospitals often employ central plant systems where the cooling, heating, and perhaps power are produced in a central location and distributed to the areas needing those utilities. A possible drawback is that distribution of the cooling and heating (air and water) may increase the energy use of the facility. Great care should be taken in the design of hydronic and air-distribution systems so that central plant efficiencies are not negated by distribution inefficiencies. Some general guidelines that will help are as follows:

- Wring as many thermal units (Btus) out of the distributed fluid as possible prior to returning it to the central plant. This can be accomplished by increasing the operational temperature difference and reducing the flow rates required to satisfy the loads. Heat recovery chillers can precool chilled water so the primary warm weather chillers have a "normal" (10°F–15°F) delta T.
- Make distribution pipes and ductwork as large as practical and possible to reduce friction losses. Lay out the piping and ductwork to reduce fitting pressure losses. Allow space so that air-handling-unit pressure drops can be reduced. Finding ways to incorporate these into the architecture, rather than hiding them in as small a space as possible, will enhance overall efficiency. This has the added benefit of reducing noise and improving patient comfort.
- Always consider each utility as a system. Concentrating and maximizing efficiency of once piece of the system (for example, the chiller in a chilled-water system or boiler in a

hot-water system) often results in increased system energy use. Understand and estimate the ancillary energy use whenever considering changes.

- Design the system for the specific requirements of the particular building. Match cooling- and heating-unit selection to efficiently deliver the required heating and cooling loads at various times of the year. For example, size the heat recovery chiller to match the desired heating load.
- Recover and reuse energy whenever possible (e.g., service water preheat, low temperature reheat, etc.).

This Guide does not cover purchased chilled water for cooling, or solar energy, steam, or purchased steam for heating. These and other systems are alternative means that may be used to help achieve the energy savings target

Schedules of Occupancy, Use, and Utility Rates

It is essential that the team understands the schedules related to utility rates, especially any embedded demand charges and on/off/high/low/seasonal peak period definitions local to the site and its service utility. This is because the prevailing benchmarks for energy savings in ASHRAE/IES Standard 90.1 (ASHRAE 2010b) and most energy codes are based on annual cost, not absolute energy savings. Most importantly, the owner pays for both demand and consumption charges. This means that discretionary decisions by the team to avoid onerous demand charges through load shifting may be appropriate when seeking to reduce annual operating expenditures.

It is important for the team to map out the anticipated schedules of use and occupancy for each area of the building. This information is crucial to the energy modeling and can greatly affect outcomes with regard to estimated energy savings over a known benchmark or life-cycle cost analysis. It is important to note that most energy models run the same schedule week after week, so schedules not only should be configured to cover typical weeks but also should be changed to account for any known periods of differing occupation or use (for example, holiday periods when the patient census or diagnostic and treatment schedules differ).

CONTROL STRATEGIES

When striving to achieve significant energy reductions on the order of 50% savings, the appropriate application of automatic controls is necessary, as occupants of the building are primarily and appropriately focused on their day-to-day activities and not on behaving in an energy-conscious manner. A number of control strategies are discussed in Chapter 5. This section is devoted to discussion of multitrade integration of controls.

The following issues should be considered for integrated approaches in controls:

- Shared information technology backbone and routing (if data security will allow it) to improve Web-based access to energy-use data
- Shared connection of occupancy sensors between HVAC and lighting controls
- Motorized blind control algorithms in response to anticipated solar heat gain and glare or to provide insulation during the heating season
- Facilities scheduling software interlinked with HVAC ventilation controls
- Server-room, load-management controls as noted in the multidisciplinary "Plug Load Reduction" section earlier in this chapter
- Consolidated reporting of motor kilowatt-hours versus anticipated benchmarks
- Energy-use dashboards showing instantaneous energy use or monthly energy cost roll up by zone to encourage departmental competition and behavioral change
- Overlays of plug-load monitoring, lighting, and HVAC controls to monitor relative energy-use intensities by use and by zone throughout the day and year (useful in trouble-shooting large energy consumers)

REFERENCES AND RESOURCES

AIA. 2010. *Guidelines for the Design and Construction of Healthcare Facilities.* Dallas, TX: Facility Guidelines Institute.

ASHRAE. 2003. *HVAC Design Manual for Hospitals and Clinics.* Atlanta: ASHRAE.

ASHRAE. 2004. ANSI/ASHRAE/IESNA Standard 90.1-2004, *Energy Standard for Buildings Except Low-Rise Residential Buildings.* Atlanta: ASHRAE.

ASHRAE. 2005. ASHRAE Guideline 0, *The Commissioning Process.*Atlanta: ASHRAE.

ASHRAE. 2007a. ANSI/ASHRAE/IESNA Standard 90.1-2007, *Energy Standard for Buildings Except Low-Rise Residential Buildings.* Atlanta: ASHRAE.

ASHRAE. 2007b. *ASHRAE Handbook—HVAC Applications.* Atlanta: ASHRAE.

ASHRAE. 2007c. ASHRAE Guideline 1.1, *HVAC&R Technical Requirements for The Commissioning Process.* Atlanta: ASHRAE.

ASHRAE. 2008a. ANSI/ASHRAE/ASHE Standard 170, *Ventilation of Heath Care Facilities.* Atlanta: ASHRAE.

ASHRAE. 2008b. *ASHRAE Handbook—HVAC Systems and Equipment*, I-P Edition. Atlanta: ASHRAE.

ASHRAE. 2009a. *ASHRAE Handbook—Fundamentals*, I-P Edition. Atlanta: ASHRAE.

ASHRAE. 2009b. *Indoor Air Quality Guide: Best Practices for Design, Construction, and Commissioning.* Atlanta: ASHRAE.

ASHRAE. 2010a. ANSI/ASHRAE Standard 55-2010, *Thermal Environmental Conditions for Human Occupancy.* Atlanta: ASHRAE.

ASHRAE. 2010b. ANSI/ASHRAE Standard 62.1-2010, *Ventilation for Acceptable Indoor Air Quality.* Atlanta: ASHRAE.

ASHRAE. 2010c. ANSI/ASHRAE/IES Standard 90.1-2010, *Energy Standard for Buildings Except Low-Rise Residential Buildings.* Atlanta: ASHRAE.

ASHRAE. 2010d. *ASHRAE GreenGuide: The Design, Construction, and Operation of Sustainable Buildings*, 3rd ed. John M. Swift, Jr., and Tom Lawrence, Editors. Atlanta: ASHRAE.

ASHRAE. 2011a. *Advanced Energy Design Guide for Small to Medium Office Buildings: Achieving 50% Energy Savings Toward a Net Zero Energy Building.* Atlanta: ASHRAE.

ASHRAE. 2011b. *ASHRAE Handbook—HVAC Applications.* Atlanta: ASHRAE.

ASHRAE. 2011c. ANSI/ASHRAE/USGBC/IES Standard 189.1-2009, *Standard for the Design of High-Performance Green Buildings Except Low-Rise Residential Buildings.* Atlanta: ASHRAE.

Bonnema, E., D. Studer, A. Parker, S. Pless, P. Torcellini. 2010. Large Hospital 50% Energy Savings: Technical Support Document. NREL/TP-550-47867, National Renewable Energy Laboratory, Golden CO. www.nrel.gov/docs/fy10osti/47867.pdf.

Briggs, R.S., R.G. Lucas, and Z.T. Taylor. 2002a. Climate classification for building energy codes and standards, PNNL Technical Paper final review draft. Richland, WA: Pacific Northwest National Laboratory.

Briggs, R.S., R.G. Lucas, and Z.T. Taylor. 2002b. Climate classification for building energy codes and standards: Part 1—Development process. *ASHRAE Transactions* 109(1).

Briggs, R.S., R.G. Lucas, and Z.T. Taylor. 2002c. Climate classification for building energy codes and standards: Part 2—Zone definitions, maps, and comparisons. *ASHRAE Transactions* 109(1).

Burpee, H., and J. Loveland. 2009. Target 100!. Integrated Design Lab, University of Washington, Seattle, WA.

CBSC. 2011. *California Energy Code*, Title 24, Part 6 of the California Code of Regulations. California Building Standards Commission, Sacramento, CA.

CEC. 2008. California Commercial End-Use Survey (CEUS). California Energy Commission, Sacramento, CA. http://www.energy.ca.gov/ceus.

CFR. 1992. National Appliance Energy Conservation Act. Code of Federal Regulations, Title 10, Chapter II, Part 430—Energy Efficiency Program for Certain Commercial and Industrial Equipment. Washington, DC: U.S. Government.

Colliver, D., R.S. Gates, T.F. Burks, and H. Zhang. 1997. Determination of the 0.4%, 1% and 2% annual occurrences of temperature and moisture and the 99% and 98% occurrences of temperature for 1400 national and international locations. Final Report, ASHRAE Research Project RP-890. Atlanta: American Society of Heating, Refrigerating and Air-Conditioning.

DOI. 1970. The National Atlas of the United States of America. Washington, DC: U.S. Department of Interior, Geological Survey.

EERE. 2010. Weather Data. EnergyPlus Energy Simulation Software. http://apps1.eere.energy. gov/buildings/energyplus/cfm/weather_data.cfm. Washington, DC: U.S. Department of Energy, Office of Energy Efficiency and Renewable Energy.

EIA. 2011. Commercial Buildings Energy Consumption Survey (CBECS). U.S. Department of Energy, U.S. Energy Information Administration, Washington DC. http:// www.eia.doe.gov/emeu/cbecs/.

EPA. 2011. ENERGY STAR Portfolio Manager, www.energystar.gov/benchmark. U.S. Environmental Protection Agency, U.S. Department of Energy, Washington DC.

Hart, R., S. Mangan, and W. Price. 2004. Who left the lights on? Typical load profiles in the 21st century. 2004 ACEEE Summer Study on Energy Efficiency in Buildings. Washington, DC: American Council for an Energy-Efficient Economy.

Heerwagen, Judith, ed. 2008. *Biophilic Design: The Theory, Science and Practice of Bringing Buildings to Life.* Hoboken, NJ: John Wiley and Sons, Inc

HMG. 2003. Windows and offices: A study of office worker performance and the indoor environment. California Energy Commission Technical Report P500-03-082-A-9. Gold River, CA: Heschong Mahone Group.

ICC. 2009. *International Energy Conservation Code*. Washington, DC: International Code Council.

IES. 2011. *The Lighting Handbook*, 10th ed. New York: Illuminating Engineering Society of North America.

Leach, M., E. Bonnema, and S. Pless. 2011. Setting Absolute Energy Use Targets for High Performance Buildings. NREL/TP-5500-52590, National Renewable Energy Laboratory, Golden, CO. www.nrel.gov/docs/fy11osti/52590.pdf.

Lobato, C., S. Pless, M. Sheppy, and P. Torcellini. 2011. Reducing plug and process loads for a large-scale, low-energy office building: NREL's Research Support Facility. *ASHRAE Transactions* 117(1):330–39.

Maniccia, D., and A. Tweed. 2000. *Occupancy Sensor Simulations and Energy Analysis for Commercial Buildings.* Troy, NY: Lighting Research Center, Rensselaer Polytechnic Institute.

Marion, W., and S. Wilcox. 2008. *Users Manual for TMY3 Data Sets*, NREL/TP-581-43156. Golden, CO: National Renewable Energy Laboratory.

NFPA. 2011. NFPA 70, *National Electrical Code*®. Quincy, MA: National Fire Protection Association.

NOAA. 2005. Climate maps of the United States. http://cdo.ncdc.noaa.gov/cgi-bin/climaps/climaps.pl. NOAA Satellite and Information Service. National Climatic Data Center. Washington, DC: National Oceanic and Atmospheric Administration.

NREL. 2005. Global Horizontal Solar Radiation – Annual. Image "solar_glo" available at www.nrel.gov/gis/images. Golden, CO: National Renewable Energy Laboratory.

Provencio, I. 2011. The hidden organism in our eyes. *Scientific American* May:55–59.

Sanchez, M.C., C.A. Webber, R. Brown, J. Busch, M. Pinckard, and J. Roberson. 2007. Space heaters, computers, cell phone chargers: How plugged in are commercial buildings? LBNL-62397. *Proceedings of the 2006 ACEEE Summer Study on Energy Efficiency in Buildings*, August, Asilomar, CA.

Sethi, A., and T. Marseille. 2010. Old concepts, new tools: Case study—The Terry Thomas. *High Performing Buildings*, Summer:26–38.

Seibert, K.L. The right fit: Case study—CMTA office building. *High Performing Buildings*, Winter:48–59.

Thornton, B.A., W. Wang, M.D. Lane, M.I. Rosenberg, and B. Liu. 2009. *Technical Support Document: 50% Energy Savings Design Technology Packages for Medium Office Buildings*, PNNL-19004. Richland, WA: Pacific Northwest National Laboratory.

Thornton, B.A., W. Wang, Y. Huang, M.D. Lane, and B. Liu. 2010. *Technical Support Document: 50% Energy Savings for Small Office Buildings*, PNNL-19341. Richland, WA: Pacific Northwest National Laboratory.

Ulrich, R. 2008. Chapter 6, Biophilic theory and research for healthcare design. In *Biophilic Design: The Theory, Science and Practice of Bringing Buildings to Life*. Stephen R. Kellert, Judith Heerwagen, Martin Mador, Editors. Hoboken, NJ: Wiley & Sons.

USGBC. 2011. Leadership in Energy and Environmental Design (LEED) Green Building Rating System. Washington, DC: U.S. Green Building Council. www.usgbc.org/DisplayPage.aspx?CategoryID=19.

SWEDISH ISSAQUAH HOSPITAL A CASE STUDY

Located in the Issaquah Highlands near Seattle, Washington, Swedish Issaquah is a 350,000 ft², four-story acute-care hospital with 175 beds, and is the first greenfield hospital to be built in King County in 25 years. When fully complete, it will be part of a 550,000 ft² campus that includes the acute-care hospital (composed of emergency, surgery, imaging, labor and delivery, pediatrics, intensive-care unit, cancer, and medical/surgical facilities), a 200,000 ft² medical office building (MOB), and a stand-alone central utility plant (CUP) connected by a utility tunnel.

INTEGRATED DESIGN

Design began in May of 2009 with an EUI target of 150 kBtu/ft²·yr or lower. Similar hospitals in the Pacific Northwest have an EUI of about 260–265 kBtu/ft²·yr. Using an integrated project delivery approach, all the stakeholders were brought together early in the process. This spirit of cooperation and involvement extended through completion of construction and included the pipe fitters and sheet metal installers. Once it was understood that efficiency was a key element of the design, even the number of pipe bends and duct offsets became important.

The design team met weekly to discuss how best to expedite design. The integrated design approach carried through into the roles and responsibilities shared by the mechanical design engineer and contractor. All major equipment, pipe racks, ductwork, skids, and assemblies

Swedish Issaquah Hospital
Photos courtesy of CollinsWoerman (reprinted with permission)

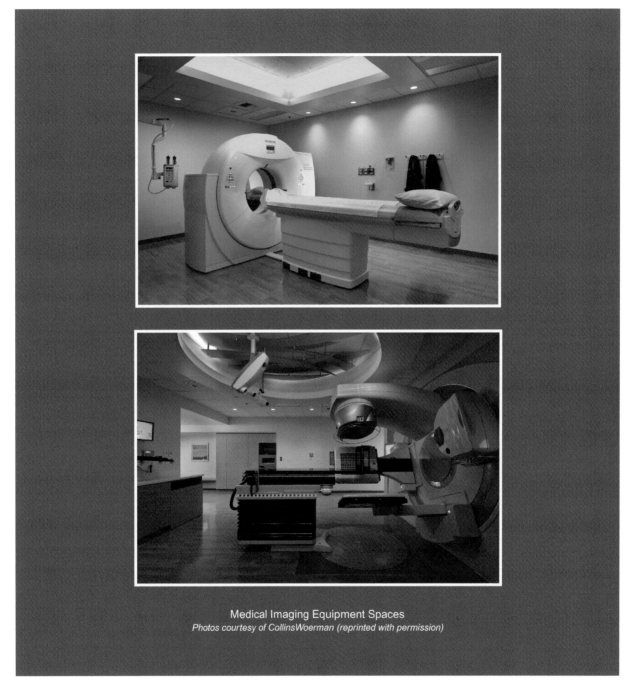

Medical Imaging Equipment Spaces
Photos courtesy of CollinsWoerman (reprinted with permission)

were to be placed ahead of the structural roof steel, and so the design team created a decision matrix that allowed them to select and model equipment and controls well ahead of the traditional schedule. Prefabrication was a key element to shaving more than a year off of project delivery:

- The CUP piping (and certain equipment packages) and utility tunnel piping and racks were delivered prefabricated to the site by the time the contract documents were ready to issue.
- Terminal units were procured early based on performance, size, and acoustics and were fully piped, valved, and bench tested off site. They were then capped, precharged, and palletized for delivery.
- The MOB mechanical room was prefabricated off site and shipped complete to the site.

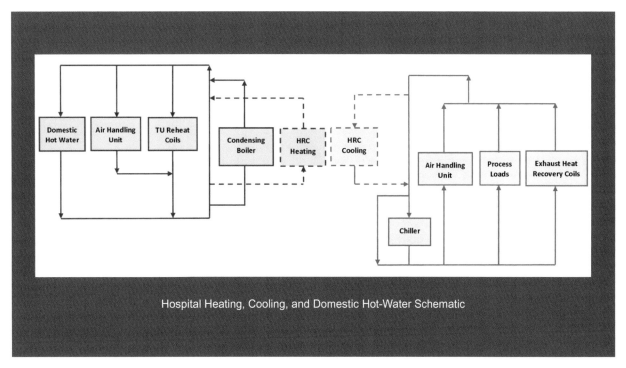

Hospital Heating, Cooling, and Domestic Hot-Water Schematic

BUILDING ENVELOPE AND DAYLIGHTING

As part of the overall strategy, the building exterior elements (insulation, glass types, and solar shading) were studied for impact on energy consumption and assessment of investment return. Because the energy model had been developed during concept development and populated first with data from a similar hospital program and loads, the baseline envelope was determined to be adequate. Any significant upgrade to insulation or glazing was found to have minimal impact on overall EUI reduction.

HVAC SYSTEMS

Because hospitals always require some degree of simultaneous cooling and heating, the design focused on integrating heating/cooling and domestic hot-water systems to recover and reuse heat that otherwise would be wasted. The hospital's heating, cooling, and domestic hot-water systems is an effort to recover and reuse heat that otherwise would be wasted. At the core of the system is a heat recovery chiller (HRC) that uses building cooling and heat recovered from building exhaust airstreams to produce usable low-temperature heating energy. The heating loop, which provides building heating and the majority of the domestic hot-water heating, is supplemented by a condensing boiler. The boilers are not expected to operate until the OA temperature drops to 40°F. In addition, zones are carefully designed so that cooling air temperature can be kept near 62°F, on average. A low EUI was achieved in large part due to cooling with a higher supply air temperature.

ENERGY MODELING

When all design decisions are scrutinized on the basis of their impact on overall EUI, the energy model becomes a forward-looking tool to keep the energy budget as a viable target rather than a record-keeping exercise that looks back at design decisions already made. The hospital was modeled down to the space level, with 45 individual space templates created. The team used actual lighting and equipment data and realistic occupancy schedules. Part of programming included detailed interviews where real occupancy patterns, equipment, and control response time were determined.

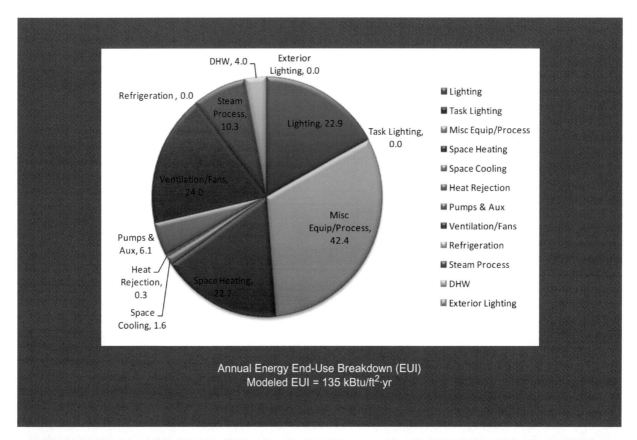

Annual Energy End-Use Breakdown (EUI)
Modeled EUI = 135 kBtu/ft^2·yr

Energy Savings Analysis			
Strategy	Total Cost	Annual Energy Savings	Simple Payback
Light Occupancy Sensors		$22,941	
VAV	$973,047	$342,183	3 years
Heat Recovery System	$1,103,971	$115,081	10 years
Low Static Pressure AHUs	$398,312	$31,742	13 years
Low Static Pressure Ducts	$314,983	$19,538	16 years
VSD Chiller	$208,998	$11,144	19 years

The final model shows energy use reductions from typical hospital usage for the following:

- Space heating from a typical EUI of 110 kBtu/ft^2·yr to 22.7 kBtu/ft^2·yr
- Space cooling from a typical EUI of 11 kBtu/ft^2·yr to 1.6 kBtu/ft^2·yr

And, with the low air transport factor in play:

- Ventilation fans energy from a typical EUI of 43 kBtu/ft^2·yr to 24 kBtu/ft^2·yr

In addition to making design decisions within the energy model, the model was used by the integrated team and the utility to assess potential energy reduction strategies that would result in utility rebate funding. Over 70 strategies were studied (including low static pressure air-handling units and ductwork, VFDs on medical vacuum equipment variable-speed-cooling tower fans, variable-flow kitchen exhaust make up, supply-air temperature reset, occupancy sensors and controls, and low air transport factors). With an involved, hands-on approach, the utility evaluated and ultimately funded a wide range of energy saving strategies, resulting in one of the largest rebate grants ever given to a hospital in Washington.

Strategies and Recommendations by Climate Zone

4

INTRODUCTION

This Guide organizes specific recommendations according to the eight U.S. Department of Energy climate zones defined in Figure 4-1. To assist those outside of the United States in using this Guide, Appendix B shows the climate zone definitions applicable to any location. Choosing the appropriate recommended measures for a given climate zone will contribute to the target 50% energy reduction above ASHRAE/IESNA Standard 90.1-2004 requirements.

Chapter 4 tabulates a unique set of energy-conserving design elements for each climate zone. The recommendations are *a way*, but not the *only way* to achieve the energy reduction goal. Other approaches may also be used to save energy, and the guidance provided in Chapter 3 can help project teams determine additional levels of savings.

Where "Comply with Standard 90.1" is indicated, the project must meet the more stringent of either the most current version of ASHRAE/IES Standard 90.1 or the local code requirements.

Each of the recommendation tables includes a set of common items arranged by building system: envelope, daylighting/lighting, plug and process loads (PPL), service water heating (SWH), and HVAC. Recommendations are included for each item or system. In some cases, the recommendations vary depending on the construction type or specific component attributes. For example, different insulation values are recommended for mass and steel-framed wall types; vertical fenestration criteria are provided; and recommendations are given for thermal transmittance, solar heat gain coefficient (SHGC), and exterior sun control.

The Guide recommends one of three HVAC system types, all of which use a form of separately treated outdoor air: water-source heat pumps (WSHP), four-pipe fan coils, and central variable-air-volume (VAV) air-handling units. These systems are further described in HV2–5 of Chapter 5. The detailed descriptions suggest refinements to the basic system-type recommendations included for each HVAC system type, based on practicality of implementation and the 50% energy reduction goal.

The fourth column of each table references how-to tips for implementing the recommended criteria. The tips are located in Chapter 5 under separate sections coded for envelope (EN), daylighting (DL), electric lighting (EL), plug loads (PL), service water heating systems and equipment (WH), HVAC systems and equipment (HV), and quality assurance (QA). In addition to how-to advice that represents good practice for design and maintenance suggestions, these tips include cautions for what to avoid. Important QA considerations and recommendations are also given for the building design, construction, and post-occupancy phases. Note that each tip is tied to the applicable climate zone in Chapter 4. The final column is provided as a simple checklist to identify the recommendations being used for a specific building design and construction.

CLIMATE ZONE RECOMMENDATIONS

The recommendations presented in the following tables are minimum, maximum, or specific values (which are both the minimum and maximum values).

Minimum values include the following:

- R-values
- Solar reflectance index (SRI)
- Light-to-solar-gain (LSG) ratio
- Projection factor (PF)
- Interior surface average reflectance
- Mean lumens per watt
- Gas water heater or boiler efficiency
- Thermal efficiency (E_t)
- Energy factor (EF)
- Energy efficiency ratio (EER)
- Integrated part-load value (IPLV)
- Coefficient of performance (COP)
- Energy recovery effectiveness
- Motor efficiency
- Duct or pipe insulation thickness

Maximum values include the following:

- Fenestration and door U-factors
- Fenestration solar heat gain coefficient (SHGC)
- Window-to-wall ratio (WWR)
- Lighting power density (LPD)
- Fan input power per cfm of supply airflow (W/cfm)

BONUS SAVINGS

Chapter 5 provides additional recommendations and strategies for savings for toplighting, natural ventilation, and renewable energy that are over and above the 50% savings recommendations contained in the following eight climate regions.

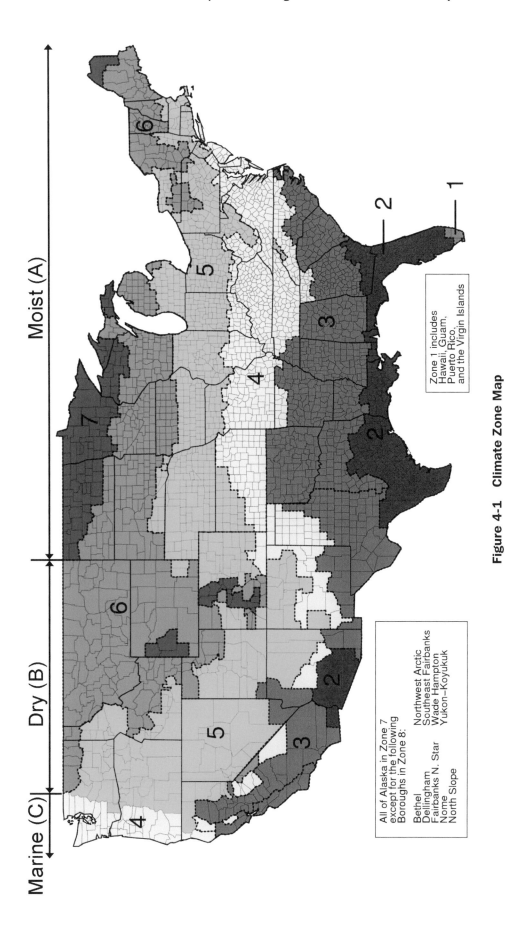

Figure 4-1 Climate Zone Map

Zone 1

Florida
Broward
Miami-Dade
Monroe

Guam

Hawaii

Puerto Rico

U.S. Virgin Islands

Climate Zone 1 Recommendation Table for Large Hospitals

	Item	Component	Recommendation	How-to Tips	✓
Envelope	Form/space planning	Proper zoning	Group similar space types within the building footprint.	DL4–6	
	Roofs	Insulation entirely above deck	R-20.0 c.i.	EN2, 15–17	
		Solar reflectance index (SRI)	78	EN1	
		Mass (HC > 7 Btu/ft^2)	R-5.7 c.i.	EN3, 15–17	
	Walls	Steel framed	R-13.0 + R-7.5 c.i.	EN4, 15–17	
		Below-grade walls	Comply with Standard 90.1*	EN5, 15–17	
	Floors	Mass	R-4.2 c.i.	EN6, 15–17	
		Steel framed	R-19.0	EN7, 15–17	
	Slabs	Unheated	Comply with Standard 90.1*		
		Heated	R-7.5 for 12 in.	EN9–10, 15–17	
	Doors	Swinging	U-0.70	EN11, 16	
		Nonswinging	U-1.45	EN12, 16	
	Vestibules	At primary visitor building entrance	Comply with Standard 90.1*	EN14	
	Continuous air barriers	Continuous air barriers	Entire building envelope	EN13	
	Vertical fenestration (full assembly—NFRC rating)	Window-to-wall ratio	40% of net wall (floor-ceiling)	DL7, EN20	
		Thermal transmittance	Nonmetal framing windows = 0.56 Metal framing windows = 0.65	EN18–20, 23–25	
		Solar heat gain coefficient (SHGC)	Nonmetal framing windows = 0.25 Metal framing windows = 0.25	EN19–20, 23–25	
		Light-to-solar gain ratio (LSG)	All orientations ≥ 1.5	EN24	
		Exterior sun control	South orientation only – PF = 0.5	EN21, DL13–14	
Daylighting/ Lighting	Form-driven daylighting option	All spaces	Comply with LEED for healthcare credits IEQ 8.1 (daylighting) and IEQ 8.2 (views)	DL3–6	
		Diagnostic and treatment block	Shape the building footprint and form such that the area within 15 ft of the perimeter exceeds 40% of the floorplate.	DL6	
		Inpatient units	Ensure that 75% of the occupied space not including patient rooms lies within 20 ft of the perimeter.	DL6	
		Staff areas (exam rooms, nurse stations, offices, corridors); public spaces (waiting, reception); and other regularly occupied spaces as applicable	Design the building form to maximize access to natural light, through sidelighting and toplighting.	DL8–14, 20–23	
	Nonform-driven daylighting option	Staff areas (exam rooms, nurse stations, offices, corridors) and public spaces (waiting, reception)	Add daylight controls to any space within 15 ft of a perimeter window.	DL20–23	
	Interior finishes	Room interior surface average reflectance	Ceilings ≥ 80% Walls ≥ 70%	DL17	
		Lighting power density (LPD)	Whole building = 0.9 W/ft^2 Space-by-space per Table 5-4	EL1, 12–20	
		Light source efficacy (mean lumens per watt)	T8 & T5 > 2 ft = 92 T8 & T5 < 2 ft = 85 All other >50	EL2–5	
	Interior lighting	Ballasts—4 ft T8 Lamps	Nondimming = NEMA Premium Dimming= NEMA Premium Program Start	EL2	
		Ballasts—Fluorescent and HID	Electronic	EL2–5	
		Dimming controls daylight harvesting	Dim all fixtures in daylighted zones.	DL20–23, EL11	
		Lighting controls—general	Manual ON, auto/timed OFF in all areas as possible.	EL6, 21	
		Surgery task lights	Use LED lights exclusively.	EL14	
		Exit signage	0.1–0.2 W light emitting capacitor (LEC) exit signs exclusively	EL22	
	Exterior lighting	Façade and landscape lighting	LPD = 0.15 W/ft^2	EL23	
		Parking lots and drives	LPD = 0.1 W/ft^2	EL23	
		All other exterior lighting	LPD = Comply with Standard 90.1* Auto reduce to 25% (12am–6am)	EL23	
PPL	Equipment choices	Computers	Laptops = minimum 2/3 of total computers All others = mini desktop computers	PL2	
		ENERGY STAR® equipment	All computers, equipment, appliances	PL5	
		Vending machines	Delamp and specify best in class efficiency.	PL3, 7	
	Controls	Computer power control	Network control with power saving modes and control during unoccupied hours or IT enterprise power management software	PL2	
		Occupancy sensors	Office plug occupancy sensors	PL3	
		Timer switches	Water coolers, coffee makers, small appliances = auto OFF during unoccupied hours	PL3	

*Note: Where the table says "Comply with Standard 90.1," the user must meet the more stringent of either the most current version of Standard 90.1 or the local code requirements.

Climate Zone 1 Recommendation Table for Large Hospitals (Continued)

	Item	Component	Recommendation	How-to Tips	✓
PPL	Kitchen equipment	Cooking equipment	ENERGY STAR or California rebate-qualified equipment	PL8–9	
		Refrigeration equipment	6 in. insulation on low-temp walk-in equipment, insulated floor, LED lighting, floating-head pressure controls, liquid pressure amplifier, subcooled liquid refrigerant, evaporative condenser	PL8–9, 12	
		Exhaust hoods	Side panels, larger overhangs, rear seal at appliances, proximity hoods, VAV demand-based exhaust	PL8, 10, 13	
	Process loads	Elevators	Use traction elevators for all elevators, and use regenerative traction elevators for all high-use elevators.	PL16	
SWH	Service water heating	Gas water heater (condensing)	95% Efficiency	WH3, HV8	
		Point-of-use water heater	0.81 EF or 81% E_t	PL11, WH3	
		Electric-heat-pump water heater	2.33 EF	WH3	
		Pipe insulation (d < 1.5 in./$d \geq$ 1.5 in.)	1.0 in./1.5 in.	WH7	
HVAC	Heating system	No central steam Use hot-water distribution system	Point-of-use steam for humidification and sterilization	HV33	
	Surgery — Central air-handling system	Water-cooled chiller	6.5 COP	HV8, 35	
		Water-circulation pumps	VFD and NEMA premium	HV35	
		Cooling towers	VFD on tower fans	HV37	
		Boiler efficiency	90% E_c	HV8	
		Maximum fan power	bhp ≤ supply cfm × 0.0012 + A	HV21–22, 24	
		Economizer	Comply with Standard 90.1*	HV19	
	Nonsurgery — Water-source heat pump (WSHP) system with DOAS	WSHP part-load/full-load cooling efficiency	17.6/15.0 EER	HV2	
		WSHP part-load/full-load heating efficiency	5.7/5.0 COP	HV2	
		WSHP compressor capacity control	Two-speed or variable-speed	HV2	
		Water-circulation pumps	VFD and NEMA premium	HV35	
		Closed-circuit cooling tower	VFD on fans	HV37	
		Boiler efficiency	90% E_c	HV8	
		Maximum fan power	0.4 W/cfm	HV21–22, 24	
		Exhaust-air energy recovery in DOAS	A (humid zones) = 60% total effectiveness B (dry zones) = 60% sensible effectiveness	HV9, 15–16	
		DOAS ventilation control	DCV with VFD	HV10–11	
	Fan-coil system with DOAS	Water-cooled chiller	6.5 COP	HV8, 35	
		Water-circulation pumps	VFD and NEMA premium	HV35	
		Cooling towers	VFD on tower fans	HV37	
		Boiler efficiency	90% E_c	HV8	
		Maximum fan power	0.4 W/cfm	HV21–22, 24	
		FCU fans	Multiple speed	HV5	
		Exhaust-air energy recovery in DOAS	A (humid zones) = 60% total effectiveness B (dry zones) = 60% sensible effectiveness	HV9, 15–16	
		DOAS ventilation control	DCV with VFD	HV10–11	
	Mixed-air VAV system with separate OA treatment and heat recovery system	Heat recovery water-cooled chiller	4.55 COP	HV8, 36, 38	
		Water-cooled chiller	6.5 COP	HV8, 35	
		Water-circulation pumps	VFD and NEMA premium	HV37	
		Cooling towers	VFD on tower fans	HV35	
		Boiler efficiency	90% E_c	HV8	
		Maximum fan power	bhp ≤ supply cfm × 0.0012 + A	HV21–22, 24	
		Economizer	Comply with Standard 90.1*	HV19	
		Exhaust-air energy recovery in DOAS	A (humid zones) = 60% total effectiveness B (dry zones) = 60% sensible effectiveness	HV9, 15–16	
		DOAS ventilation control	DCV with VFD	HV10–11	
	Ducts and dampers	OA damper	Motorized	HV14, 31	
		Duct seal class	Seal class A	HV22, 24	
		Insulation level	R-6	HV22–23	
QA	Measurement and verification	Electrical submeters	Design and circuit for separate submeters for lighting, HVAC, general 120V, service water heating, renewables, and whole building	QA12–14	
		Benchmarks	Benchmark monthly energy use.	QA15	
		Training	Facility operator on continuous benchmarking	QA12–15	

*Note: Where the table says "Comply with Standard 90.1," the user must meet the more stringent of either the most current version of Standard 90.1 or the local code requirements.

Zone 2

Alabama

Baldwin
Mobile

Arizona

La Paz
Maricopa
Pima
Pinal
Yuma

California

Imperial

Florida

Alachua
Baker
Bay
Bradford
Brevard
Calhoun
Charlotte
Citrus
Clay
Collier
Columbia
DeSoto
Dixie
Duval
Escambia
Flagler
Franklin
Gadsden
Gilchrist
Glades
Gulf

Hamilton
Hardee
Hendry
Hernando
Highlands
Hillsborough
Holmes
Indian River
Jackson
Jefferson
Lafayette
Lake
Lee
Leon
Levy
Liberty
Madison
Manatee
Marion
Martin
Nassau
Okaloosa
Okeechobee
Orange
Osceola
Palm Beach
Pasco
Pinellas
Polk
Putnam
Santa Rosa
Sarasota
Seminole
St. Johns
St. Lucie
Sumter
Suwannee
Taylor

Union
Volusia
Wakulla
Walton
Washington

Georgia

Appling
Atkinson
Bacon
Baker
Berrien
Brantley
Brooks
Bryan
Camden
Charlton
Chatham
Clinch
Colquitt
Cook
Decatur
Echols
Effingham
Evans
Glynn
Grady
Jeff Davis
Lanier
Liberty
Long
Lowndes
McIntosh
Miller
Mitchell
Pierce
Seminole
Tattnall

Thomas
Toombs
Ware
Wayne

Louisiana

Acadia
Allen
Ascension
Assumption
Avoyelles
Beauregard
Calcasieu
Cameron
East Baton
Rouge
East Feliciana
Evangeline
Iberia
Iberville
Jefferson
Jefferson Davis
Lafayette
Lafourche
Livingston
Orleans
Plaquemines
Pointe Coupee
Rapides
St. Bernard
St. Charles
St. Helena
St. James
St. John the
Baptist
St. Landry
St. Martin
St. Mary

St. Tammany
Tangipahoa
Terrebonne
Vermilion
Washington
West Baton
Rouge
West Feliciana

Mississippi

Hancock
Harrison
Jackson
Pearl River
Stone

Texas

Anderson
Angelina
Aransas
Atascosa
Austin
Bandera
Bastrop
Bee
Bell
Bexar
Bosque
Brazoria
Brazos
Brooks
Burleson
Caldwell
Calhoun
Cameron
Chambers
Cherokee

Colorado
Comal
Coryell
DeWitt
Dimmit
Duval
Edwards
Falls
Fayette
Fort Bend
Freestone
Frio
Galveston
Goliad
Gonzales
Grimes
Guadalupe
Hardin
Harris
Hays
Hidalgo
Hill
Houston
Jackson
Jasper
Jefferson
Jim Hogg
Jim Wells
Karnes
Kenedy
Kinney
Kleberg
La Salle
Lavaca
Lee
Leon
Liberty
Limestone

Live Oak
Madison
Matagorda
Maverick
McLennan
McMullen
Medina
Milam
Montgomery
Newton
Nueces
Orange
Polk
Real
Refugio
Robertson
San Jacinto
San Patricio
Starr
Travis
Trinity
Tyler
Uvalde
Val Verde
Victoria
Walker
Waller
Washington
Webb
Wharton
Willacy
Williamson
Wilson
Zapata
Zavala

Climate Zone 2 Recommendation Table for Large Hospitals

	Item	Component	Recommendation	How-to Tips	✓
Envelope	Form/space planning	Proper zoning	Group similar space types within the building footprint.	DL4–6	
	Roofs	Insulation entirely above deck	R-25.0 c.i.	EN2, 15–17	
		Solar reflectance index (SRI)	78	EN1	
	Walls	Mass (HC > 7 Btu/ft^2)	R-7.6 c.i.	EN3, 15–17	
		Steel framed	R-13.0 + R-7.5 c.i.	EN4, 15–17	
		Below-grade walls	Comply with Standard 90.1*	EN5, 15–17	
	Floors	Mass	R-10.4 c.i.	EN6, 15–17	
		Steel framed	R-19.0	EN7, 15–17	
	Slabs	Unheated	Comply with Standard 90.1*		
		Heated	R-10.0 for 12 in.	EN9–10, 15–17	
	Doors	Swinging	U-0.70	EN11, 16	
		Nonswinging	U-0.50	EN12, 16	
	Vestibules	At primary visitor building entrance	Comply with Standard 90.1*	EN14	
	Continuous air barriers	Continuous air barriers	Entire building envelope	EN13	
	Vertical fenestration (full assembly—NFRC rating)	Window-to-wall ratio	40% of net wall (floor-ceiling)	DL7, EN20	
		Thermal transmittance	Nonmetal framing windows = 0.45 Metal framing windows = 0.65	EN18–20, 22–25	
		Solar heat gain coefficient (SHGC)	Nonmetal framing windows = 0.25 Metal framing windows = 0.25	EN19–20, 23–25	
		Light-to-solar gain ratio (LSG)	All orientations ≥ 1.5	EN24	
		Exterior sun control	South orientation only – PF = 0.5	EN21, DL13–14	
Daylighting/ Lighting	Form-driven daylighting option	All spaces	Comply with LEED for healthcare credits IEQ 8.1 (daylighting) and IEQ 8.2 (views)	DL3–6	
		Diagnostic and treatment block	Shape the building footprint and form such that the area within 15 ft of the perimeter exceeds 40% of the floorplate.	DL6	
		Inpatient units	Ensure that 75% of the occupied space not including patient rooms lies within 20 ft of the perimeter.	DL6	
		Staff areas (exam rooms, nurse stations, offices, corridors); public spaces (waiting, reception); and other regularly occupied spaces as applicable	Design the building form to maximize access to natural light, through sidelighting and toplighting.	DL8–14, 20–23	
	Nonform-driven daylighting option	Staff areas (exam rooms, nurse stations, offices, corridors) and public spaces (waiting, reception)	Add daylight controls to any space within 15 ft of a perimeter window.	DL20–23	
	Interior finishes	Room interior surface average reflectance	Ceilings ≥ 80% Walls ≥ 70%	DL17	
	Interior lighting	Lighting power density (LPD)	Whole building = 0.9 W/ft^2 Space-by-space per Table 5-4	EL1, 12–20	
		Light source efficacy (mean lumens per watt)	T8 & T5 > 2 ft = 92 T8 & T5 < 2 ft = 85 All other >50	EL2–5	
		Ballasts—4 ft T8 Lamps	Nondimming = NEMA Premium Dimming= NEMA Premium Program Start	EL2	
		Ballasts—Fluorescent and HID	Electronic	EL2–5	
		Dimming controls daylight harvesting	Dim all fixtures in daylighted zones.	DL20–23, EL11	
		Lighting controls—General	Manual ON, auto/timed OFF in all areas as possible.	EL6, 21	
		Surgery task lights	Use LED lights exclusively.	EL14	
		Exit signage	0.1–0.2 W Light Emitting Capacitor (LEC) exit signs exclusively	EL22	
	Exterior lighting	Façade and landscape lighting	LPD = 0.15 W/ft^2	EL23	
		Parking lots and drives	LPD = 0.1 W/ft^2	EL23	
		All other exterior lighting	LPD = Comply with Standard 90.1* Auto reduce to 25% (12 am–6 am)	EL23	
PPL	Equipment choices	Computers	Laptops = minimum 2/3 of total computers All others = mini desktop computers	PL2	
		ENERGY STAR® equipment	All computers, equipment, appliances	PL5	
		Vending machines	Delamp and specify best in class efficiency.	PL3, 7	
	Controls	Computer power control	Network control with power saving modes and control during unoccupied hours or IT enterprise power management software	PL2	
		Occupancy sensors	Office plug occupancy sensors	PL3	
		Timer switches	Water coolers, coffee makers, small appliances = auto OFF during unoccupied hours	PL3	

*Note: Where the table says "Comply with Standard 90.1," the user must meet the more stringent of either the most current version of Standard 90.1 or the local code requirements.

Climate Zone 2 Recommendation Table for Large Hospitals *(Continued)*

	Item	Component	Recommendation	How-to Tips	✓
PPL	Kitchen equipment	Cooking equipment	ENERGY STAR or California rebate-qualified equipment	PL8–9	
		Refrigeration equipment	6 in. insulation on low-temp walk-in equipment, insulated floor, LED lighting, floating-head pressure controls, liquid pressure amplifier, subcooled liquid refrigerant, evaporative condenser	PL8–9, 12	
		Exhaust hoods	Side panels, larger overhangs, rear seal at appliances, proximity hoods, VAV demand-based exhaust	PL8, 10, 13	
	Process loads	Elevators	Use traction elevators for all elevators, and use regenerative traction elevators for all high-use elevators.	PL16	
SWH	Service water heating	Gas water heater (condensing)	95% Efficiency	WH3, HV8	
		Point-of-use water heater	0.81 EF or 81% E_t	PL11, WH3	
		Electric-heat-pump water heater	2.33 EF	WH3	
		Pipe insulation ($d < 1.5$ in./$d \geq 1.5$ in.)	1.0 in./1.5 in.	WH7	
HVAC	Heating system	No central steam Use hot-water distribution system	Point-of-use steam for humidification and sterilization	HV33	
	Surgery — Central air-handling system	Water-cooled chiller	6.5 COP	HV8, 35	
		Water-circulation pumps	VFD and NEMA premium	HV35	
		Cooling towers	VFD on tower fans	HV37	
		Boiler efficiency	90% E_c	HV8	
		Maximum fan power	bhp $\leq$ supply cfm × 0.0012 + A	HV21–22, 24	
		Economizer	Comply with Standard 90.1*	HV19	
	Nonsurgery — Water-source heat pump (WSHP) system with DOAS	WSHP part-load/full-load cooling efficiency	17.6/15.0 EER	HV2	
		WSHP part-load/full-load heating efficiency	5.7/5.0 COP	HV2	
		WSHP compressor capacity control	Two-speed or variable-speed	HV2	
		Water-circulation pumps	VFD and NEMA premium	HV35	
		Closed-circuit cooling tower	VFD on fans	HV37	
		Boiler efficiency	90% E_c	HV8	
		Maximum fan power	0.4 W/cfm	HV21–22, 24	
		Exhaust-air energy recovery in DOAS	A (humid zones) = 60% total effectiveness B (dry zones) = 60% sensible effectiveness	HV9, 15–16	
		DOAS ventilation control	DCV with VFD	HV10–11	
	Nonsurgery — Fan-coil system with DOAS	Water-cooled chiller	6.5 COP	HV8, 35	
		Water-circulation pumps	VFD and NEMA premium	HV35	
		Cooling towers	VFD on tower fans	HV35	
		Boiler efficiency	90% E_c	HV8	
		Maximum fan power	0.4 W/cfm	HV21–22, 24	
		FCU fans	Multiple speed	HV5	
		Exhaust-air energy recovery in DOAS	A (humid zones) = 60% total effectiveness B (dry zones) = 60% sensible effectiveness	HV9, 15–16	
		DOAS ventilation control	DCV with VFD	HV10–11	
	Nonsurgery — Mixed-air VAV system with separate OA treatment and heat recovery system	Heat recovery water-cooled chiller	4.55 COP	HV8, 36, 38	
		Water-cooled chiller	6.5 COP	HV9, 35	
		Water-circulation pumps	VFD and NEMA premium	HV35	
		Cooling towers	VFD on tower fans	HV37	
		Boiler efficiency	90% E_c	HV8	
		Maximum fan power	bhp $\leq$ supply cfm × 0.0012 + A	HV21–22, 24	
		Economizer	Comply with Standard 90.1*	HV19	
		Exhaust-air energy recovery in DOAS	A (humid zones) = 60% total effectiveness B (dry zones) = 60% sensible effectiveness	HV9, 15–16	
		DOAS ventilation control	DCV with VFD	HV10–11	
	Ducts and dampers	OA damper	Motorized	HV14, 31	
		Duct seal class	Seal class A	HV22, 24	
		Insulation level	R-6	HV22–23	
Q&A	Measurement and verification	Electrical submeters	Design and circuit for separate submeters for lighting, HVAC, general 120V, service water heating, renewables, and whole building	QA12–14	
		Benchmarks	Benchmark monthly energy use.	QA15	
		Training	Facility operator on continuous benchmarking	QA12–15	

*Note: Where the table says "Comply with Standard 90.1," the user must meet the more stringent of either the most current version of Standard 90.1 or the local code requirements.

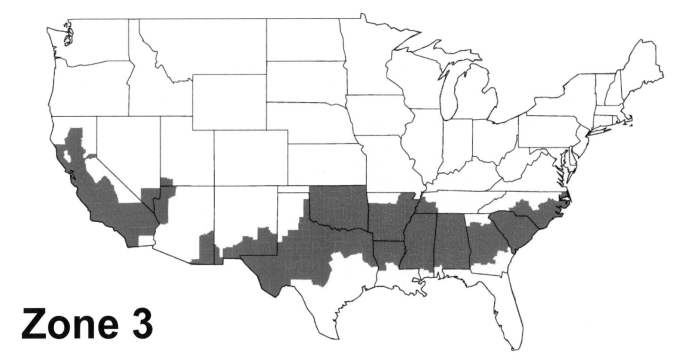

Zone 3

Alabama

All counties except:
Baldwin
Mobile

Arizona

Cochise
Graham
Greenlee
Mohave
Santa Cruz

Arkansas

All counties except:
Baxter
Benton
Boone
Carroll
Fulton
Izard
Madison
Marion
Newton
Searcy
Stone
Washington

California

All counties except:
Alpine
Amador
Calaveras
Del Norte
El Dorado
Humboldt
Imperial
Inyo
Lake
Lassen
Mariposa
Modoc
Mono
Nevada
Plumas
Sierra
Siskiyou
Trinity
Tuolumne

Georgia

All counties except:
Appling
Atkinson
Bacon
Baker
Banks
Berrien
Brantley
Brooks
Bryan
Catoosa
Camden
Charlton
Chatham
Chattooga
Clinch
Colquitt
Cook
Dade
Dawson
Decatur
Echols
Effingham
Evans
Fannin
Floyd
Franklin
Gilmer
Glynn
Gordon
Grady
Habersham
Hall
Jeff Davis
Lanier
Liberty
Long
Lowndes
Lumpkin
McIntosh
Miller
Mitchell
Murray
Pickens
Pierce
Rabun
Seminole
Stephens
Tattnall
Thomas
Toombs
Towns
Union

Walker
Ware
Wayne
White
Whitfield

Louisiana

Bienville
Bossier
Caddo
Caldwell
Catahoula
Claiborne
Concordia
De Soto
East Carroll
Franklin
Grant
Jackson
La Salle
Lincoln
Madison
Morehouse
Natchitoches
Ouachita
Red River
Richland
Sabine
Tensas
Union
Vernon
Webster
West Carroll
Winn

Mississippi

All counties except:
Hancock
Harrison
Jackson
Pearl River
Stone

New Mexico

Chaves
Dona Ana
Eddy
Hidalgo
Lea
Luna
Otero

Nevada

Clark

Texas

Andrews
Archer
Baylor
Blanco
Borden
Bowie
Brewster
Brown
Burnet
Callahan
Camp
Cass
Childress
Clay
Coke
Coleman
Collingsworth
Collin
Comanche
Concho
Cottle
Cooke
Crane
Crockett
Crosby
Culberson
Dallas
Dawson
Delta
Denton
Dickens
Eastland
Ector
El Paso
Ellis
Erath
Fannin
Fisher
Foard
Franklin
Gaines
Garza
Gillespie
Glasscock
Grayson
Gregg
Hall
Hamilton
Hardeman

Harrison
Haskell
Hemphill
Henderson
Hood
Hopkins
Howard
Hudspeth
Hunt
Irion
Jack
Jeff Davis
Johnson
Jones
Kaufman
Kendall
Kent
Kerr
Kimble
King
Knox
Lamar
Lampasas
Llano
Loving
Lubbock
Lynn
Marion
Martin
Mason
McCulloch
Menard
Midland
Mills
Mitchell
Montague
Morris
Motley
Nacogdoches
Navarro
Nolan
Palo Pinto
Panola
Parker
Pecos
Presidio
Rains
Reagan
Reeves
Red River
Rockwall
Runnels
Rusk
Sabine
San Augustine

San Saba
Schleicher
Scurry
Shackelford
Shelby
Smith
Somervell
Stephens
Sterling
Stonewall
Sutton
Tarrant
Taylor
Terrell
Terry
Throckmorton
Titus
Tom Green
Upshur
Upton
Van Zandt
Ward
Wheeler
Wichita
Wilbarger
Winkler
Wise
Wood
Young

Utah

Washington

North Carolina

Anson
Beaufort
Bladen
Brunswick
Cabarrus
Camden
Carteret
Chowan
Columbus
Craven
Cumberland
Currituck
Dare
Davidson
Duplin
Edgecombe
Gaston
Greene
Hoke
Hyde

Johnston
Jones
Lenoir
Martin
Mecklenburg
Montgomery
Moore
New Hanover
Onslow
Pamlico
Pasquotank
Pender
Perquimans
Pitt
Randolph
Richmond
Robeson
Rowan
Sampson
Scotland
Stanly
Tyrrell
Union
Washington
Wayne
Wilson

Oklahoma

All counties except:
Beaver
Cimarron
Texas

South Carolina

All counties

Tennessee

Chester
Crockett
Dyer
Fayette
Hardeman
Hardin
Haywood
Henderson
Lake
Lauderdale
Madison
McNairy
Shelby
Tipton

Climate Zone 3 Recommendation Table for Table for Large Hospitals

	Item	Component	Recommendation	How-to Tips	✓
	Form/space planning	Proper zoning	Group similar space types within the building footprint.	DL4–6	
Envelope	Roofs	Insulation entirely above deck	R-25.0 c.i.	EN2, 15–17	
		Solar reflectance index (SRI)	78	EN1	
		Mass (HC > 7 Btu/ft^2)	R-11.4 c.i.	EN3, 15–17	
	Walls	Steel framed	R-13.0 + R-7.5 c.i.	EN4, 15–17	
		Below-grade walls	R-7.5 c.i. (Comply with Standard 90.1* in 3A)	EN5, 15–17	
	Floors	Mass	R-12.5 c.i.	EN6, 15–17	
		Steel framed	R-30.0	EN7, 15–17	
	Slabs	Unheated	Comply with Standard 90.1*		
		Heated	R-15.0 for 24 in.	EN9–10, 15–17	
	Doors	Swinging	U-0.70	EN11, 16	
		Nonswinging	U-0.50	EN12, 16	
	Vestibules	At primary visitor building entrance	Comply with Standard 90.1*	EN14	
	Continuous air barriers	Continuous air barriers	Entire building envelope	EN13	
	Vertical fenestration (full assembly—NFRC rating)	Window-to-wall ratio	40% of net wall (floor-ceiling)	DL7, EN20	
		Thermal transmittance	Nonmetal framing windows = 0.56 Metal framing windows = 0.65	EN18-20, 22–25	
		Solar heat gain coefficient (SHGC)	Nonmetal framing windows = 0.41 Metal framing windows = 0.6	EN19–20, 23–25	
		Light-to-solar gain ratio (LSG)	All orientations ≥ 1.5	EN24	
		Exterior sun control	South orientation only – PF = 0.5	EN21, DL13–14	
Daylighting/ Lighting	Form-driven daylighting option	All spaces	Comply with LEED for healthcare credits IEQ 8.1 (daylighting) and IEQ 8.2 (views)	DL3–6	
		Diagnostic and treatment block	Shape the building footprint and form such that the area within 15 ft of the perimeter exceeds 40% of the floorplate.	DL6	
		Inpatient units	Ensure that 75% of the occupied space not including patient rooms lies within 20 ft of the perimeter.	DL6	
		Staff areas (exam rooms, nurse stations, offices, corridors); public spaces (waiting, reception); and other regularly occupied spaces as applicable	Design the building form to maximize access to natural light, through sidelighting and toplighting.	DL8–14, 20–23	
	Nonform-driven daylighting option	Staff areas (exam rooms, nurse stations, offices, corridors) and public spaces (waiting, reception)	Add daylight controls to any space within 15 ft of a perimeter window.	DL20–23	
	Interior finishes	Room interior surface average reflectance	Ceilings ≥ 80% Walls ≥ 70%	DL17	
		Lighting power density (LPD)	Whole building = 0.9 W/ft^2 Space-by-space per Table 5-4	EL1, 12–20	
		Light source efficacy (mean lumens per watt)	T8 & T5 > 2 ft = 92 T8 & T5 < 2 ft = 85 All other >50	EL2–5	
	Interior lighting	Ballasts—4 ft T8 Lamps	Nondimming = NEMA Premium Dimming= NEMA Premium Program Start	EL2	
		Ballasts—Fluorescent and HID	Electronic	EL2–5	
		Dimming controls daylight harvesting	Dim all fixtures in daylighted zones.	DL20–23, EL11	
		Lighting controls—General	Manual ON, auto/timed OFF in all areas as possible.	EL6,21	
		Surgery task lights	Use LED lights exclusively.	EL14	
		Exit signage	0.1–0.2 W Light Emitting Capacitor (LEC) exit signs exclusively	EL22	
	Exterior lighting	Façade and landscape lighting	LPD = 0.15 W/ft^2	EL23	
		Parking lots and drives	LPD = 0.1 W/ft^2	EL23	
		All other exterior lighting	LPD = Comply with Standard 90.1* Auto reduce to 25% (12 am–6 am)	EL23	
PPL	Equipment choices	Computers	Laptops = minimum 2/3 of total computers All others = mini desktop computers	PL2	
		ENERGY STAR® equipment	All computers, equipment, appliances	PL5	
		Vending machines	Delamp and specify best in class efficiency.	PL3, 7	
		Computer power control	Network control with power saving modes and control during unoccupied hours or IT enterprise power management software	PL2	
	Controls	Occupancy sensors	Office plug occupancy sensors	PL3	
		Timer switches	Water coolers, coffee makers, small appliances = auto OFF during unoccupied hours	PL3	

*Note: Where the table says "Comply with Standard 90.1," the user must meet the more stringent of either the most current version of Standard 90.1 or the local code requirements.

Climate Zone 3 Recommendation Table for Table for Large Hospitals *(Continued)*

	Item	Component	Recommendation	How-to Tips	✓
PPL	Kitchen equipment	Cooking equipment	ENERGY STAR or California rebate-qualified equipment	PL8–9	
		Refrigeration equipment	6 in. insulation on low-temp walk-in equipment, insulated floor, LED lighting, floating-head pressure controls, liquid pressure amplifier, subcooled liquid refrigerant, evaporative condenser	PL8–9, 12	
		Exhaust hoods	Side panels, larger overhangs, rear seal at appliances, proximity hoods, VAV demand-based exhaust	PL8, 10, 13	
	Process loads	Elevators	Use traction elevators for all elevators, and use regenerative traction elevators for all high-use elevators.	PL16	
SWH	Service water heating	Gas water heater (condensing)	95% Efficiency	WH3, HV8	
		Point-of-use water heater	0.81 EF or 81% E_t	PL11, WH3	
		Electric-heat-pump water heater	2.33 EF	WH3	
		Pipe insulation ($d < 1.5$ in./$d \geq 1.5$ in.)	1.0 in./1.5 in.	WH7	
HVAC	Heating system	No central steam Use hot-water distribution system	Point-of-use steam for humidification and sterilization	HV33	
	Surgery — Central air-handling system	Water-cooled chiller	6.5 COP	HV8, 35	
		Water-circulation pumps	VFD and NEMA premium	HV35	
		Cooling towers	VFD on tower fans	HV37	
		Boiler efficiency	90% E_c	HV8	
		Maximum fan power	bhp ≤ supply cfm × 0.0012 + A	HV21–22, 24	
		Economizer	Comply with Standard 90.1*	HV19	
	Nonsurgery — Water-source heat pump (WSHP) system with DOAS	WSHP part-load/full-load cooling efficiency	17.6/15.0 EER	HV2	
		WSHP part-load/full-load heating efficiency	5.7/5.0 COP	HV2	
		WSHP compressor capacity control	Two-speed or variable-speed	HV2	
		Water-circulation pumps	VFD and NEMA premium	HV35	
		Closed-circuit cooling tower	VFD on fans	HV37	
		Boiler efficiency	90% E_c	HV8	
		Maximum fan power	0.4 W/cfm	HV21–22, 24	
		Exhaust-air energy recovery in DOAS	A (humid zones) = 60% total effectiveness B (dry zones) = 60% sensible effectiveness C (marine zones) = 60% total effectiveness	HV9, 15–16	
		DOAS ventilation control	DCV with VFD	HV10–11	
	Fan-coil system with DOAS	Water-cooled chiller	6.5 COP	HV8, 35	
		Water-circulation pumps	VFD and NEMA premium	HV35	
		Cooling towers	VFD on tower fans	HV37	
		Boiler efficiency	90% E_c	HV8	
		Maximum fan power	0.4 W/cfm	HV21–22, 24	
		FCU fans	Multiple speed	HV5	
		Exhaust-air energy recovery in DOAS	A (humid zones) = 60% total effectiveness B (dry zones) = 60% sensible effectiveness C (marine zones) = 60% total effectiveness	HV9, 15–16	
		DOAS ventilation control	DCV with VFD	HV10–11	
	Mixed-air VAV system with separate OA treatment and heat recovery system	Heat recovery water-cooled chiller	4.55 COP	HV8, 36, 38	
		Water-cooled chiller	6.5 COP	HV8, 35	
		Water-circulation pumps	VFD and NEMA premium	HV35	
		Cooling towers	VFD on tower fans	HV37	
		Boiler efficiency	90% E_c	HV8	
		Maximum fan power	bhp ≤ supply cfm × 0.0012 + A	HV21–22, 24	
		Economizer	Comply with Standard 90.1*	HV19	
		Exhaust-air energy recovery in DOAS	A (humid zones) = 60% total effectiveness B (dry zones) = 60% sensible effectiveness C (marine zones) = 60% total effectiveness	HV9, 15–16	
		DOAS ventilation control	DCV with VFD	HV10–11	
	Ducts and dampers	OA damper	Motorized	HV14, 31	
		Duct seal class	Seal class A	HV22, 24	
		Insulation level	R-6	HV22–23	
Q&A	Measurement and verification	Electrical submeters	Design and circuit for separate submeters for lighting, HVAC, general 120V, service water heating, renewables, and whole building	QA12–14	
		Benchmarks	Benchmark monthly energy use.	QA15	
		Training	Facility operator on continuous benchmarking	QA12–15	

*Note: Where the table says "Comply with Standard 90.1," the user must meet the more stringent of either the most current version of Standard 90.1 or the local code requirements.

Zone 4

Arizona
Gila
Yavapai

Arkansas
Baxter
Benton
Boone
Carroll
Fulton
Izard
Madison
Marion
Newton
Searcy
Stone
Washington

California
Amador
Calaveras
Del Norte
El Dorado
Humboldt
Inyo
Lake
Mariposa
Trinity
Tuolumne

Colorado
Baca
Las Animas
Otero

Delaware
All counties

District of Columbia

Georgia
Banks
Catoosa
Chattooga
Dade
Dawson
Fannin
Floyd
Franklin
Gilmer
Gordon
Habersham
Hall
Lumpkin
Murray
Pickens
Rabun
Stephens
Towns
Union

Walker
White
Whitfield

Illinois
Alexander
Bond
Brown
Christian
Clay
Clinton
Crawford
Edwards
Effingham
Fayette
Franklin
Gallatin
Hamilton
Hardin
Jackson
Jasper
Jefferson
Johnson
Lawrence
Macoupin
Madison
Marion
Massac
Monroe
Montgomery
Perry
Pope
Pulaski
Randolph
Richland
Saline
Shelby
St. Clair
Union
Wabash
Washington
Wayne
White
Williamson

Indiana
Clark
Crawford
Daviess
Dearborn
Dubois
Floyd
Gibson
Greene
Harrison
Jackson
Jennings
Knox
Lawrence
Martin
Monroe
Ohio

Orange
Perry
Pike
Posey
Ripley
Scott
Spencer
Sullivan
Switzerland
Vanderburgh
Warrick
Washington

Kansas
All counties except:
Cheyenne
Cloud
Decatur
Ellis
Gove
Graham
Greeley
Hamilton
Jewell
Lane
Logan
Mitchell
Ness
Norton
Osborne
Phillips
Rawlins
Republic
Rooks
Scott
Sheridan
Sherman
Smith
Thomas
Trego
Wallace
Wichita

Kentucky
All counties

Maryland
All counties except:
Garrett

Missouri
All counties except:
Adair
Andrew
Atchison
Buchanan
Caldwell
Chariton
Clark
Clinton
Daviess
DeKalb
Gentry

Grundy
Harrison
Holt
Knox
Lewis
Linn
Livingston
Macon
Marion
Mercer
Nodaway
Pike
Putnam
Ralls
Schuyler
Scotland
Shelby
Sullivan
Worth

New Jersey
All counties except:
Bergen
Hunterdon
Mercer
Morris
Passaic
Somerset
Sussex
Warren

New Mexico
Bernalillo
Cibola
Curry
DeBaca
Grant
Guadalupe
Lincoln
Quay
Roosevelt
Sierra
Socorro
Union
Valencia

New York
Bronx
Kings
Nassau
New York
Queens
Richmond
Suffolk
Westchester

North Carolina
Alamance
Alexander
Bertie
Buncombe
Burke

Caldwell
Caswell
Catawba
Chatham
Cherokee
Clay
Cleveland
Davie
Durham
Forsyth
Franklin
Gates
Graham
Granville
Guilford
Halifax
Harnett
Haywood
Henderson
Hertford
Iredell
Jackson
Lee
Lincoln
Macon
Madison
McDowell
Nash
Northampton
Orange
Person
Polk
Rockingham
Rutherford
Stokes
Surry
Swain
Transylvania
Vance
Wake
Warren
Wilkes
Yadkin

Ohio
Adams
Brown
Clermont
Gallia
Hamilton
Lawrence
Pike
Scioto
Washington

Oklahoma
Beaver
Cimarron
Texas

Oregon
Benton

Clackamas
Clatsop
Columbia
Coos
Curry
Douglas
Jackson
Josephine
Lane
Lincoln
Linn
Marion
Multnomah
Polk
Tillamook
Washington
Yamhill

Pennsylvania
Bucks
Chester
Delaware
Montgomery
Philadelphia
York

Tennessee
All counties except:
Chester
Crockett
Dyer
Fayette
Hardeman
Hardin
Haywood
Henderson
Lake
Lauderdale
Madison
McNairy
Shelby
Tipton

Texas
Armstrong
Bailey
Briscoe
Carson
Castro
Cochran
Dallam
Deaf Smith
Donley
Floyd
Gray
Hale
Hansford
Hartley
Hockley
Hutchinson
Lamb
Lipscomb
Moore
Ochiltree

Oldham
Parmer
Potter
Randall
Roberts
Sherman
Swisher
Yoakum

Virginia
All counties

Washington
Clallam
Clark
Cowlitz
Grays Harbor
Island
Jefferson
King
Kitsap
Lewis
Mason
Pacific
Pierce
San Juan
Skagit
Snohomish
Thurston
Wahkiakum
Whatcom

West Virginia
Berkeley
Boone
Braxton
Cabell
Calhoun
Clay
Gilmer
Jackson
Jefferson
Kanawha
Lincoln
Logan
Mason
McDowell
Mercer
Mingo
Monroe
Morgan
Pleasants
Putnam
Ritchie
Roane
Tyler
Wayne
Wirt
Wood
Wyoming

Climate Zone 4 Recommendation Table for Large Hospitals

	Item	Component	Recommendation	How-to Tips	✓
	Form/space planning	Proper zoning	Group similar space types within the building footprint.	DL4–6	
Envelope	Roofs	Insulation entirely above deck	R-30.0 c.i.	EN2, 15–17	
		Solar reflectance index (SRI)	Comply with Standard 90.1*		
	Walls	Mass (HC > 7 Btu/ft^2)	R-13.3 c.i.	EN3, 15–17	
		Steel framed	R-13.0 + R-7.5 c.i.	EN4, 15–17	
		Below-grade walls	R-7.5 c.i.	EN5, 15–17	
	Floors	Mass	R-14.6 c.i.	EN6, 15–17	
		Steel framed	R-38.0	EN7, 15–17	
	Slabs	Unheated	Comply with Standard 90.1*	EN8, 10, 15–16	
		Heated	R-20 for 24 in.	EN9–10, 15–17	
	Doors	Swinging	U-0.50	EN11, 16	
		Nonswinging	U-0.50	EN12, 16	
	Vestibules	At primary visitor building entrance	Comply with Standard 90.1*	EN14	
	Continuous air barriers	Continuous air barriers	Entire building envelope	EN13	
	Vertical fenestration (full assembly—NFRC rating)	Window-to-wall ratio	40% of net wall (floor-ceiling)	DL7, EN20, 26–27	
		Thermal transmittance	Nonmetal framing windows = 0.38 Metal framing windows = 0.44	EN19–20, 25–28	
		Solar heat gain coefficient (SHGC)	Nonmetal framing windows = 0.26 Metal framing windows = 0.38	EN19–20, 25–28	
		Light-to-solar gain ratio (LSG)	All orientations ≥ 1.5	EN24	
		Exterior sun control	South orientation only – PF = 0.5	EN21, DL13–14	
Daylighting/ Lighting	Form-driven daylighting option	All spaces	Comply with LEED for healthcare credits IEQ 8.1 (daylighting) and IEQ 8.2 (views)	DL3–6	
		Diagnostic and treatment block	Shape the building footprint and form such that the area within 15 ft of the perimeter exceeds 40% of the floorplate.	DL6	
		Inpatient units	Ensure that 75% of the occupied space not including patient rooms lies within 20 ft of the perimeter.	DL6	
		Staff areas (exam rooms, nurse stations, offices, corridors); public spaces (waiting, reception); and other regularly occupied spaces as applicable	Design the building form to maximize access to natural light, through sidelighting and toplighting.	DL8–13, 15, 20–23	
	Nonform-driven daylighting option	Staff areas (exam rooms, nurse stations, offices, corridors) and public spaces (waiting, reception)	Add daylight controls to any space within 15 ft of a perimeter window.	DL20–23	
	Interior finishes	Room interior surface average reflectance	Ceilings ≥ 80% Walls ≥ 70%	DL17	
	Interior lighting	Lighting power density (LPD)	Whole building = 0.9 W/ft^2 Space-by-space per Table 5-4	EL1, 12–20	
		Light source efficacy (mean lumens per watt)	T8 & T5 > 2 ft = 92 T8 & T5 < 2 ft = 85 All other >50	EL2–5	
		Ballasts—4 ft T8 Lamps	Nondimming = NEMA Premium Dimming= NEMA Premium Program Start	EL2	
		Ballasts—Fluorescent and HID	Electronic	EL2–5	
		Dimming controls daylight harvesting	Dim all fixtures in daylighted zones.	DL20–23, EL11	
		Lighting controls—General	Manual ON, auto/timed OFF in all areas as possible.	EL6, 21	
		Surgery task lights	Use LED lights exclusively.	EL14	
		Exit signage	0.1–0.2 W Light Emitting Capacitor (LEC) exit signs exclusively	EL22	
	Exterior lighting	Façade and landscape lighting	LPD = 0.15 W/ft^2	EL23	
		Parking lots and drives	LPD = 0.1 W/ft^2	EL23	
		All other exterior lighting	LPD = Comply with Standard 90.1* Auto reduce to 25% (12 am–6 am)	EL23	
PPL	Equipment choices	Computers	Laptops = minimum 2/3 of total computers All others = mini desktop computers	PL2	
		ENERGY STAR® equipment	All computers, equipment, appliances	PL5	
		Vending machines	Delamp and specify best in class efficiency.	PL3, 7	
	Controls	Computer power control	Network control with power saving modes and control during unoccupied hours or IT enterprise power management software	PL2	
		Occupancy sensors	Office plug occupancy sensors	PL3	
		Timer switches	Water coolers, coffee makers, small appliances = auto OFF during unoccupied hours	PL3	

*Note: Where the table says "Comply with Standard 90.1," the user must meet the more stringent of either the most current version of Standard 90.1 or the local code requirements.

Climate Zone 4 Recommendation Table for Large Hospitals *(Continued)*

	Item	Component	Recommendation	How-to Tips	✓
PPL	Kitchen equipment	Cooking equipment	ENERGY STAR or California rebate-qualified equipment	PL8–9	
		Refrigeration equipment	6 in. insulation on low-temp walk-in equipment, insulated floor, LED lighting, floating-head pressure controls, liquid pressure amplifier, subcooled liquid refrigerant, evaporative condenser	PL8–9, 12	
		Exhaust hoods	Side panels, larger overhangs, rear seal at appliances, proximity hoods, VAV demand-based exhaust	PL8, 10, 13	
	Process loads	Elevators	Use traction elevators for all elevators, and use regenerative traction elevators for all high-use elevators.	PL16	
SWH	Service water heating	Gas water heater (condensing)	95% Efficiency	WH3, HV8	
		Point-of-use water heater	0.81 EF or 81% E_t	PL11, WH3	
		Electric-heat-pump water heater	2.33 EF	WH3	
		Pipe insulation ($d < 1.5$ in./$d \geq 1.5$ in.)	1.0 in./1.5 in.	WH7	
HVAC	Heating system	No central steam Use hot-water distribution system	Point-of-use steam for humidification and sterilization	HV33	
	Surgery — Central air-handling system	Water-cooled chiller	6.5 COP	HV8, 35	
		Water-circulation pumps	VFD and NEMA premium	HV35	
		Cooling towers	VFD on tower fans	HV37	
		Boiler efficiency	90% E_c	HV8	
		Maximum fan power	bhp ≤ supply cfm × 0.0012 + A	HV21–22, 24	
		Economizer	Comply with Standard 90.1*	HV19	
	Nonsurgery — Water-source heat pump (WSHP) system with DOAS	WSHP part-load/full-load cooling efficiency	17.6/15.0 EER	HV2	
		WSHP part-load/full-load heating efficiency	5.7/5.0 COP	HV2	
		WSHP compressor capacity control	Two-speed or variable-speed	HV2	
		Water-circulation pumps	VFD and NEMA premium	HV35	
		Closed-circuit cooling tower	VFD on fans	HV37	
		Boiler efficiency	90% E_c	HV8	
		Maximum fan power	0.4 W/cfm	HV21–22, 24	
		Exhaust-air energy recovery in DOAS	A (humid zones) = 60% total effectiveness B (dry zones) = 60% sensible effectiveness C (marine zones) = 60% total effectiveness	HV9, 15–16	
		DOAS ventilation control	DCV with VFD	HV10–11	
	Nonsurgery — Fan-coil system with DOAS	Water-cooled chiller	6.5 COP	HV8, 35	
		Water-circulation pumps	VFD and NEMA premium	HV35	
		Cooling towers	VFD on tower fans	HV37	
		Boiler efficiency	90% E_c	HV8	
		Maximum fan power	0.4 W/cfm	HV21–22, 24	
		FCU fans	Multiple speed	HV5	
		Exhaust-air energy recovery in DOAS	A (humid zones) = 60% total effectiveness B (dry zones) = 60% sensible effectiveness C (marine zones) = 60% total effectiveness	HV9, 15–16	
		DOAS ventilation control	DCV with VFD	HV10–11	
	Mixed-air VAV system with separate OA treatment and heat recovery system	Heat recovery water-cooled chiller	4.55 COP	HV8, 36, 38	
		Water-cooled chiller	6.5 COP	HV8, 35	
		Water-circulation pumps	VFD and NEMA premium	HV35	
		Cooling towers	VFD on tower fans	HV37	
		Boiler efficiency	90% E_c	HV8	
		Maximum fan power	bhp ≤ supply cfm × 0.0012 + A	HV21–22, 24	
		Economizer	Comply with Standard 90.1*	HV19	
		Exhaust-air energy recovery in DOAS	A (humid zones) = 60% total effectiveness B (dry zones) = 60% sensible effectiveness C (marine zones) = 60% total effectiveness	HV9, 15–16	
		DOAS ventilation control	DCV with VFD	HV10–11	
	Ducts and dampers	OA damper	Motorized	HV14, 31	
		Duct seal class	Seal class A	HV22, 24	
		Insulation level	R-6	HV22–23	
Q&A	Measurement and verification	Electrical submeters	Design and circuit for separate submeters for lighting, HVAC, general 120V, service water heating, renewables, and whole building	QA12–14	
		Benchmarks	Benchmark monthly energy use.	QA15	
		Training	Facility operator on continuous benchmarking	QA12–15	

*Note: Where the table says "Comply with Standard 90.1," the user must meet the more stringent of either the most current version of Standard 90.1 or the local code requirements.

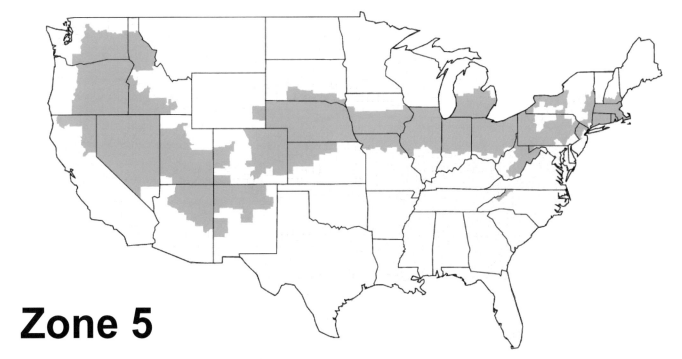

Zone 5

Arizona
Apache
Coconino
Navajo

California
Lassen
Modoc
Nevada
Plumas
Sierra
Siskiyou

Colorado
Adams
Arapahoe
Bent
Boulder
Cheyenne
Crowley
Delta
Denver
Douglas
Elbert
El Paso
Fremont
Garfield
Gilpin
Huerfano
Jefferson
Kiowa
Kit Carson
La Plata
Larimer
Lincoln
Logan
Mesa
Montezuma
Montrose
Morgan
Phillips
Prowers
Pueblo
Sedgwick
Teller
Washington
Weld
Yuma

Connecticut
All counties

Idaho
Ada
Benewah
Canyon
Cassia
Clearwater
Elmore
Gem
Gooding
Idaho
Jerome
Kootenai
Latah
Lewis
Lincoln
Minidoka
Nez Perce
Owyhee
Payette
Power

Shoshone
Twin Falls
Washington

Illinois
All counties except:
Alexander
Bond
Christian
Clay
Clinton
Crawford
Edwards
Effingham
Fayette
Franklin
Gallatin
Hamilton
Hardin
Jackson
Jasper
Jefferson
Johnson
Lawrence
Macoupin
Madison
Marion
Massac
Monroe
Montgomery
Perry
Pope
Pulaski
Randolph
Richland
Saline
Shelby
St. Clair
Union
Wabash
Washington
Wayne
White
Williamson
Brown

Indiana
All counties except:
Clark
Crawford
Daviess
Dearborn
Dubois
Floyd
Gibson
Greene
Harrison
Jackson
Jefferson
Jennings
Knox
Lawrence
Martin
Monroe
Ohio
Orange
Perry
Pike
Posey
Ripley
Scott
Spencer
Sullivan

Switzerland
Vanderburgh
Warrick
Washington

Iowa
All counties except:
Allamakee
Black Hawk
Bremer
Buchanan
Buena Vista
Butler
Calhoun
Cerro Gordo
Cherokee
Chickasaw
Clay
Clayton
Delaware
Dickinson
Emmet
Fayette
Floyd
Franklin
Grundy
Hamilton
Hancock
Hardin
Howard
Humboldt
Ida
Kossuth
Lyon
Mitchell
O'Brien
Osceola
Palo Alto
Plymouth
Pocahontas
Sac
Sioux
Webster
Winnebago
Winneshiek
Worth
Wright

Kansas
Cheyenne
Cloud
Decatur
Ellis
Gove
Graham
Greeley
Hamilton
Jewell
Lane
Logan
Mitchell
Ness
Norton
Osborne
Phillips
Rawlins
Republic
Rooks
Scott
Sheridan
Sherman
Smith
Thomas

Trego
Wallace
Wichita

Maryland
Garrett

Massachusetts
All counties

Michigan
Allegan
Barry
Bay
Berrien
Branch
Calhoun
Cass
Clinton
Eaton
Genesee
Gratiot
Hillsdale
Ingham
Ionia
Jackson
Kalamazoo
Kent
Lapeer
Lenawee
Livingston
Macomb
Midland
Monroe
Montcalm
Muskegon
Oakland
Ottawa
Saginaw
Shiawassee
St. Clair
St. Joseph
Tuscola
Van Buren
Washtenaw
Wayne

Missouri
Adair
Andrew
Atchison
Buchanan
Caldwell
Chariton
Clark
Clinton
Daviess
DeKalb
Gentry
Grundy
Harrison
Holt
Knox
Lewis
Linn
Livingston
Macon
Marion
Mercer
Nodaway
Pike
Putnam
Ralls
Schuyler

Scotland
Shelby
Sullivan
Worth

Nebraska
All counties

Nevada
All counties except:
Clark

New Hampshire
Cheshire
Hillsborough
Rockingham
Strafford

New Jersey
Bergen
Hunterdon
Mercer
Morris
Passaic
Somerset
Sussex
Warren

New Mexico
Catron
Colfax
Harding
Los Alamos
McKinley
Mora
Rio Arriba
Sandoval
San Juan
San Miguel
Santa Fe
Taos
Torrance

New York
Albany
Cayuga
Chautauqua
Chemung
Columbia
Cortland
Dutchess
Erie
Genesee
Greene
Livingston
Monroe
Niagara
Onondaga
Ontario
Orange
Orleans
Oswego
Putnam
Rensselaer
Rockland
Saratoga
Schenectady
Seneca
Tioga
Washington
Wayne
Yates

North Carolina
Alleghany
Ashe
Avery
Mitchell
Watauga
Yancey

Ohio
All counties except:
Adams
Brown
Clermont
Gallia
Hamilton
Lawrence
Pike
Scioto
Washington

Oregon
Baker
Crook
Deschutes
Gilliam
Grant
Harney
Hood River
Jefferson
Klamath
Lake
Malheur
Morrow
Sherman
Umatilla
Union
Wallowa
Wasco
Wheeler

Pennsylvania
All counties except:
Bucks
Cameron
Chester
Clearfield
Delaware
Elk
McKean
Montgomery
Philadelphia
Potter
Susquehanna
Tioga
Wayne
York

Rhode Island
All counties

South Dakota
Bennett
Bon Homme
Charles Mix
Clay
Douglas
Gregory
Hutchinson
Jackson
Mellette

Todd
Tripp
Union
Yankton

Utah
All counties except:
Box Elder
Cache
Carbon
Daggett
Duchesne
Morgan
Rich
Summit
Uintah
Wasatch
Washington

Washington
Adams
Asotin
Benton
Chelan
Columbia
Douglas
Franklin
Garfield
Grant
Kittitas
Klickitat
Lincoln
Skamania
Spokane
Walla Walla
Whitman
Yakima

Wyoming
Goshen
Platte

West Virginia
Barbour
Brooke
Doddridge
Fayette
Grant
Greenbrier
Hampshire
Hancock
Hardy
Harrison
Lewis
Marion
Marshall
Mineral
Monongalia
Nicholas
Ohio
Pendleton
Pocahontas
Preston
Raleigh
Randolph
Summers
Taylor
Tucker
Upshur
Webster
Wetzel

Climate Zone 5 Recommendation Table for Large Hospitals

Item	Component	Recommendation	How-to Tips	✓
Form/space planning	Proper zoning	Group similar space types within the building footprint.	DL4–6	
Roofs	Insulation entirely above deck	R-30.0 c.i.	EN2, 15–17	
	Solar reflectance index (SRI)	Comply with Standard 90.1*		
	Mass (HC > 7 Btu/ft^2)	R-13.3 c.i.	EN3, 15–17	
Walls	Steel framed	R-13.0 + R-15.6 c.i.	EN4, 15–17	
	Below-grade walls	R-7.5 c.i.	EN5, 15–17	
Floors	Mass	R-14.6 c.i.	EN6, 15–17	
	Steel framed	R-38.0	EN7, 15–17	
Slabs	Unheated	Comply with Standard 90.1*	EN8,10, 15–17	
	Heated	R-20 for 24 in.	EN9–10, 15–17	
Doors	Swinging	U-0.50	EN11, 16	
	Nonswinging	U-0.50	EN12, 16	
Vestibules	At primary visitor building entrance	Comply with Standard 90.1*	EN14	
Continuous air barriers	Continuous air barriers	Entire building envelope	EN13	
Vertical fenestration (full assembly—NFRC rating)	Window-to-wall ratio	40% of net wall (floor-ceiling)	DL7, EN20, 26–27	
	Thermal transmittance	Nonmetal framing windows = 0.35 Metal framing windows = 0.42	EN19–20, 25–28	
	Solar heat gain coefficient (SHGC)	Nonmetal framing windows = 0.25 Metal framing windows = 0.25	EN19–20, 25–28	
	Light-to-solar gain ratio (LSG)	All orientations ≥ 1.5	EN24	
	Exterior sun control	South orientation only – PF = 0.5	EN21, DL13–14	
Form-driven daylighting option	All spaces	Comply with LEED for healthcare credits IEQ 8.1 (daylighting) and IEQ 8.2 (views)	DL3–6	
	Diagnostic and treatment block	Shape the building footprint and form such that the area within 15 ft of the perimeter exceeds 40% of the floorplate.	DL6	
	Inpatient units	Ensure that 75% of the occupied space not including patient rooms lies within 20 ft of the perimeter.	DL6	
	Staff areas (exam rooms, nurse stations, offices, corridors); public spaces (waiting, reception); and other regularly occupied spaces as applicable	Design the building form to maximize access to natural light, through sidelighting and toplighting.	DL8–13, 15, 20–23	
Nonform-driven daylighting option	Staff areas (exam rooms, nurse stations, offices, corridors) and public spaces (waiting, reception)	Add daylight controls to any space within 15 ft of a perimeter window.	DL20–23	
Interior finishes	Room interior surface average reflectance	Ceilings ≥ 80% Walls ≥ 70%	DL17	
	Lighting power density (LPD)	Whole building = 0.9 W/ft^2 Space-by-space per Table 5-4	EL1, 12–20	
	Light source efficacy (mean lumens per watt)	T8 & T5 > 2 ft = 92 T8 & T5 < 2 ft = 85 All other >50	EL2–5	
Interior lighting	Ballasts—4 ft T8 Lamps	Nondimming = NEMA Premium Dimming= NEMA Premium Program Start	EL2	
	Ballasts—Fluorescent and HID	Electronic	EL2–5	
	Dimming controls daylight harvesting	Dim all fixtures in daylighted zones.	DL20–23, EL11	
	Lighting controls—General	Manual ON, auto/timed OFF in all areas as possible.	EL6,21	
	Surgery task lights	Use LED lights exclusively.	EL14	
	Exit signage	0.1–0.2 W Light Emitting Capacitor (LEC) exit signs exclusively	EL22	
Exterior lighting	Façade and landscape lighting	LPD = 0.15 W/ft^2	EL23	
	Parking lots and drives	LPD = 0.1 W/ft^2	EL23	
	All other exterior lighting	LPD = Comply with Standard 90.1* Auto reduce to 25% (12 am–6 am)	EL23	
Equipment choices	Computers	Laptops = minimum 2/3 of total computers All others = mini desktop computers	PL2	
	ENERGY STAR® equipment	All computers, equipment, appliances	PL5	
	Vending machines	Delamp and specify best in class efficiency.	PL3, 7	
	Computer power control	Network control with power saving modes and control during unoccupied hours or IT enterprise power management software	PL2	
Controls	Occupancy sensors	Office plug occupancy sensors	PL3	
	Timer switches	Water coolers, coffee makers, small appliances = auto OFF during unoccupied hours	PL3	

*Note: Where the table says "Comply with Standard 90.1," the user must meet the more stringent of either the most current version of Standard 90.1 or the local code requirements.

Climate Zone 5 Recommendation Table for Large Hospitals *(Continued)*

	Item	Component	Recommendation	How-to Tips	✓
PPL	Kitchen equipment	Cooking equipment	ENERGY STAR or California rebate-qualified equipment	PL8–9	
		Refrigeration equipment	6 in. insulation on low-temp walk-in equipment, insulated floor, LED lighting, floating-head pressure controls, liquid pressure amplifier, subcooled liquid refrigerant, evaporative condenser	PL8–9, 12	
		Exhaust hoods	Side panels, larger overhangs, rear seal at appliances, proximity hoods, VAV demand-based exhaust	PL8, 10, 13	
	Process loads	Elevators	Use traction elevators for all elevators, and use regenerative traction elevators for all high-use elevators.	PL16	
SWH	Service water heating	Gas water heater (condensing)	95% Efficiency	WH3, HV8	
		Point-of-use water heater	0.81 EF or 81% E_t	PL11, WH3	
		Electric-heat-pump water heater	2.33 EF	WH3	
		Pipe insulation (d < 1.5 in./$d \geq$ 1.5 in.)	1.0 in./1.5 in.	WH7	
HVAC	Heating system	No central steam Use hot-water distribution system	Point-of-use steam for humidification and sterilization	HV33	
	Surgery — Central air-handling system	Water-cooled chiller	6.5 COP	HV8, 35	
		Water-circulation pumps	VFD and NEMA premium	HV35	
		Cooling towers	VFD on tower fans	HV37	
		Boiler efficiency	90% E_c	HV8	
		Maximum fan power	bhp ≤ supply cfm × 0.0012 + A	HV21–22, 24	
		Economizer	Comply with Standard 90.1*	HV19	
	Nonsurgery — Water-source heat pump (WSHP) system with DOAS	WSHP part-load/full-load cooling efficiency	17.6/15.0 EER	HV2	
		WSHP part-load/full-load heating efficiency	5.7/5.0 COP	HV2	
		WSHP compressor capacity control	Two-speed or variable-speed	HV2	
		Water-circulation pumps	VFD and NEMA premium	HV35	
		Closed-circuit cooling tower	VFD on fans	HV37	
		Boiler efficiency	90% E_c	HV8	
		Maximum fan power	0.4 W/cfm	HV21–22, 24	
		Exhaust-air energy recovery in DOAS	A (humid zones) = 60% total effectiveness B (dry zones) = 60% sensible effectiveness	HV9, 15–16	
		DOAS ventilation control	DCV with VFD	HV10–11	
	Fan-coil system with DOAS	Water-cooled chiller	6.5 COP	HV8,35	
		Water-circulation pumps	VFD and NEMA premium	HV35	
		Cooling towers	VFD on tower fans	HV37	
		Boiler efficiency	90% E_c	HV8	
		Maximum fan power	0.4 W/cfm	HV21–22, 24	
		FCU fans	Multiple speed	HV5	
		Exhaust-air energy recovery in DOAS	A (humid zones) = 60% total effectiveness B (dry zones) = 60% sensible effectiveness	HV9, 15–16	
		DOAS ventilation control	DCV with VFD	HV10–11	
	Mixed-air VAV system with separate OA treatment and heat recovery system	Heat recovery water-cooled chiller	4.55 COP	HV8,36,38	
		Water-cooled chiller	6.5 COP	HV8,35	
		Water-circulation pumps	VFD and NEMA premium	HV35	
		Cooling towers	VFD on tower fans	HV37	
		Boiler efficiency	90% E_c	HV8	
		Maximum fan power	bhp ≤ supply cfm × 0.0012 + A	HV21–22, 24	
		Economizer	Comply with Standard 90.1*	HV19	
		Exhaust-air energy recovery in DOAS	A (humid zones) = 60% total effectiveness B (dry zones) = 60% sensible effectiveness	HV9, 15–16	
		DOAS ventilation control	DCV with VFD	HV10–11	
	Ducts and dampers	OA damper	Motorized	HV14,31	
		Duct seal class	Seal class A	HV22, 24	
		Insulation level	R-6	HV22–23	
Q&A	Measurement and verification	Electrical submeters	Design and circuit for separate submeters for lighting, HVAC, general 120V, service water heating, renewables, and whole building	QA12–14	
		Benchmarks	Benchmark monthly energy use.	QA15	
		Training	Facility operator on continuous benchmarking	QA12–15	

*Note: Where the table says "Comply with Standard 90.1," the user must meet the more stringent of either the most current version of Standard 90.1 or the local code requirements.

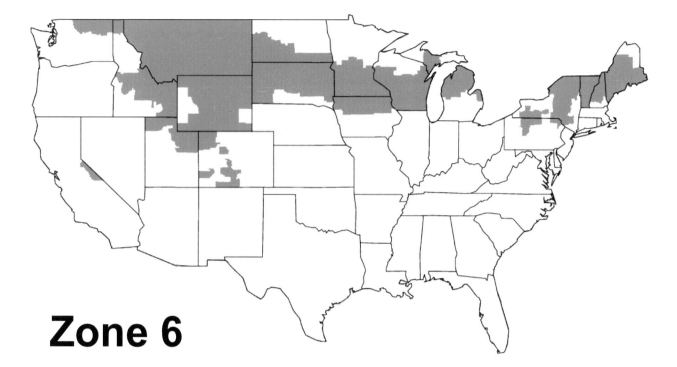

Zone 6

California

Alpine
Mono

Colorado

Alamosa
Archuleta
Chaffee
Conejos
Costilla
Custer
Dolores
Eagle
Moffat
Ouray
Rio Blanco
Saguache
San Miguel

Idaho

Adams
Bannock
Bear Lake
Bingham
Blaine
Boise
Bonner
Bonneville
Boundary
Butte
Camas
Caribou
Clark
Custer
Franklin
Fremont
Jefferson
Lemhi
Madison
Oneida
Teton
Valley

Iowa

Allamakee
Black Hawk
Bremer
Buchanan
Buena Vista
Butler
Calhoun
Cerro Gordo
Cherokee
Chickasaw
Clay
Clayton
Delaware
Dickinson
Emmet
Fayette
Floyd
Franklin
Grundy
Hamilton
Hancock
Hardin
Howard
Humboldt
Ida
Kossuth
Lyon
Mitchell
O'Brien
Osceola
Palo Alto
Plymouth
Pocahontas
Sac
Sioux
Webster
Winnebago
Winneshiek
Worth
Wright

Maine

All counties except:
Aroostook

Michigan

Alcona
Alger
Alpena
Antrim
Arenac
Benzie
Charlevoix
Cheboygan
Clare
Crawford
Delta
Dickinson
Emmet
Gladwin
Grand Traverse
Huron
Iosco
Isabella
Kalkaska
Lake
Leelanau
Manistee
Marquette
Mason
Mecosta
Menominee
Missaukee
Montmorency
Newaygo
Oceana
Ogemaw
Osceola
Oscoda
Otsego
Presque Isle
Roscommon
Sanilac
Wexford

Minnesota

Anoka
Benton
Big Stone
Blue Earth
Brown
Carver
Chippewa

Chisago
Cottonwood
Dakota
Dodge
Douglas
Faribault
Fillmore
Freeborn
Goodhue
Hennepin
Houston
Isanti
Jackson
Kandiyohi
Lac qui Parle
Le Sueur
Lincoln
Lyon
Martin
McLeod
Meeker
Morrison
Mower
Murray
Nicollet
Nobles
Olmsted
Pipestone
Pope
Ramsey
Redwood
Renville
Rice
Rock
Scott
Sherburne
Sibley
Stearns
Steele
Stevens
Swift
Todd
Traverse
Wabasha
Waseca
Washington
Watonwan
Winona
Wright
Yellow Medicine

Montana

All counties

New Hampshire

Belknap
Carroll
Coos
Grafton
Merrimack
Sullivan

New York

Allegany
Broome
Cattaraugus
Chenango
Clinton
Delaware
Essex
Franklin
Fulton
Hamilton
Herkimer
Jefferson
Lewis
Madison
Montgomery
Oneida
Otsego
Schoharie
Schuyler
Steuben
St. Lawrence
Sullivan
Tompkins
Ulster
Warren
Wyoming

North Dakota

Adams
Billings
Bowman
Burleigh
Dickey
Dunn
Emmons

Golden Valley
Grant
Hettinger
LaMoure
Logan
McIntosh
McKenzie
Mercer
Morton
Oliver
Ransom
Richland
Sargent
Sioux
Slope
Stark

Pennsylvania

Cameron
Clearfield
Elk
McKean
Potter
Susquehanna
Tioga
Wayne

South Dakota

All counties except:
Bennett
Bon Homme
Charles Mix
Clay
Douglas
Gregory
Hutchinson
Jackson
Mellette
Todd
Tripp
Union
Yankton

Utah

Box Elder
Cache
Carbon
Daggett

Duchesne
Morgan
Rich
Summit
Uintah
Wasatch

Vermont

All counties

Washington

Ferry
Okanogan
Pend Oreille
Stevens

Wisconsin

All counties except:
Ashland
Bayfield
Burnett
Douglas
Florence
Forest
Iron
Langlade
Lincoln
Oneida
Price
Sawyer
Taylor
Vilas
Washburn

Wyoming

All counties except:
Goshen
Platte
Lincoln
Sublette
Teton

Climate Zone 6 Recommendation Table for Large Hospitals

	Item	Component	Recommendation	How-to Tips	✓
	Form/space planning	Proper zoning	Group similar space types within the building footprint.	DL4–6	
Envelope	Roofs	Insulation entirely above deck	R-30.0 c.i.	EN2, 15–17	
		Solar reflectance index (SRI)	Comply with Standard 90.1*		
	Walls	Mass (HC > 7 Btu/ft^2)	R-19.5 c.i.	EN3, 15–17	
		Steel framed	R-13.0 + R-18.8 c.i.	EN4, 15–17	
		Below-grade walls	R-10.0 c.i.	EN5, 15–17	
	Floors	Mass	R-16.7 c.i.	EN6, 15–17	
		Steel framed	R-38.0	EN7, 15–17	
	Slabs	Unheated	R-10 for 24 in.	EN8,10, 15–17	
		Heated	R-20 for 48 in.	EN9–10, 15–17	
	Doors	Swinging	U-0.50	EN11, 16	
		Nonswinging	U-0.50	EN12, 16	
	Vestibules	At primary visitor building entrance	Comply with Standard 90.1*	EN14	
	Continuous air barriers	Continuous air barriers	Entire building envelope	EN13	
	Vertical fenestration (full assembly—NFRC rating)	Window-to-wall ratio	40% of net wall (floor-ceiling)	DL7, EN20, 26–27	
		Thermal transmittance	Nonmetal framing windows = 0.35 Metal framing windows = 0.42	EN19–20, 25–28	
		Solar heat gain coefficient (SHGC)	Nonmetal framing windows = 0.25 Metal framing windows = 0.25	EN19–20, 25–28	
		Light-to-solar gain ratio (LSG)	All orientations ≥ 1.5	EN24	
		Exterior sun control	South orientation only – PF = 0.5	EN21, DL13–14	
Daylighting/ Lighting	Form-driven daylighting option	All spaces	Comply with LEED for healthcare credits IEQ 8.1 (daylighting) and IEQ 8.2 (views)	DL3–6	
		Diagnostic and treatment block	Shape the building footprint and form such that the area within 15 ft of the perimeter exceeds 40% of the floorplate.	DL6	
		Inpatient units	Ensure that 75% of the occupied space not including patient rooms lies within 20 ft of the perimeter.	DL6	
		Staff areas (exam rooms, nurse stations, offices, corridors); public spaces (waiting, reception); and other regularly occupied spaces as applicable	Design the building form to maximize access to natural light, through sidelighting and toplighting.	DL8–13, 15, 20–23	
	Nonform-driven daylighting option	Staff areas (exam rooms, nurse stations, offices, corridors) and public spaces (waiting, reception)	Add daylight controls to any space within 15 ft of a perimeter window.	DL20–23	
	Interior finishes	Room interior surface average reflectance	Ceilings ≥ 80% Walls ≥ 70%	DL17	
		Lighting power density (LPD)	Whole building = 0.9 W/ft^2 Space-by-space per Table 5-4	EL1, 12–20	
	Interior lighting	Light source efficacy (mean lumens per watt)	T8 & T5 > 2 ft = 92 T8 & T5 < 2 ft = 85 All other >50	EL2–5	
		Ballasts—4 ft T8 Lamps	Nondimming = NEMA Premium Dimming= NEMA Premium Program Start	EL2	
		Ballasts—Fluorescent and HID	Electronic	EL2–5	
		Dimming controls daylight harvesting	Dim all fixtures in daylighted zones.	DL20–23, EL11	
		Lighting controls—General	Manual ON, auto/timed OFF in all areas as possible.	EL6,21	
		Surgery task lights	Use LED lights exclusively.	EL14	
		Exit signage	0.1–0.2 W Light Emitting Capacitor (LEC) exit signs exclusively	EL22	
	Exterior lighting	Façade and landscape lighting	LPD = 0.15 W/ft^2	EL23	
		Parking lots and drives	LPD = 0.1 W/ft^2	EL23	
		All other exterior lighting	LPD = Comply with Standard 90.1* Auto reduce to 25% (12 am–6 am)	EL23	
PPL	Equipment choices	Computers	Laptops = minimum 2/3 of total computers All others = mini desktop computers	PL2	
		ENERGY STAR® equipment	All computers, equipment, appliances	PL5	
		Vending machines	Delamp and specify best in class efficiency.	PL3, 7	
		Computer power control	Network control with power saving modes and control during unoccupied hours or IT enterprise power management software	PL2	
	Controls	Occupancy sensors	Office plug occupancy sensors	PL3	
		Timer switches	Water coolers, coffee makers, small appliances = auto OFF during unoccupied hours	PL3	

*Note: Where the table says "Comply with Standard 90.1," the user must meet the more stringent of either the most current version of Standard 90.1 or the local code requirements.

Climate Zone 6 Recommendation Table for Large Hospitals *(Continued)*

	Item	Component	Recommendation	How-to Tips	✓
PPL	Kitchen equipment	Cooking equipment	ENERGY STAR or California rebate-qualified equipment	PL8–9	
		Refrigeration equipment	6 in. insulation on low-temp walk-in equipment, insulated floor, LED lighting, floating-head pressure controls, liquid pressure amplifier, subcooled liquid refrigerant, evaporative condenser	PL8–9, 12	
		Exhaust hoods	Side panels, larger overhangs, rear seal at appliances, proximity hoods, VAV demand-based exhaust	PL8, 10, 13	
	Process loads	Elevators	Use traction elevators for all elevators, and use regenerative traction elevators for all high-use elevators.	PL16	
SWH	Service water heating	Gas water heater (condensing)	95% Efficiency	WH3, HV8	
		Point-of-use water heater	0.81 EF or 81% E_t	PL11, WH3	
		Electric-heat-pump water heater	2.33 EF	WH3	
		Pipe insulation (d < 1.5 in./$d \geq$ 1.5 in.)	1.0 in./1.5 in.	WH7	
HVAC	Heating system	No central steam Use hot-water distribution system	Point-of-use steam for humidification and sterilization	HV33	
	Surgery — Central air-handling system	Water-cooled chiller	6.5 COP	HV8, 35	
		Water-circulation pumps	VFD and NEMA premium	HV35	
		Cooling towers	VFD on tower fans	HV37	
		Boiler efficiency	90% E_c	HV8	
		Maximum fan power	bhp ≤ supply cfm × 0.0012 + A	HV21–22, 24	
		Economizer	Comply with Standard 90.1*	HV19	
	Nonsurgery — Water-source heat pump (WSHP) system with DOAS	WSHP part-load/full-load cooling efficiency	17.6/15.0 EER	HV2	
		WSHP part-load/full-load heating efficiency	5.7/5.0 COP	HV2	
		WSHP compressor capacity control	Two-speed or variable-speed	HV2	
		Water-circulation pumps	VFD and NEMA premium	HV35	
		Closed-circuit cooling tower	VFD on fans	HV37	
		Boiler efficiency	90% E_c	HV8	
		Maximum fan power	0.4 W/cfm	HV21–22, 24	
		Exhaust-air energy recovery in DOAS	A (humid zones) = 60% total effectiveness B (dry zones) = 60% sensible effectiveness	HV9, 15–16	
		DOAS ventilation control	DCV with VFD	HV10–11	
	Nonsurgery — Fan-coil system with DOAS	Water-cooled chiller	6.5 COP	HV8,35	
		Water-circulation pumps	VFD and NEMA premium	HV35	
		Cooling towers	VFD on tower fans	HV37	
		Boiler efficiency	90% E_c	HV8	
		Maximum fan power	0.4 W/cfm	HV21–22, 24	
		FCU fans	Multiple speed	HV5	
		Exhaust-air energy recovery in DOAS	A (humid zones) = 60% total effectiveness B (dry zones) = 60% sensible effectiveness	HV9, 15–16	
		DOAS ventilation control	DCV with VFD	HV10–11	
	Nonsurgery — Mixed-air VAV system with separate OA treatment and heat recovery system	Heat recovery water-cooled chiller	4.55 COP	HV8,36,38	
		Water-cooled chiller	6.5 COP	HV8,35	
		Water-circulation pumps	VFD and NEMA premium	HV35	
		Cooling towers	VFD on tower fans	HV37	
		Boiler efficiency	90% E_c	HV8	
		Maximum fan power	bhp ≤ supply cfm × 0.0012 + A	HV21–22, 24	
		Economizer	Comply with Standard 90.1*	HV19	
		Exhaust-air energy recovery in DOAS	A (humid zones) = 60% total effectiveness B (dry zones) = 60% sensible effectiveness	HV9, 15–16	
		DOAS ventilation control	DCV with VFD	HV10–11	
	Ducts and dampers	OA damper	Motorized	HV14, 31	
		Duct seal class	Seal class A	HV22, 24	
		Insulation level	R-6	HV22–23	
Q&A	Measurement and verification	Electrical submeters	Design and circuit for separate submeters for lighting, HVAC, general 120V, service water heating, renewables, and whole building	QA12–14	
		Benchmarks	Benchmark monthly energy use.	QA15	
		Training	Facility operator on continuous benchmarking	QA12–15	

*Note: Where the table says "Comply with Standard 90.1," the user must meet the more stringent of either the most current version of Standard 90.1 or the local code requirements.

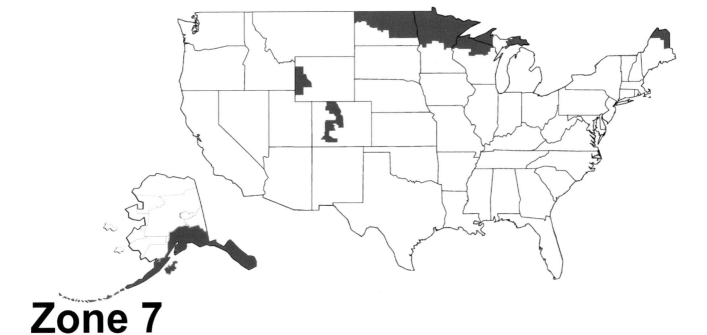

Zone 7

Alaska

Aleutians East
Aleutians West (CA)
Anchorage
Angoon (CA)
Bristol Bay
Denali
Haines
Juneau
Kenai Peninsula
Ketchikan (CA)
Ketchikan Gateway
Kodiak Island
Lake and Peninsula
Matanuska-Susitna
Prince of Wales-Outer
Sitka
Skagway-Hoonah-
Valdez-Cordova (CA)
Wrangell-Petersburg (CA)
Yakutat

Colorado

Clear Creek
Grand
Gunnison
Hinsdale
Jackson
Lake
Mineral
Park
Pitkin
Rio Grande
Routt
San Juan
Summit

Maine

Aroostook

Michigan

Baraga
Chippewa
Gogebic
Houghton

Iron
Keweenaw
Luce
Mackinac
Ontonagon
Schoolcraft

Minnesota

Aitkin
Becker
Beltrami
Carlton
Cass
Clay
Clearwater
Cook
Crow Wing
Grant
Hubbard
Itasca
Kanabec
Kittson
Koochiching
Lake
Lake of the Woods
Mahnomen
Marshall
Mille Lacs
Norman
Otter Tail
Pennington
Pine
Polk
Red Lake
Roseau
St. Louis
Wadena
Wilkin

North Dakota

Barnes
Benson
Bottineau
Burke
Cass
Cavalier

Divide
Eddy
Foster
Grand Forks
Griggs
Kidder
McHenry
McLean
Mountrail
Nelson
Pembina
Pierce
Ramsey
Renville
Rolette
Sheridan
Steele
Stutsman
Towner
Traill
Walsh
Ward
Wells
Williams

Wisconsin

Ashland
Bayfield
Burnett
Douglas
Florence
Forest
Iron
Langlade
Lincoln
Oneida
Price
Sawyer
Taylor
Vilas
Washburn

Wyoming

Lincoln
Sublette
Teton

Climate Zone 7 Recommendation Table for Large Hospitals

	Item	Component	Recommendation	How-to Tips	✓
Envelope	Form/space planning	Proper zoning	Group similar space types within the building footprint.	DL4–6	
	Roofs	Insulation entirely above deck	R-35.0 c.i.	EN2, 15–17	
		Solar reflectance index (SRI)	Comply with Standard 90.1*		
	Walls	Mass (HC > 7 Btu/ft^2)	R-19.5 c.i.	EN3, 15–17	
		Steel framed	R-13.0 + R-18.8 c.i.	EN4, 15–17	
		Below-grade walls	R-15.0 c.i.	EN5, 15–17	
	Floors	Mass	R-20.9 c.i.	EN6, 15–17	
		Steel framed	R-49.0	EN7, 15–17	
	Slabs	Unheated	R-20 for 24 in.	EN8,10, 15–17	
		Heated	R-25 for 48 in.	EN9–10, 15–17	
	Doors	Swinging	U-0.50	EN11, 16	
		Nonswinging	U-0.50	EN12, 16	
	Vestibules	At primary visitor building entrance	Comply with Standard 90.1*	EN14	
	Continuous air barriers	Continuous air barriers	Entire building envelope	EN13	
		Window-to-wall ratio	40% of net wall (floor-ceiling)	DL7, EN20, 26–27	
	Vertical fenestration (full assembly—NFRC rating)	Thermal transmittance	Nonmetal framing windows = 0.33 Metal framing windows = 0.34	EN19–20, 25–28	
		Solar heat gain coefficient (SHGC)	Nonmetal framing windows = 0.4 Metal framing windows = 0.4	EN19–20, 25–28	
		Light-to-solar gain ratio (LSG)	All orientations ≥ 1.5	EN24	
		Exterior sun control	South orientation only – PF = 0.5	EN21, DL13–14	
Daylighting/ Lighting		All spaces	Comply with LEED for healthcare credits IEQ 8.1 (daylighting) and IEQ 8.2 (views)	DL3–6	
	Form-driven daylighting option	Diagnostic and treatment block	Shape the building footprint and form such that the area within 15 ft of the perimeter exceeds 40% of the floorplate.	DL6	
		Inpatient units	Ensure that 75% of the occupied space not including patient rooms lies within 20 ft of the perimeter.	DL6	
		Staff areas (exam rooms, nurse stations, offices, corridors); public spaces (waiting, reception); and other regularly occupied spaces as applicable	Design the building form to maximize access to natural light, through sidelighting and toplighting.	DL8–13, 15, 20–23	
	Nonform-driven daylighting option	Staff areas (exam rooms, nurse stations, offices, corridors) and public spaces (waiting, reception)	Add daylight controls to any space within 15 ft of a perimeter window.	DL20–23	
	Interior finishes	Room interior surface average reflectance	Ceilings ≥ 80% Walls ≥ 70%	DL17	
		Lighting power density (LPD)	Whole building = 0.9 W/ft^2 Space-by-space per Table 5-4	EL1, 12–20	
	Interior lighting	Light source efficacy (mean lumens per watt)	T8 & T5 > 2 ft = 92 T8 & T5 < 2 ft = 85 All other >50	EL2–5	
		Ballasts—4 ft T8 Lamps	Nondimming = NEMA Premium Dimming= NEMA Premium Program Start	EL2	
		Ballasts—Fluorescent and HID	Electronic	EL2–5	
		Dimming controls daylight harvesting	Dim all fixtures in daylighted zones.	DL20–23, EL11	
		Lighting controls—General	Manual ON, auto/timed OFF in all areas as possible.	EL6,21	
		Surgery task lights	Use LED lights exclusively.	EL14	
		Exit signage	0.1–0.2 W Light Emitting Capacitor (LEC) exit signs exclusively	EL22	
	Exterior lighting	Façade and landscape lighting	LPD = 0.15 W/ft^2	EL23	
		Parking lots and drives	LPD = 0.1 W/ft^2	EL23	
		All other exterior lighting	LPD = Comply with Standard 90.1* Auto reduce to 25% (12 am–6 am)	EL23	
PPL	Equipment choices	Computers	Laptops = minimum 2/3 of total computers All others = mini desktop computers	PL2	
		ENERGY STAR® equipment	All computers, equipment, appliances	PL5	
		Vending machines	Delamp and specify best in class efficiency.	PL3, 7	
	Controls	Computer power control	Network control with power saving modes and control during unoccupied hours or IT enterprise power management software	PL2	
		Occupancy sensors	Office plug occupancy sensors	PL3	
		Timer switches	Water coolers, coffee makers, small appliances = auto OFF during unoccupied hours	PL3	

*Note: Where the table says "Comply with Standard 90.1," the user must meet the more stringent of either the most current version of Standard 90.1 or the local code requirements.

Climate Zone 7 Recommendation Table for Large Hospitals *(Continued)*

		Item	Component	Recommendation	How-to Tips	✓
PPL		Kitchen equipment	Cooking equipment	ENERGY STAR or California rebate-qualified equipment	PL8–9	
			Refrigeration equipment	6 in. insulation on low-temp walk-in equipment, insulated floor, LED lighting, floating-head pressure controls, liquid pressure amplifier, subcooled liquid refrigerant, evaporative condenser	PL8–9, 12	
			Exhaust hoods	Side panels, larger overhangs, rear seal at appliances, proximity hoods, VAV demand-based exhaust	PL8, 10, 13	
		Process loads	Elevators	Use traction elevators for all elevators, and use regenerative traction elevators for all high-use elevators.	PL16	
SWH		Service water heating	Gas water heater (condensing)	95% Efficiency	WH3, HV8	
			Point-of-use water heater	0.81 EF or 81% E_t	PL11, WH3	
			Electric-heat-pump water heater	2.33 EF	WH3	
			Pipe insulation ($d <$ 1.5 in./$d \geq$ 1.5 in.)	1.0 in./1.5 in.	WH7	
HVAC		Heating system	No central steam Use hot-water distribution system	Point-of-use steam for humidification and sterilization	HV33	
	Surgery	Central air-handling system	Water-cooled chiller	6.5 COP	HV8,35	
			Water-circulation pumps	VFD and NEMA premium	HV35	
			Cooling towers	VFD on tower fans	HV37	
			Boiler efficiency	90% E_c	HV8	
			Maximum fan power	bhp ≤ supply cfm × 0.0012 + A	HV21–22, 24	
			Economizer	Comply with Standard 90.1*	HV19	
	Nonsurgery	Water-source heat pump (WSHP) system with DOAS	WSHP part-load/full-load cooling efficiency	17.6/15.0 EER	HV2	
			WSHP part-load/full-load heating efficiency	5.7/5.0 COP	HV2	
			WSHP compressor capacity control	Two-speed or variable-speed	HV2	
			Water-circulation pumps	VFD and NEMA premium	HV35	
			Closed-circuit cooling tower	VFD on fans	HV37	
			Boiler efficiency	90% E_c	HV8	
			Maximum fan power	0.4 W/cfm	HV21–22, 24	
			Exhaust-air energy recovery in DOAS	A (humid zones) = 60% total effectiveness B (dry zones) = 60% sensible effectiveness	HV9, 15–16	
			DOAS ventilation control	DCV with VFD	HV10–11	
		Fan-coil system with DOAS	Water-cooled chiller	6.5 COP	HV8,35	
			Water-circulation pumps	VFD and NEMA premium	HV35	
			Cooling towers	VFD on tower fans	HV37	
			Boiler efficiency	90% E_c	HV8	
			Maximum fan power	0.4 W/cfm	HV21–22, 24	
			FCU fans	Multiple speed	HV5	
			Exhaust-air energy recovery in DOAS	A (humid zones) = 60% total effectiveness B (dry zones) = 60% sensible effectiveness	HV9, 15–16	
			DOAS ventilation control	DCV with VFD	HV10–11	
		Mixed-air VAV system with separate OA treatment and heat recovery system	Heat recovery water-cooled chiller	4.55 COP	HV8,36,38	
			Water-cooled chiller	6.5 COP	HV8,35	
			Water-circulation pumps	VFD and NEMA premium	HV35	
			Cooling towers	VFD on tower fans	HV35	
			Boiler efficiency	90% E_c	HV8	
			Maximum fan power	bhp ≤ supply cfm × 0.0012 + A	HV21–22, 24	
			Economizer	Comply with Standard 90.1*	HV19	
			Exhaust-air energy recovery in DOAS	A (humid zones) = 60% total effectiveness B (dry zones) = 60% sensible effectiveness	HV9, 15–16	
			DOAS ventilation control	DCV with VFD	HV10–11	
		Ducts and dampers	OA damper	Motorized	HV14, 31	
			Duct seal class	Seal class A	HV22, 24	
			Insulation level	R-6	HV22–23	
Q&A		Measurement and verification	Electrical submeters	Design and circuit for separate submeters for lighting, HVAC, general 120V, service water heating, renewables, and whole building	QA12–14	
			Benchmarks	Benchmark monthly energy use.	QA15	
			Training	Facility operator on continuous benchmarking	QA12–15	

*Note: Where the table says "Comply with Standard 90.1," the user must meet the more stringent of either the most current version of Standard 90.1 or the local code requirements.

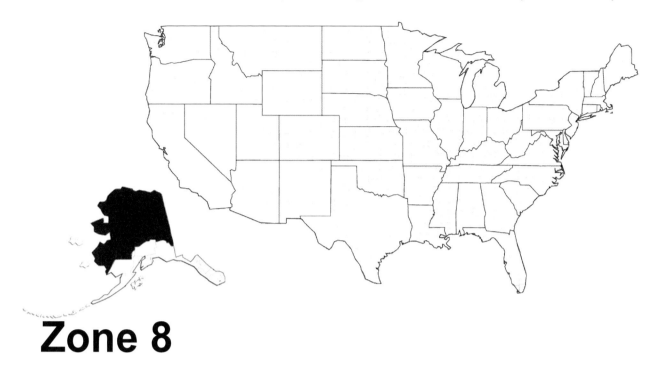

Zone 8

Alaska

Bethel (CA)
Dillingham (CA)
Fairbanks North Star
Nome (CA)
North Slope
Northwest Arctic
Southeast Fairbanks (CA)
Wade Hampton (CA)
Yukon-Koyukuk (CA)

Climate Zone 8 Recommendation Table for Large Hospitals

	Item	Component	Recommendation	How-to Tips	✓
	Form/space planning	Proper zoning	Group similar space types within the building footprint.	DL4–6	
Envelope	Roofs	Insulation entirely above deck	R-35.0 c.i.	EN2, 15–17	
		Solar reflectance index (SRI)	Comply with Standard 90.1*		
	Walls	Mass (HC > 7 Btu/ft^2)	R-19.5 c.i.	EN3, 15–17	
		Steel framed	R-13.0 + R-18.8 c.i.	EN4, 15–17	
		Below-grade walls	R-15.0 c.i.	EN5, 15–17	
	Floors	Mass	R-23.0 c.i.	EN6, 15–17	
		Steel framed	R-60.0	EN7, 15–17	
	Slabs	Unheated	R-20 for 24 in.	EN8,10, 15–17	
		Heated	R-20 full slab	EN9–10, 15–17	
	Doors	Swinging	U-0.50	EN11, 16	
		Nonswinging	U-0.50	EN12, 16	
	Vestibules	At primary visitor building entrance	Comply with Standard 90.1*	EN14	
	Continuous air barriers	Continuous air barriers	Entire building envelope	EN13	
	Vertical fenestration (full assembly—NFRC rating)	Window-to-wall ratio	40% of net wall (floor-ceiling)	DL7, EN20, 26–27	
		Thermal transmittance	Nonmetal framing windows = 0.25 Metal framing windows = 0.34	EN19–20, 25–28	
		Solar heat gain coefficient (SHGC)	Nonmetal framing windows = 0.4 Metal framing windows = 0.4	EN19–20, 25–28	
		Light-to-solar gain ratio (LSG)	All orientations ≥ 1.5	EN24	
		Exterior sun control	South orientation only – PF = 0.5	EN21, DL13–14	
Surgery task lights	Use LED lights exclusively	All spaces	Comply with LEED for healthcare credits IEQ 8.1 (daylighting) and IEQ 8.2 (views)	DL3–6	
		Diagnostic and treatment block	Shape the building footprint and form such that the area within 15 ft of the perimeter exceeds 40% of the floorplate.	DL6	
		Inpatient units	Ensure that 75% of the occupied space not including patient rooms lies within 20 ft of the perimeter.	DL6	
		Staff areas (exam rooms, nurse stations, offices, corridors); public spaces (waiting, reception); and other regularly occupied spaces as applicable	Design the building form to maximize access to natural light, through sidelighting and toplighting.	DL8–13, 15, 20–23	
	Nonform-driven daylighting option	Staff areas (exam rooms, nurse stations, offices, corridors) and public spaces (waiting, reception)	Add daylight controls to any space within 15 ft of a perimeter window.	DL20–23	
	Interior finishes	Room interior surface average reflectance	Ceilings ≥ 80% Walls ≥ 70%	DL17	
		Lighting power density (LPD)	Whole building = 0.9 W/ft^2 Space-by-space per Table 5-4	EL1, 12–20	
		Light source efficacy (mean lumens per watt)	T8 & T5 > 2 ft = 92 T8 & T5 < 2 ft = 85 All other >50	DL2–5	
	Interior lighting	Ballasts—4 ft T8 Lamps	Nondimming = NEMA Premium Dimming= NEMA Premium Program Start	EL2	
		Ballasts—Fluorescent and HID	Electronic	EL2–5	
		Dimming controls daylight harvesting	Dim all fixtures in daylighted zones.	DL20–23, EL11	
		Lighting controls—General	Manual ON, auto/timed OFF in all areas as possible.	EL6, 21	
		Surgery task lights	Use LED lights exclusively.	EL14	
		Exit signage	0.1–0.2 W Light Emitting Capacitor (LEC) exit signs exclusively	EL22	
	Exterior lighting	Façade and landscape lighting	LPD = 0.15 W/ft^2	EL23	
		Parking lots and drives	LPD = 0.1 W/ft^2	EL23	
		All other exterior lighting	LPD = Comply with Standard 90.1* Auto reduce to 25% (12 am–6 am)	EL23	
PPL	Equipment choices	Computers	Laptops = minimum 2/3 of total computers All others = mini desktop computers	PL2	
		ENERGY STAR® equipment	All computers, equipment, appliances	PL5	
		Vending machines	Delamp and specify best in class efficiency.	PL3, 7	
	Controls	Computer power control	Network control with power saving modes and control during unoccupied hours or IT enterprise power management software	PL2	
		Occupancy sensors	Office plug occupancy sensors	PL3	
		Timer switches	Water coolers, coffee makers, small appliances = auto OFF during unoccupied hours	PL3	

*Note: Where the table says "Comply with Standard 90.1," the user must meet the more stringent of either the most current version of Standard 90.1 or the local code requirements.

Climate Zone 8 Recommendation Table for Large Hospitals *(Continued)*

	Item	Component	Recommendation	How-to Tips	✓
PPL	Kitchen equipment	Cooking equipment	ENERGY STAR or California rebate-qualified equipment	PL8–9	
		Refrigeration equipment	6 in. insulation on low-temp walk-in equipment, insulated floor, LED lighting, floating-head pressure controls, liquid pressure amplifier, subcooled liquid refrigerant, evaporative condenser	PL8–9, 12	
		Exhaust hoods	Side panels, larger overhangs, rear seal at appliances, proximity hoods, VAV demand-based exhaust	PL8, 10, 13	
	Process loads	Elevators	Use traction elevators for all elevators, and use regenerative traction elevators for all high-use elevators.	PL16	
SWH	Service water heating	Gas water heater (condensing)	95% Efficiency	WH3, HV8	
		Point-of-use water heater	0.81 EF or 81% E_t	PL11, WH3	
		Electric-heat-pump water heater	2.33 EF	WH3	
		Pipe insulation ($d <$ 1.5 in./$d \geq$ 1.5 in.)	1.0 in./1.5 in.	WH7	
HVAC	Heating system	No central steam Use hot-water distribution system	Point-of-use steam for humidification and sterilization	HV33	
	Surgery — Central air-handling system	Water-cooled chiller	Comply with Standard 90.1*	HV8, 35	
		Water-circulation pumps	VFD and NEMA premium	HV35	
		Cooling towers	VFD on tower fans	HV37	
		Boiler efficiency	90% E_c	HV8	
		Maximum fan power	bhp ≤ supply cfm × 0.0012 + A	HV21–22, 24	
		Economizer	Comply with Standard 90.1*	HV19	
	Nonsurgery — Water-source heat pump (WSHP) system with DOAS	WSHP part-load/full-load cooling efficiency	17.6/15.0 EER	HV2	
		WSHP part-load/full-load heating efficiency	5.7/5.0 COP	HV2	
		WSHP compressor capacity control	Two-speed or variable-speed	HV2	
		Water-circulation pumps	VFD and NEMA premium	HV35	
		Closed-circuit cooling tower	VFD on fans	HV37	
		Boiler efficiency	90% E_c	HV8	
		Maximum fan power	0.4 W/cfm	HV21–22, 24	
		Exhaust-air energy recovery in DOAS	60% sensible effectiveness	HV9, 15–16	
		DOAS ventilation control	DCV with VFD	HV10–11	
	Fan-coil system with DOAS	Water-cooled chiller	6.5 COP	HV8, 35	
		Water-circulation pumps	VFD and NEMA premium	HV35	
		Cooling towers	VFD on tower fans	HV37	
		Boiler efficiency	90% E_c	HV8	
		Maximum fan power	0.4 W/cfm	HV21–22, 24	
		FCU fans	Multiple speed	HV5	
		Exhaust-air energy recovery in DOAS	60% sensible effectiveness	HV9, 15–16	
		DOAS ventilation control	DCV with VFD	HV10–11	
	Mixed-air VAV system with separate OA treatment and heat recovery system	Heat recovery water-cooled chiller	4.55 COP	HV8, 36, 38	
		Water-cooled chiller	6.5 COP	HV8, 35	
		Water-circulation pumps	VFD and NEMA premium	HV35	
		Cooling towers	VFD on tower fans	HV37	
		Boiler efficiency	90% E_c	HV8	
		Maximum fan power	bhp ≤ supply cfm × 0.0012 + A	HV21–22, 24	
		Economizer	Comply with Standard 90.1*	HV19	
		Exhaust-air energy recovery in DOAS	60% sensible effectiveness	HV9, 15–16	
		DOAS ventilation control	DCV with VFD	HV10–11	
	Ducts and dampers	OA damper	Motorized	HV14, 31	
		Duct seal class	Seal class A	HV22, 24	
		Insulation level	R-6	HV22–23	
Q&A	Measurement and verification	Electrical submeters	Design and circuit for separate submeters for lighting, HVAC, general 120V, service water heating, renewables, and whole building	QA12–14	
		Benchmarks	Benchmark monthly energy use.	QA15	
		Training	Facility operator on continuous benchmarking	QA12–15	

*Note: Where the table says "Comply with Standard 90.1," the user must meet the more stringent of either the most current version of Standard 90.1 or the local code requirements.

How to Implement Recommendations

5

Recommendations are contained in the individual tables in Chapter 4, "Recommendations by Climate." The following how-to tips are intended to provide guidance on good practices for implementing the recommendations as well as cautions to avoid known problems and obstacles to energy-efficient construction.

ENVELOPE

OPAQUE ENVELOPE COMPONENTS

Good Design Practice

EN1   *Cool Roofs* **(Climate Zones: ❶ ❷ ③)**

For a roof to be considered a cool roof, a Solar Reflectance Index (SRI) of 78 or higher is recommended. A high reflectance keeps much of the sun's energy from being absorbed, while a high thermal emissivity surface radiates away any solar energy that is absorbed, allowing the roof to cool more rapidly. Cool roofs are typically white and have a smooth surface. Commercial roof products that qualify as cool roofs fall into three categories: single ply, liquid applied, and metal panels. Examples are presented in Table 5-1.

Table 5-1   Examples of Cool Roofs

Category	Product	Reflectance	Emissivity	SRI
Single ply	White polyvinyl chloride (PVC)	0.86	0.86	107
	White chlorinated polyethylene (CPE)	0.86	0.88	108
	White chlorosulfonated polyethylene (CPSE)	0.85	0.87	106
	White thermoplastic polyolefin (TSO)	0.77	0.87	95
Liquid applied	White elastomeric, polyurethane, acrylic coating	0.71	0.86	86
	White paint (on metal or concrete)	0.71	0.85	86
Metal panels	Factory-coated white finish	0.90	0.87	113

The solar reflectance and thermal emissivity property values represent initial conditions as determined by a laboratory accredited by the Cool Roof Rating Council (CRRC). An SRI can be determined by the following equation:

$$SRI = 123.97 - 141.35(\chi) + 9.655(\chi^2)$$

where

$$\chi = \frac{20.797 \times \alpha - 0.603 \times \varepsilon}{9.5205 \times \varepsilon + 12.0}$$

and

α = solar absorptance = 1 – solar reflectance

ε = thermal emissivity

These equations were derived from ASTM E1980 (ASTM 2011a), assuming a medium wind speed. Note that cool roofs are not a substitute for the appropriate amount of insulation.

EN2 *Roofs, Insulation Entirely above Deck* (Climate Zones: all)

The insulation entirely above deck should be continuous insulation (c.i.) rigid boards. Continuous insulation is important because no framing members are present that would introduce thermal bridges or short circuits to bypass the insulation. When two layers of c.i. are used in this construction, the board edges should be staggered to reduce the potential for convection losses or thermal bridging. If an inverted or protected membrane roof system is used, at least one layer of insulation is placed above the membrane and a maximum of one layer is placed beneath the membrane.

EN3 *Walls, Mass* (Climate Zones: all)

Mass walls are defined as those with a heat capacity exceeding 7 Btu/ft$^2\cdot$°F. Insulation may be placed either on the inside or the outside of the mass wall. When insulation is placed on the exterior, rigid c.i. is recommended. When insulation is placed on the interior, a furring or framing system may be used, provided the total wall assembly has a U-factor that is less than or equal to the appropriate climate zone construction listed in Appendix A.

The greatest advantages of mass can be obtained when insulation is placed on its exterior. In this case, the mass absorbs heat from the interior spaces that is later released in the evenings when the buildings are not occupied. The thermal mass of a building (typically contained in the building envelope) absorbs heat during the day and reduces the magnitude of indoor air temperature swings, reduces peak cooling loads, and transfers some of the absorbed heat into the night hours. The cooling load can then be covered by passive cooling techniques (natural ventilation) when the outdoor conditions are more favorable. An unoccupied building can also be precooled during the night by natural or mechanical ventilation to reduce the cooling energy use. This same effect reduces heating load as well.

Thermal mass also has a positive effect on thermal comfort. High-mass buildings attenuate interior air and wall temperature variations and sustain a stable overall thermal environment. This increases thermal comfort, particularly during mild seasons (spring and fall), during large air temperature changes (high solar gain), and in areas with large day-night temperature swings.

Designers should keep in mind that the occupants will be the final determinants on the extent of the usability of any building system, including thermal mass. Changing the use of internal spaces and surfaces can drastically reduce the effectiveness of thermal storage. The final use of the space must be considered when making the heating and cooling load calculations and incorporating possible energy savings from thermal mass effects.

EN4   ***Walls, Steel Framed*** (Climate Zones: all)

Cold-formed steel framing members are thermal bridges to the cavity insulation. Adding exterior foam sheathing as c.i. is the preferred method to upgrade the wall thermal performance because it increases the overall wall thermal performance and tends to minimize the impact of the thermal bridging.

Alternative combinations of cavity insulation and sheathing in thicker steel-framed walls can be used, provided that the proposed total wall assembly has a U-factor that is less than or equal to the U-factor for the appropriate climate zone construction listed in Appendix A. Batt insulation installed in cold-formed, steel-framed wall assemblies should be ordered as "full width batts" and installation is normally by friction fit. Batt insulation should fill the entire cavity and not be cut short.

EN5   ***Below Grade Walls*** (Climate Zones: all)

Insulation, when recommended, may be placed either on the inside or the outside of the below-grade wall. If placed on the exterior of the wall, rigid c.i. is recommended. If placed on the interior of the wall, a furring or framing system is recommended, provided the total wall assembly has a C-factor that is less than or equal to the appropriate climate zone construction listed in Appendix A.

EN6   ***Floors, Mass*** (Climate Zones: all)

Insulation should be continuous and either integral to or above the slab. This can be achieved by placing high-density extruded polystyrene above the slab with either plywood or a thin layer of concrete on top. Placing insulation below the deck is not recommended due to losses through any concrete support columns or through the slab perimeter.

Exception: Buildings or zones within buildings that have durable floors for heavy machinery or equipment could place insulation below the deck.

EN7   ***Floors, Metal Joist, or Steel Framed*** (Climate Zones: all)

Insulation should be installed parallel to the framing members and in intimate contact with the flooring system supported by the framing member in order to avoid the potential thermal short-circuiting associated with open or exposed air spaces. Nonrigid insulation should be supported from below and no less frequently than 24 in. on center.

EN8   ***Slab-on-Grade Floors, Unheated*** (Climate Zones: ④ ⑤ ⑥ ❼ ❽)

Rigid c.i. should be used around the perimeter of the slab and should reach the depth listed in the recommendation or to the bottom of the footing, whichever is less.

EN9   ***Slab-on-Grade Floors, Heated*** (Climate Zones: all)

Continuous rigid insulation should be used around the perimeter of the slab and should reach to the depth listed or to the frost line, whichever is deeper. Additionally, in climate zone 8, continuous insulation should be placed below the slab as well.

Note: In areas where termites are a concern and rigid insulation is not recommended for use under the slab, a different heating system should be used.

EN10   ***Slab Edge Insulation*** (Climate Zones: all)

Use of slab edge insulation improves thermal performance, but problems can occur in regions that have termites.

EN11   ***Doors, Opaque, Swinging*** (Climate Zones: all)

A U-factor of 0.37 corresponds to an insulated double-panel metal door. A U-factor of 0.61 corresponds to a double-panel metal door. If at all possible, single swinging doors should be used. Double swinging doors are difficult to seal at the center of the doors unless there is a center post

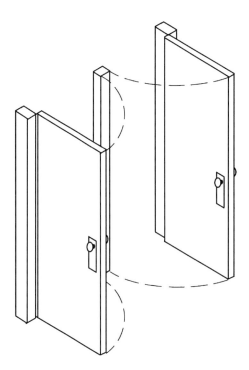

Figure 5-1 Swinging Opaque Doors with Hinges on One Side, Closing to a Center Post

(see Figure 5-1). Double swinging doors without a center post should be minimized and limited to areas where width is important. Vestibules or revolving doors can be added to further improve energy efficiency.

EN12   Doors, Opaque, Sectional or Sliding **(Climate Zones: all)**

Sectional or sliding doors are recommended to have R-14 rigid insulation or meet the recommended U-factor. When meeting the recommended U-factor, the thermal bridging at the door and section edges should be included in the analysis. Insulated panel doors can provide a tighter seal to minimize infiltration.

EN13   Vestibules **(Climate Zones: all)**

Vestibules are recommended for building entrances routinely used by occupants but not for emergency exits, maintenance doors, loading docks, or other specialty entrances. Occupant entrances that separate conditioned space from the exterior should be protected with an enclosed vestibule, where all doors opening into and out of the vestibule are equipped with self-closing devices. Vestibules should be designed so that in passing through the vestibule it is not necessary for the interior and exterior doors to open at the same time. Interior and exterior doors should have a minimum distance between them of not less than 7 ft (2.1m) when in the closed position. Vestibules should be designed only as areas to traverse between the exterior and the interior. The exterior envelope of conditioned vestibules should comply with the requirements for a conditioned space. Either the interior or exterior envelope of unconditioned vestibules should comply with the requirements for a conditioned space.

EN14   Air Infiltration Control **(Climate Zones: all)**

The building envelope should be designed and constructed with a continuous air barrier system to control air leakage into or out of the conditioned space and should extend over all surfaces of the building envelope (at the lowest floor, exterior walls, and ceiling or roof). An air barrier system should also be provided for interior separations between conditioned space and space designed to maintain temperature or humidity levels that differ from those in the conditioned space by more than 50% of the difference between the conditioned space and design ambient conditions. If possible, a blower door should be used to depressurize the building to find leaks in the infiltration barrier. The blower door testing should be conducted using a pressure differential of 0.3 in. water (1.57 lb/ft^2) in accordance with ASTM E779 (ASTM 2010) or an equivalent approved method.

At a minimum, the air barrier system should have the following characteristics:

- It should be continuous, with all joints made airtight.
- Air barrier materials used in frame walls should have an air permeability not to exceed 0.004 cfm/ft^2 under a pressure differential of 0.3 in. H$_2$O (1.57 lb/ft^2) when tested in accordance with ASTM E 2178 (ASTM 2011b).
- The system should be able to withstand positive and negative combined design wind, fan, and stack pressures on the envelope without damage or displacement and should transfer the load to the structure. It should not displace adjacent materials under full load.
- It should be durable or maintainable.
- The air barrier material of an envelope assembly should be joined in an airtight and flexible manner to the air barrier material of adjacent assemblies, allowing for the relative movement of these assemblies and components due to thermal and moisture variations, creep, and structural deflection.
- Connections should be made between the following:
  a. Foundation and walls
  b. Walls and windows or doors
  c. Different wall systems
  d. Wall and roof
  e. Wall and roof over unconditioned space
  f. Walls, floors, and roof across construction, control, and expansion joints
  g. Walls, floors, and roof to utility, pipe, and duct penetrations
- All penetrations of the air barrier system and paths of air infiltration/exfiltration should be made airtight.

Options

EN15 *Alternative Constructions* (Climate Zones: all)

The climate zone recommendations provide only one solution for upgrading the thermal performance of the envelope. Other constructions can be equally effective, but they are not shown in this document. Any alternative construction that is less than or equal to the U-factor, C-factor, or F-factor presented in Appendix A for the appropriate climate zone construction is equally acceptable. U-factors, C-factors, and F-factors that correspond to all the recommendations are presented in Appendix A.

Procedures to calculate U-factors and C-factors are presented in *ASHRAE Handbook—Fundamentals* (ASHRAE 2009), and expanded U-factor, C-factor, and F-factor tables are presented in Appendix A of ASHRAE/IES Standard 90.1 (ASHRAE 2010c).

Cautions

The design of building envelopes for durability, indoor environmental quality, and energy conservation should not create conditions of accelerated deterioration or reduced thermal performance or problems associated with moisture, air infiltration, or termites.

The following cautions should be incorporated into the design and construction of the building.

EN16 *Moisture Control* (Climate Zones: all)

Building envelope assemblies (see Figures 5-2a and 5-2b) should be designed to prevent wetting, high moisture content, liquid water intrusion, and condensation caused by diffusion of

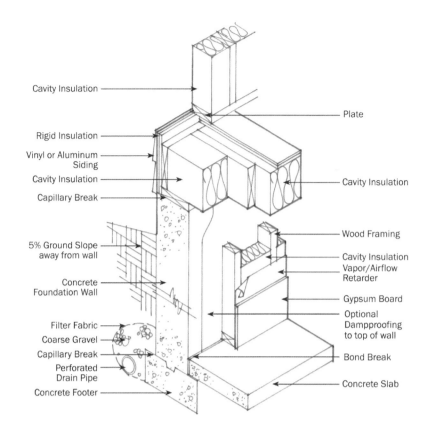

Figure 5-2a   (EN16) Moisture Control for Mixed Climates

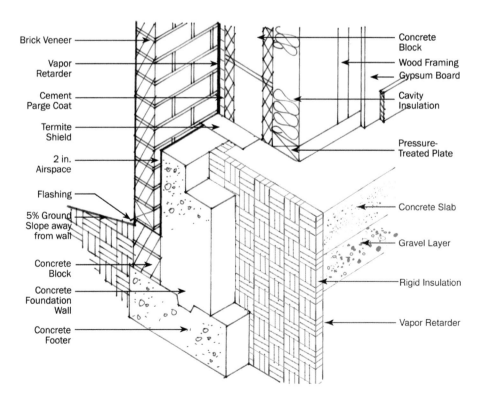

Figure 5-2b   (EN16) Moisture Control for Warm, Humid Climates

water vapor. See Chapter 24 of the *ASHRAE Handbook—Fundamentals* (ASHRAE 2009) for additional information.

EN17   *Thermal Bridging, Opaque Components* **(Climate Zones: all)**

Thermal bridging in opaque components occurs when continuous conductive elements connect internal and external surfaces. The adverse effects of thermal bridging are most notable in cold climates where frost can develop on internal surfaces and lead to water droplets when the indoor temperature increases. The solution to thermal bridging is to provide thermal breaks or continuous insulation. Common problem areas are parapets, foundations, and penetrations of insulation.

Figure 5-3a shows thermal bridging at a parapet. The problem is that a portion of the wall construction is extended to create a parapet that extends above the roof to ensure worker safety per local code requirements. Since the wall insulation is on the outer face of the structure, it does not naturally connect to the insulation at the roof structure. The solution is to wrap the parapet with continuous insulation in the appropriate locations, as shown in Figure 5-3b, or to build an independent parapet that periodically penetrates the roof insulation line to limit the thermal bridging effects.

A thermal bridge in a foundation is shown in Figure 5-4a. The connection between the below-grade and above-grade thermal protection is an oversight attributed to the structural elements being installed separately by different parties. To achieve the solution shown in Figure 5-4b, design and construction teams must make clear that action to establish thermal continuity of the insulation line is a performance requirement inclusive of all disciplines and all parties. The insulation above grade needs to be protected with a surface or coating that is weather resistant and abuse tolerant.

Penetrations of insulation in which metal structural members must protrude from the building in order to support an external shade or construction (balcony, signage, etc.) need to be insulated. In these cases, the insulation should wrap the protruding metal piece when it is within the indoor cavity, and an additional length of insulation should be provided on its connection in each direction in order to prevent excessive heat transfer from the metal into the internal wall cavity. A façade consultant can model these types of applications and advise on the various lengths and thicknesses of insulation are needed to limit adverse impacts from condensation within the wall cavity.

EN18   *Thermal Bridging, Fenestration* **(Climate Zones: all)**

Thermal bridging typically occurs at fenestration locations where well-insulated glazing abuts the opaque facade, whether through a metal mullion system or just framed into the wall. Windows that are installed out of the plane of the wall insulation are an example of this construction (Figure 5-5a).

The normal solution is not to rebuild the wall but to blow hot air against the window to increase the interior surface temperature of the frame and glazing, which increases the temperature difference across the glazing and reduces the interior film coefficient thermal resistance from 0.68 to 0.25 $h \cdot ft^2 \cdot °F/Btu$.

Careful specification is also necessary to ensure that framing of the glazed units also incorporates a thermal break. Installing the fenestration outside of the plane of the wall insulation defeats the thermal break in the window frame. Fenestration should be installed to align the frame thermal break with the wall thermal barrier (see Figure 5-5b). This minimizes the thermal bridging of the frame due to fenestration projecting beyond the insulating layers in the wall.

In colder climates, it is essential to select a glazing unit that will avoid condensation and frosting. This requires analysis to determine internal surface temperatures, since glass is a higher thermal conductor as compared to the adjacent wall in which it is mounted. There is a risk of condensation occurring on the inner face of the glass whenever the inner surface temperature approaches the room dew-point temperature.

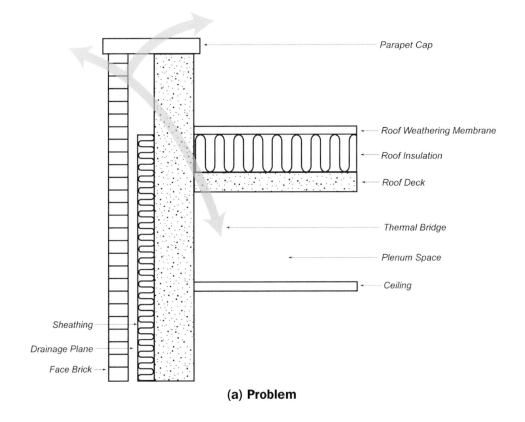

(a) Problem

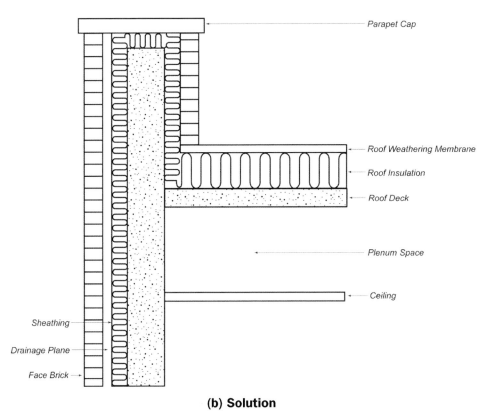

(b) Solution

Figure 5-3   (EN17) Thermal Bridges—Parapets

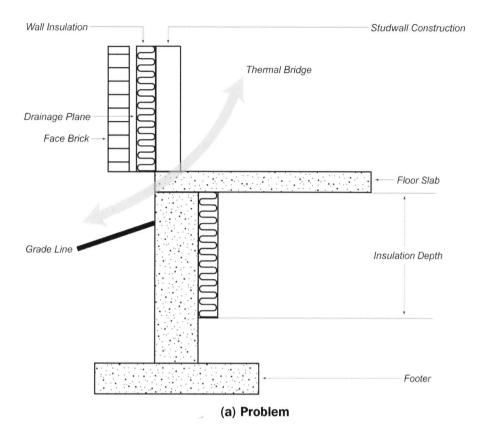

(a) Problem

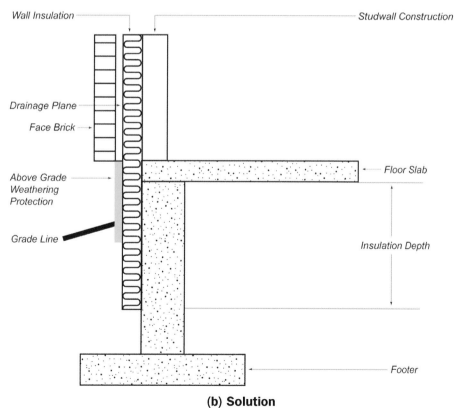

(b) Solution

Figure 5-4   (EN17) Thermal Bridges—Foundations

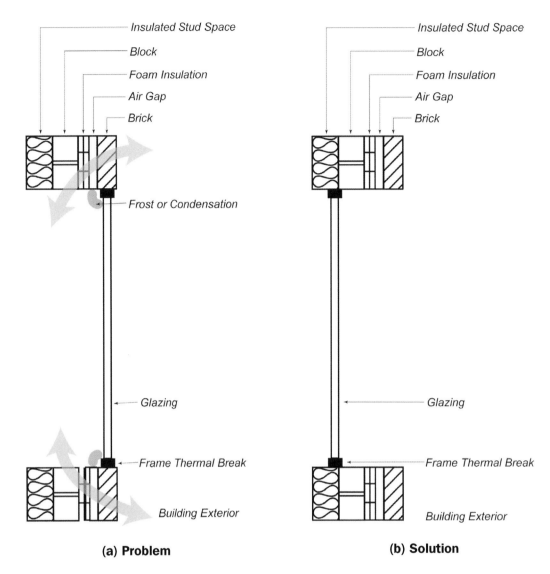

(a) **Problem**   (b) **Solution**

**Figure 5-5   (EN18) Thermal Break (a) at Window Frame and
(b) in Window Frame Aligned with Wall Insulation**

VERTICAL FENESTRATION

Good Design Practice

EN19   Vertical Fenestration Descriptions (**Climate Zones: all**)

Fenestration refers to the light-transmitting areas of a wall or roof, mainly windows and sky-lights but also including glass doors, glass block walls, and translucent plastic panels. Vertical fenestration includes sloped glazing if it has a slope equal to or more than 60° from the horizontal. If it slopes less than 60° from the horizontal, the fenestration falls in the skylight category. This means clerestories, roof monitors, and other such fenestration fall in the vertical category.

The recommendations for vertical fenestration are listed in Chapter 4 by climate zone. To be useful and consistent, the U-factors for windows should be measured over the entire window assembly, not just the center of glass. Look for a label that denotes the window rating is certified by the National Fenestration Rating Council (NFRC). The selection of high-performance window products should be considered separately for each orientation of the building and for daylighting and viewing functions.

To meet the solar heat gain coefficient recommendations for vertical fenestration in Chapter 4, use the SHGC multipliers for permanent projections as provided in Table 5.5.4.4.1 of ASHRAE/IES Standard 90.1-2010 (ASHRAE 2010c). These multipliers allow for a higher SHGC for vertical fenestration with overhangs.

EN20   *Window-to-Wall Ratio* (**Climate Zones: all**)

The window-to-wall ratio (WWR) is the percentage resulting from dividing the glazed area of the wall by the exterior wall area. A WWR for the floor-to-ceiling portion of the wall of less than 40%, in conjunction with the recommended values for U-factor and SHGC, contributes toward the 50% savings target of the entire building. A reduction in the overall WWR may further save energy, as long as daylight performance is not compromised, especially where fenestration is difficult to shade, such as on east- and west-oriented façades. Glazing reductions for energy conservation should only be made where they will not jeopardize views, daylighting, or passive solar strategies.

WINDOW DESIGN GUIDELINES FOR THERMAL CONDITIONS

Uncontrolled solar heat gain is a major cause of energy use for cooling in warmer climates and of thermal discomfort for occupants. Hot spots can also cause significant disruption to displacement ventilation HVAC systems. However, high indirect levels of daylight are critical for patient and staff well being. Appropriate configuration of windows, with external shading according to their orientation, is critical to a design that supports both energy efficiency as well as health and healing.

EN21   *Unwanted Solar Heat Gain Is Most Effectively Controlled on the Outside of the Building* (**Climate Zones: all**)

Significantly greater energy savings are realized when sun penetration is blocked before it enters the windows. Horizontal overhangs and shading systems at the top of the windows are most effective for south-facing façades and must continue beyond the width of the windows to adequately shade them (see Figure 5-6). Vertical fins oriented slightly north are most effective for east- and west-facing façades. Consider louvered or perforated sun control devices, especially in primarily overcast and colder climates, to prevent a totally dark appearance in those environments. Dynamic shading that moves with the angle of the sun is often the most effective solution to block unwanted direct sun, especially on the east and west façades. The benefits of these systems should be balanced with potential drawbacks, including first cost, life expectancy of the system, wind loads on buildings over three stories, and potential maintenance needs. See DL14 for more information on shading strategies.

EN22   *Operable vs. Fixed Windows* (**Climate Zones: ❷B ❸ ❹ ❺ ❻ ❼ ❽**)

Operable windows play a significant role in embracing the core idea of indoor-to-outdoor connection and reaching out to the outdoor environment and nature. Compared to buildings with fixed-position windows, buildings with well-designed operable window systems can provide energy conservation advantages in office buildings if occupants understand their appropriate use. The use of natural ventilation in healthcare facilities has long been disputed and is addressed in very different ways in facilities around the world. Some researchers and health professionals suggest that it is problematic, while others suggest that it is either neutral or beneficial.

Although operable windows offer the advantage of personal comfort control and beneficial connections to the environment, individual operation of the windows not in coordination with

$$\text{Projection Factor} = \frac{\text{Horizontal Projection}}{\text{Height Above Sill}}$$

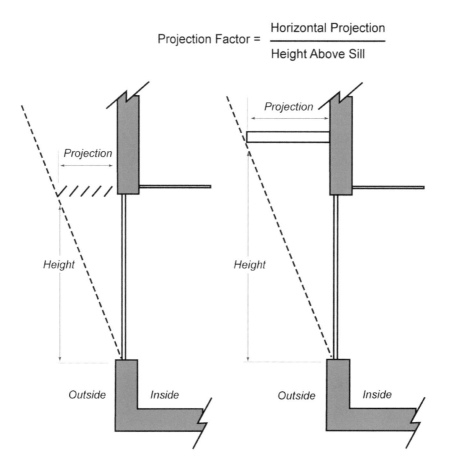

Figure 5-6   (EN21) Windows with Overhang

heating, ventilating, and air-conditioning (HVAC) system settings and requirements can have extremely negative impacts on the energy use of a building's system. Energy-efficient buildings with operable windows should strive for a high level of integration between envelope and HVAC system design. Mechanical systems should be shut off when windows are opened where critical pressurizations are not required to be maintained. If specific pressurizations are required, then the addition of operable windows will not improve energy efficiency, though they may be a positive amenity to patients and staff. Furthermore, operable windows can create infection control challenges and induce pollutants such as molds or pollens into the building. While the latter are not a significant problem for most populations, in-patient units (IPUs) and diagnostic and treatment (D&T) facilities typically have patients who are immunosuppressed and therefore are far more sensitive to these pollutants than the general population is. As a result, only nonclinical spaces can have operable windows in support of a mixed-mode ventilation system. Although small, there is some chance of problematic spores (e.g., aspergillus) moving from one part of a building with open windows to another part of a building where sensitive patients are located. Care should be taken to create appropriate mechanical separation between these types of spaces.

First, for spaces with operable windows, the envelope should be designed to take advantage of natural ventilation with well-placed, operable openings. A bottom window and a top window should be opened at the same time. This allows the stack effect to set up a convection current of airflow when the difference between the indoor and outdoor temperatures is 10°F or more. Operable window systems can be controlled manually or by button-based interlock through a centralized building management system. It should be noted that ASHRAE

Standard 62.1 (ASHRAE 2010b) requires that occupants have control over openings if they are used for natural ventilation (i.e., outdoor air intake), and the adaptive comfort model in ASHRAE Standard 55 (ASHRAE 2010a) requires that occupants have continuous control over the openings if they are used as part of a natural conditioning system.

Second, the mechanical system should use interlocks and window switches on operable windows to ensure that the HVAC system responds by shutting down in the affected zone if the window is opened. The window interlock zones need to be designed to correspond as closely as possible to the HVAC zones affected by the open windows.

Third, in some cases open windows at night may be used to remove thermal loads that have accumulated over the course of the day. Occupancy types best suited to this night flush or night purge include areas with no occupancy during the cool evening and early morning hours. To allow for this, the following conditions are required:

- Footprint: narrow floor plate and open-plan layout
- Operable windows controlled by a building management system that tracks the temperature of the slab, the temperature of the outdoors, and the external and internal relative humidities
- Solid slabs/exposed ceiling slabs in concrete structures
- Minimal concerns over building security risks due to open windows

Warm Climates

EN23 ***Building Form and Window Orientation*** **(Climate Zones: ❶ ❷ ③)**

South-facing glass can be more easily shielded than east- and west-facing glass. As a result, south-facing glass typically results in less solar heat gain and glare. During early building configuration studies and predesign, preference should be given to site layouts that permit elongating the building in the east-west direction and permit orienting more windows to the north and south. A good design strategy avoids areas of glass that do not contribute to the view from the building or to the daylighting of the space. If possible, configure the building to maximize north- and south-facing walls and glass by elongating the floor plan. Since sun control devices are less effective on the east and west façades, the solar penetration through the east- and west-facing glazing should be minimized. This can be done by reducing the area of glazing or, if the glass is needed for view or egress, by reducing the SHGC or by utilizing automated operable shading systems. For buildings where a predominantly east-west exposure is unavoidable, more aggressive energy conservation measures are required in other building components to achieve an overall 50% energy savings. See DL5 and DL6 for more information on building orientation and shape as they relate to daylighting strategies.

EN24 ***Glazing*** **(Climate Zones: ❶ ❷ ③)**

For north- and south-facing windows, select windows with low SHGCs and an appropriate visible transmittance (VT). These characteristics are captured in the light-to-solar gain (LSG) ratio, which is the ratio of VT to SHGC. The higher the LSG, the better the glazing is at admitting visible light without additional thermal gain. A glazing system with LSG > 1.5 will provide a good balance between daylighting and thermal control.

Certain window coatings, called "selective low-e," transmit the visible portions of the solar spectrum selectively and reject the nonvisible infrared sections. These glass and coating selections are important to providing a balance between visible light and solar heat gain. The placement of the coating on the glazing panes is dependent on whether the objective is to prevent heat loss in cold climates or to reduce external heat gain in hot climates. Windows with low SHGC values tend to have a low center-of-glass U-factor because they are designed to reduce the conduction of the solar heat gain absorbed on the outer layer of glass through to the inside of the window. Window manufacturers have products designed specifically for either condition.

Recommended values are for the entire fenestration assembly, in compliance with NFRC procedures, and are not simply center-of-glass values. Unfortunately, it can be difficult to obtain NRFC values for larger vertical fenestration systems such as curtain walls. In these cases, the designers should specify framing systems that are insulated and thermally-broken to ensure that system performance is not compromised.

EN25   *Obstructions and Plantings* (Climate Zones: all)

Adjacent taller buildings and trees, shrubs, or other plantings effectively shade glass on south, east, and west façades. For south-facing windows, remember that the sun is higher in the sky during the summer, so shading plants should be located high above the windows to effectively shade the glass. Also, be careful not to block south light that is being counted on for daylighting. While the shading effect of plants can reduce energy consumption, it doesn't impact equipment size. The sizing of HVAC equipment relies on the SHGC of the glass and shading system only. The glazing of fully shaded windows can be selected with higher SHGC ratings without increasing energy use.

The solar reflections from adjacent buildings with reflective surfaces (metal, windows, or especially reflective curtain walls) should be considered in the design. Such reflections may modify shading strategies, especially on the north façade.

Cold Climates

EN26   *Window Orientation* (Climate Zones: ④ ⑤ ⑥ ❼ ❽)

Only the south glass receives much sunlight during the cold winter months. If possible, maximize south-facing windows by elongating the floor plan in the east-west direction, and relocate windows to the south face. Careful configuration of overhangs or other simple solar control devices allow for passive heating when desired but prevent unwanted glare and solar overheating in the warmer months. To improve performance, dynamic or operable shading systems should be employed that achieve superior daylight harvesting and passive solar gains and also operate more effectively when facing east and west. Unless such operable shading systems are used, use of glass facing east and west should be significantly limited. Areas of glazing facing north should be optimized for daylighting and view and focus on low U-factors to minimize heat loss and maintain thermal comfort by considering triple glazing to eliminate drafts and discomfort. During early building configuration studies and predesign, preference should be given to sites that permit elongating the building in the east-west direction and that permit orienting more windows to the south. See DL14 for more information on building orientation and shape as they relate to daylighting strategies.

EN27   *Passive Solar* (Climate Zones: ④ ⑤ ⑥ ❼ ❽)

Passive solar energy-saving strategies should be limited to nonpermanently occupied spaces such as lobbies and circulation areas, unless those strategies are designed so that the occupants are not affected by direct beam radiation. Consider light-colored blinds, blinds within the fenestration, light shelves, or silk screen ceramic coating (frit) to control solar heat gain. In spaces where glare is not an issue, the usefulness of the solar heat gain collected by these windows can be increased by using hard massive and darker-colored floor surfaces, such as tile or concrete, in locations where the transmitted sunlight will fall. These floor surfaces absorb the transmitted solar heat gain and release it slowly over time, providing a more gradual heating of the structure. Consider higher SHGC and low-e glazing with optimally designed exterior overhangs.

EN28   *Glazing* (Climate Zones: ④ ⑤ ⑥ ❼ ❽)

Higher SHGCs are allowed in colder regions, but continuous horizontal overhangs are still necessary to block the high summer sun angles. As with warm climates, an LSG ratio of at least 1.5 is desirable to balance access to daylight and excessive solar gain, especially in parts of the building that have high internal loads. See EN29 for additional discussion of appropriate VT values by climate.

WINDOW DESIGN GUIDELINES FOR DAYLIGHTING

Good Design Practice

EN29   *Visible Transmittance* (Climate Zones: all)

Using daylight in place of electrical lighting significantly reduces the internal loads and saves cost on lighting and cooling power. In the U.S., it is estimated that 10% of the total energy generated in 24 hours is consumed by electrical lighting during daytime.

The amount of light transmitted in the visible range affects the view through the window, glare, and daylight harvesting. For the effective utilization of daylight, the VT of the glazing should be selected to admit the desired daylight while carefully balancing the WWR, shading systems, and fenestration orientation.

Higher VTs are useful in predominantly overcast climates. VTs below 0.50 may appear noticeably tinted and dim to occupants, and may degrade luminous quality, but may be necessary to prevent glare, especially on the east and west façades or for higher WWRs. Lower VTs may also be appropriate for other conditions of low sun angles or light-colored ground cover (such as snow or sand). Other techniques, such as adjustable blinds, may be used to handle intermittent glare conditions that are variable, but should be incorporated into the fenestration in such a way that daylighting is not compromised.

REFERENCES AND RESOURCES

ASHRAE. 2009. *ASHRAE Handbook—Fundamentals*. Atlanta: ASHRAE.

ASHRAE. 2010a. ANSI/ASHRAE Standard 55-2010, *Thermal Environmental Conditions for Human Occupancy*. Atlanta: ASHRAE.

ASHRAE. 2010b. ANSI/ASHRAE Standard 62.1-2010, *Ventilation for Acceptable Indoor Air Quality*. Atlanta: ASHRAE.

ASHRAE. 2010c. ANSI/ASHRAE/IES Standard 90.1-2010, *Energy Standard for Buildings Except Low-Rise Residential Buildings*. Atlanta: ASHRAE.

ASTM. 2010. ASTM E779-10, *Standard Test Method for Determining Air Leakage Rate by Fan Pressurization*. West Conshohocken, PA: ASTM International.

ASTM. 2011a. ASTM E1980-11, *Standard Practice for Calculating Solar Reflectance Index of Horizontal and Low-Sloped Opaque Surfaces*. West Conshohocken, PA: ASTM International.

ASTM. 2011b. ASTM E2178-11, *Standard Test Method for Air Permeance of Building Materials*. West Conshohocken, PA: ASTM International.

Brown, G.Z., J. Kline, G. Livingston, B. McDonald, C. Smith, M. Wilkerson, J. Brickman, and D. Staczek. 2005. Daylighting hospital patient rooms in Northwest hospitals. A joint study of the University of Oregon's Energy Studies in Buildings Laboratory and Zimmmer, Gunsul, and Frasca Architects LLP. (Summary located at Betterbricks: http://www.better-bricks.com/graphics/assets/documents/Daylighting_Patient_Rooms_brochure_final.pdf).

DOE. 2004. Energy Conservation Standards for Distribution Transformers. Advanced Notice of Proposed Rulemaking, July 29, 2004. U.S. Department of Energy, Washington, DC.

NEMA. 2002. NEMA TP 1-2002, *Guide for Determining Energy Efficiency for Distribution Transformers*. Rosslyn, Virginia: National Electrical manufacturers Association.

U.S. Congress. 2005. Energy Policy Act of 2005. PL 109–58. United States Congress, Washington, DC.

DAYLIGHTING

Daylighting is an essential component of high-performance healthcare facilities. It is an important energy-efficiency strategy, as well as a factor in the health of building occupants. When properly designed, a positive synergy of energy conservation and improved health is possible.

GENERAL RECOMMENDATIONS

DL1   *Integrated Daylighting Design* (Climate Zones: all)

Successful daylighting requires an integrated approach to design and affects and is influenced by each phase of the design process. Daylighting strategies drive building shape and form and must be integrated with the design from structural, mechanical, electrical, and architectural standpoints. This integrated approach essentially makes the whole building a luminaire, because a well-designed daylighted building is the most efficient luminaire possible, providing illumination with far less energy input than is required of electric sources.

While the daylighting strategies recommended in this Guide have been successfully implemented in buildings before, most daylighting strategies are generic and apply to all building types. Because of the challenge of locating occupied spaces on the perimeter of the building, daylighting has not been implemented widely in the healthcare industry. Patient rooms require occupancy-specific lighting conditions, which also reduces opportunities for daylighting. The following tips and strategies are designed to address healthcare-specific opportunities and to overcome these types of obstacles.

DL2   *Consider Daylighting Early in the Design Process* (Climate Zones: all)

In healthcare facilities, the building program and medical planning are primary drivers of the shape and footprint of the building. Planning criteria often result in the creation of compact, deep floor plates, while daylighting strategies attempt the opposite by articulating and narrowing the floor plate.

The building footprint configuration is established early in the design process, and building depth is locked in early, along with the potential for future daylighting. Building depth can significantly impact future daylighting and other design upgrades and improvements. Deep floor plates are a common barrier to daylighting and naturally ventilating existing buildings. Therefore, it is important to integrate daylight design criteria before the footprint is locked in, so that the building can meet its full energy savings potential. It also shows that medical planning and energy-efficient design are deeply integrated, as they both impact the shape and footprint and are integral to shaping of the framework of the building. Daylighting strategies impact each phase of design as described below.

Predesign (PD). Daylighting strategies focus on massing studies and the shaping of the floor plate. The goal is to minimize depth and maximize access to windows and daylight by strategically placing light wells, shafts, and atria and orienting fenestration in a predominantly north-south direction. An emphasis is placed on maximizing the amount of occupied space that has access to windows and minimizing the distance from the building core to the perimeter. This can create conflicts with programmatic and logistical requirements, such as keeping staff circulation and material transportation distances short. However, these are not necessarily compromised to gain the benefits of daylight.

Schematic Design (SD). Daylighting strategies focus on the interior and spatial considerations to optimize daylight penetration, define ceiling height, and layout and partition wall transparency with clerestory windows for borrowed light. Planning focuses on coordinating space types that require daylight and views and location them along the perimeter.

Design Development (DD). Daylighting strategies focus on envelope design to optimize quantity and quality of daylight while minimizing solar gains. Interior design focuses on surface reflectivity and optimizing furniture layout in alignment with visual and thermal comfort requirements.

Construction Documents (CD). Coordination of electrical lighting includes the placement of photo and occupancy sensors for controlling automated daylight switching and dimmable ballasts.

DL3 *Use a Climate-Responsive Approach to Optimize Design* (Climate Zones: all)

This Guide is intended for use in achieving energy savings of 50% without requiring the designers to perform energy modeling, but energy and daylighting modeling programs make evaluating energy-saving trade-offs faster and daylighting designs far more precise.

A climate-responsive design approach takes into consideration the external environmental factors that influence building performance at a particular locale. In the case of daylighting, these considerations include solar availability, amount of sunny versus cloudy daylight hours, solar paths and patterns, typical weather conditions, and unique site considerations such as shading effect of adjacent structures.

DL4 *Space Types, Layout, and Daylight* (Climate Zones: all)

Daylight is a key requirement for all occupied spaces in healthcare facilities. However, the individual lighting needs are different for staff, patients, and for the public. The purpose of this Guide is to identify the spaces that lend themselves best to daylight harvesting and energy conservation, and to recommend layout strategies that allow spaces to be located at the perimeter of the building. The potential for energy saving through daylighting varies and depends on program and occupied space types, which can be broadly characterized by the following four categories:

- *Patient Rooms and Recovery Areas.* Patient rooms by nature (and often by code) require quality views and daylight. In patient rooms, lighting level requirements are typically low, and daylight control is driven by the patient's condition and individual needs. Prioritizing response to patient needs makes the patient room an unreliable space for maximization daylight and unsuitable as a source for daylight harvesting and energy savings.
- *Diagnostic and Treatment Spaces.* Typically dominated by planning criteria, such as circulation distance, proximity, and adjacency requirements, operating rooms and procedure rooms are often located at the core of a deep floor plate with no access to views and daylight. Breaking up the D&T area requires careful planning, but locating these spaces at the building perimeter for daylighting and views is feasible without surrendering flexibility The Chapter 3 sidebar "Impacts of Building Shape and Configuration" features an example in the Rikshospitalet hospital.
- *Staff Areas (Exam Rooms, Nurse Stations, and Offices).* Locating staff spaces on the building perimeter is essential to staff performance, and a design strategy that facilitates efforts to conserve energy by reducing electric light and cooling loads.
- *Public Spaces (Lobbies, Reception, Waiting Areas, Transitional Spaces).* These spaces provide the best opportunity for high ceilings with high, large-scale fenestration and offer the greatest potential for daylight harvesting and energy savings due to their depth and height.

The following recommendations apply to spaces that are not located on the building perimeter but allow for additional energy savings if they are designed to follow specific rules.

- *Internal Corridors.* In single-story buildings or on top-level floors, where sidelighting is not available, toplighting should be used to provide daylight for corridors and contiguous spaces. Make sure that nurse stations, which are frequently placed in niches of circulation areas and waiting areas, have access to daylight and views.
- *Conference Rooms.* Conference rooms are densely populated spaces that build up high interior heat loads for only a limited period of time. When located on the perimeter, the interior loads and solar radiation penetrating the perimeter wall accumulate, leading to escalation of peak loads and oversizing of HVAC. As a strategy to minimize peak loads,

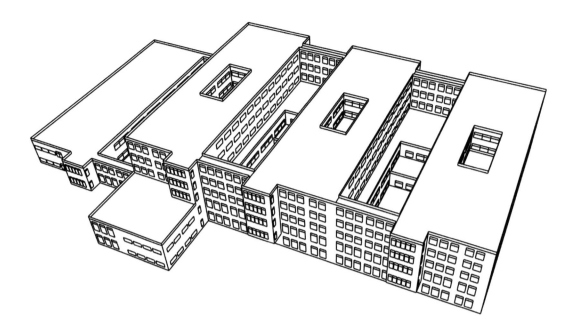

Figure 5-7   (DL6) Articulated Footprints
Source: University of Washington, Integrated Design Lab

conference rooms should be located on north-façade perimeters only, or in-board, avoiding west-, south-, and east-facing perimeter walls. This approach is also supported by prioritizing perimeter space for use by permanently occupied spaces, which make better use of daylight and views than conference rooms, which remain unoccupied in many cases.

From an energy performance standpoint, public areas and staff spaces are the most beneficial spaces for harvesting daylight, which underscores the importance of locating these spaces on the perimeter, preferably in a north- and south-facing configuration. Although patient rooms in hospitals typically have large fenestration and occupy a significant part of the building perimeter, they can't be considered as effective sources for energy savings.

DL5   *Building Orientation and Daylight* **(Climate Zones: all)**

Effective daylighting begins with selecting the correct solar orientation of the building and the building's exterior spaces. For most spaces, the vertical façades that provide daylighting should be oriented within 15° of north-south. Sidelighted daylighting solutions can work successfully for other orientations as well, but they require a more sophisticated approach to shading that is beyond the scope of the recommendations presented in this Guide.

Context and Site. Ensure that apertures are not shaded by adjacent buildings or trees or by components of the small healthcare facility itself.

DL6   *Building Shape and Daylight* **(Climate Zones: all)**

Best daylighting results are achieved by limiting the depth of the floor plate and minimizing the distance between the exterior wall and any interior space. Narrowing the floor plate in most cases results in introducing courtyards and articulating the footprint for better daylight penetration (see Figure 5-7).

Optimizing the building shape for daylighting means balancing the exterior surface exposed to daylight, and self-shading the building mass to avoid direct-beam radiation. Effective daylighting requires a maximum amount of occupied area to be located within a minimum distance to the building perimeter.

The following design criteria are recommended for achieving 50% energy savings:

- *Diagnostic and Treatment Block.* Shape the building footprint to allow for all space within 15 ft of the perimeter to be greater than or equal to 40% of the total floor plate area.
- *Inpatient Units.* Ensure that 75% of the occupied space, excluding patient rooms, is located within 20 ft of the perimeter wall. Where toplighting is not an option, the floor plate should be targeted to achieve a depth of 60 ft.

For sunny climates, designs can be evaluated on a sunny day at the summer solar peak. For overcast climates, a typical overcast day should be used to evaluate the system. Typically, the glazing-to-floor ratio percentage will increase for overcast climates. Daylighting can still work for a small healthcare building in an overcast climate. Overcast climates can produce diffuse skies, which create good daylighting conditions and minimize glare and heat gain.

Daylighting systems need to provide the correct lighting levels. To meet the criteria, daylighting modeling and simulation may be required. Daylighting systems should be designed to meet the following criteria:

- Under clear conditions, to provide sufficient daylight, illuminance levels should achieve a minimum of 25 fc but no more than 250 fc.
- Under overcast conditions, daylighted spaces should achieve a daylight factor of 2 but no more than 20.

The same criteria for lighting quality and quantity apply to both electric lighting and daylighting. When the criteria cannot be met with daylighting, electric lighting should be used. The objective is to maximize daylighting and minimize electric lighting. To maximize daylighting without oversizing the fenestration, in-depth analysis may be required.

DL7 Window-to-Wall Ratio (Climate Zones: all)

There are many considerations to window configuration and sizing. Window configuration and size should first follow interior-driven design criteria like occupancy type, requirements for view, daylight and outdoor connectivity. Secondly, the design should consider daylight availability, peak cooling load, and energy use, which may limit window size and location to keep the mechanical systems from being used to cool excess solar heat gain. For healthcare projects to achieve 50% savings, generally the floor-to-ceiling WWR should not exceed 40%.

DL8 Sidelighting, Ceiling, and Window Height (Climate Zones: all)

For good daylighting in cellular-type spaces, a minimum ceiling height of 9.0 ft is recommended. In public spaces, which extend to greater depth, such as waiting areas and lobbies, ceiling height, at least partially, should be 10 to 12 ft. When daylighting is provided exclusively through sidelighting, it is important to elevate the ceiling on the perimeter and extend glazing to the ceiling. Additional reflectance to increase lighting levels can be achieved by sloping the ceiling up toward the outside wall (see Figure 5-8).

High continuous windows generally are more effective than individual ("punched") or vertical slot windows for distributing light deeper into the space and provide greater visual comfort for the occupants. Aligning the top or head of the windows with the ceiling line also reduces contrast between the window and ceiling and produces the greatest penetration for daylighting.

DL9 Sidelighting, Clerestory Windows (Climate Zones: all)

In cases where it is not possible to place windows in exterior walls for programmatic or functional reasons, clerestory windows or window bands should be considered for daylighting. Daylight delivered above 7 ft at clerestory level, delivers the highest illuminance level available through sidelighting (see Figure 5-9).

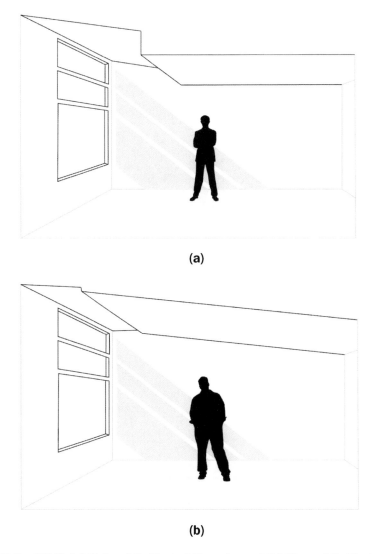

(a)

(b)

Figure 5-8 (DL8) (a) Raised Ceiling at Façade and (b) Sloped Ceiling at Façade

DL10   Sidelighting, Borrowed Light **(Climate Zones: all)**

Borrowed light is an effective strategy for delivering daylight to corridors that are located behind spaces on the building perimeter. The corridor wall frequently blocks and prevents daylight from entering deeper into the building. The corridor partitioning wall provides significant opportunities to daylight the corridor though borrowed light. Partitions between a perimeter space and a corridor that have a depth-to-height ratio of no greater than 2:5:1 should be designed with clerestory windows or window bands (see Figure 5-10).

DL11   Sidelighting, Wall-to-Wall Windows **(Climate Zones: all)**

Raising the window levels to ceiling level is the first priority for deepening daylight penetration. However, maximizing the window width and providing additional glazing on an adjacent wall goes a long way toward balancing light levels in the room and to mitigating contrast. By extending the window width from wall to wall, the adjacent partitioning walls receive greater exposure and act as indirect sources of daylight, while also achieving greater depth of daylight penetration.

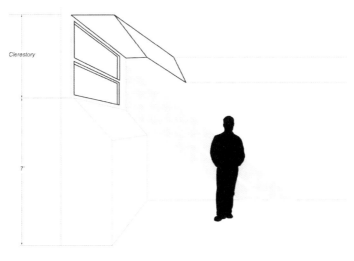

Figure 5-9   (DL9) Clerestory

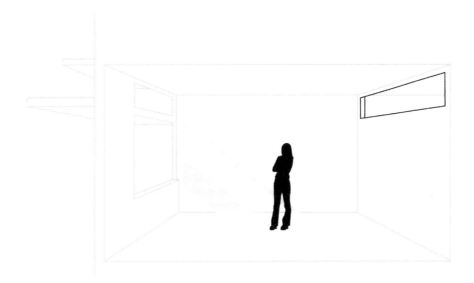

Figure 5-10   (DL10) Borrowed Light in Corridor

Additional daylight and a wider range of view can be gained by making transparent the first 2 to 3 ft of the cellular partitioning walls where they meet the perimeter wall. This enlarges the daylighted portion of the room enclosure by 50% to 60% per space (see Figure 5-11).

DL12   *Sidelighting, Punched Windows* **(Climate Zones: all)**

In cases where window size is limited, and punched windows can't be avoided, special care should be taken in placing the aperture to avoid high contrasts and lowering visual comfort.

To ensure that daylight is maximized and light levels are distributed evenly, the window aperture should align with either of the partitioning walls. This mitigates contrast differences, maximizes the depth of daylight reach, and also makes the space appear larger (Figure 5-12).

DL13   *Toplighting* **(Climate Zones: all)**

Toplighting draws from zenithal skylight, which makes toplighting the most effective source of daylight. Toplighting therefore requires smaller apertures than sidelighting to achieve the same

Figure 5-11   (DL11) Exterior Wall Section and Plan

Figure 5-12   (DL12) Punched Window Placed Next to Partition Wall

level of light. In healthcare facilities, toplighting is recommended for use in occupied spaces that have no access to sidelight. Toplighting is useful in circulation areas and contiguous spaces that are used for nurse stations and waiting areas or lobbies. Toplighting in circulation areas needs careful coordination with overhead ductwork and lighting but does not limit future flexibility as required in program spaces.

Toplighting is a highly effective strategy that not only provides excellent daylight and way finding support, but also saves energy for electrical lighting and cooling. The limitation of toplighting is that it can be used only in single-story designs or on the top floors of multistory designs. Two types of toplighting can be distinguished: monitors and skylights. A monitor uses a ceiling aperture, but the glazing is oriented vertically; a skylight's glazing is oriented horizontally. Toplighting also has limitations in large hospitals due to a lack of access to the roof from the majority of the interior spaces in the common multistory building configuration.

DL14   Toplighting, Thermal Transmittance (Climate Zones: ❶ ❷ ❸)

Use north-facing monitors for toplighting whenever possible in hot climates to eliminate excessive solar heat gain and glare. Typically, north-facing monitors have 1/6 the heat gain of skylights.

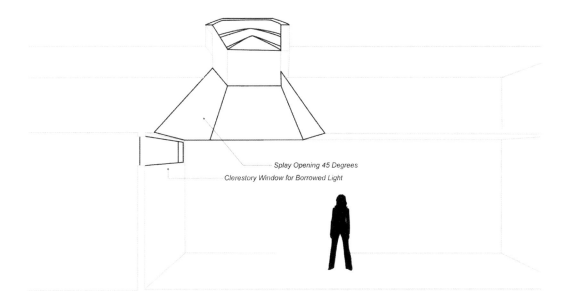

Splay Opening 45 Degrees
Clerestory Window for Borrowed Light

Figure 5-13   (DL13) Roof Skylight Section

Reduce thermal gain during the cooling season by using skylights with a low overall thermal transmittance (U-factor). Insulate the skylight curb above the roof line with continuous rigid insulation. Shade skylights with exterior/interior sun control, such as screens, baffles, or fins.

DL15   ***Toplighting, Thermal Transmittance*** (Climate Zones: ○ ⑤ ⑥ ❼ ❽)

In moderate and cooler climates, use either north- or south-facing monitors for toplighting but not east or west. East-west glazing adds excessive summer heat gain and makes it difficult to control direct solar gain. Monitors with operable glazing may also help provide natural ventilation in temperate seasons when air conditioning is not in use. Typically, north-facing monitors have 1/6 the heat gain of skylights.

Reduce summer heat gain as well as winter heat loss by using skylights with a low overall thermal transmittance. Use a skylight frame that has a thermal break to prevent excessive heat loss/gain and winter moisture condensation on the frame. Insulate the skylight curb above the roof line with continuous rigid insulation.

Shade south-facing monitors with exterior/interior sun control, such as screens, baffles, or fins. As shown in Figure 5-13, splay the skylight opening at 45° to maximize daylight distribution and minimize glare.

DL16   ***Shading Systems to Eliminate Direct Beam Radiation*** (Climate Zones: all)

Eliminating uncontrolled, direct solar radiation prevents thermal discomfort and glare and is essential for good daylight quality. This is especially critical in patient and staff spaces, but less critical for some public spaces and corridors. Strategies should be used that bounce, redirect, and filter sunlight so that direct radiation does not directly enter the space.

The sun is a moving source of energy with constantly changing directions and intensity of light and heat radiation. Exterior walls should be designed to minimize the solar heat load but maximize glare-free daylight under permanently changing conditions. The goal is to maximize the light-to-solar-heat-gain ratio for every minute of the day.

Shading systems are designed to reduce solar radiation. However, in most cases they also inadvertently cause loss of valuable daylight. As a result, the electric lights are switched on during the peak time of day, causing cooling load and power consumption to peak and driving HVAC sizing excessively/uncontrollably. This explains why, in the process of developing a

Dynamic Glazing—Electrochromic Windows

Electrochromic (EC) windows are windows that can be darkened or lightened electrically so that they can be operated in response to daylight availability. This allows for variable control of the light and heat that passes through the windows, which has the potential to reduce building energy consumption and increase user acceptance of daylighting in buildings. EC windows are best suited for west- and east-facing facades where solar gain is highly variable and subject to frequent control needs.

EC windows have a "default" state (most often clear, although it can be tinted) and a small voltage applied to the windows will cause them to change (i.e., darken or lighten). This technical performance is achieved by combining different layers of materials. The essential functionality of the window results from the transport of ions from an ion-storage layer, through an ion-conducting layer, and into an EC layer. The presence of the ions in the EC layer changes the optical properties of the glass, causing it to absorb more (or less) light. In other words, instead of the glass having a single tint/color, the glass has a variety of tint states. To change the state of the window, a voltage is applied across the two conducting layers. To reverse the process, the voltage is removed, driving the ions in the opposite direction, out of the EC layer, through the ion-conducting layer, and into the ion-storage layer. As the ions migrate out of the EC layer, the EC layer changes state, and the window returns to its default state.

EC glass can meet the window U-factors recommended in this Guide while varying the visible transmittance from 62% to 2% and the solar heat gain coefficient from 0.47 to 0.09. The U.S. Department of Energy estimates that EC window systems are capable of providing up to 20% savings in operating costs, 24% reduction in peak demand, and 25% decrease in the size of HVAC systems. A 2006 California Energy Commission study on EC windows estimated a lighting energy savings of about 44%, compared to a reference case with no daylighting controls (CEC 2006). Also, peak demand reduction of 19% to 26% related to window cooling loads occurred on clear sunny days.

Historically, EC windows have been difficult to cost justify, but as new manufacturing capabilities come online, costs are decreasing. The challenges in fabricating EC windows lie in achieving lower production costs, high durability, and practical panel sizes. However, great strides are being made, particularly in manufacturing and material science, that are reducing the cost and improving the functionality of EC glass. For example, newer units can have multiple tint states, not just "on/off", allowing greater tenability in the daylight system. In a typical scenario, EC windows may be cost competitive with other external shading devices. It is important to understand the full impact that EC windows can have on a building, including the downsizing of HVAC cooling equipment.

(continued next page)

shading strategy, it becomes inevitable to acknowledge and include daylighting as an integral component of the system.

The effectiveness of shading systems varies widely and depends on the system's ability to adapt to changing conditions. This explains why dynamic systems that operate on demand and track the path of the sun are significantly more successful than static/fixed systems.

To obtain best overall performance results, the selection of the right shading type should be based on considerations concerning both heat load and the ability to facilitate daylight and views.

Fixed External Shading. Solar heat gain is most effectively controlled when penetration is blocked before entering the building. Disadvantages of exterior shading systems can be accessibility issues for maintaining and cleaning the façade. Fixed devices are designed to perform

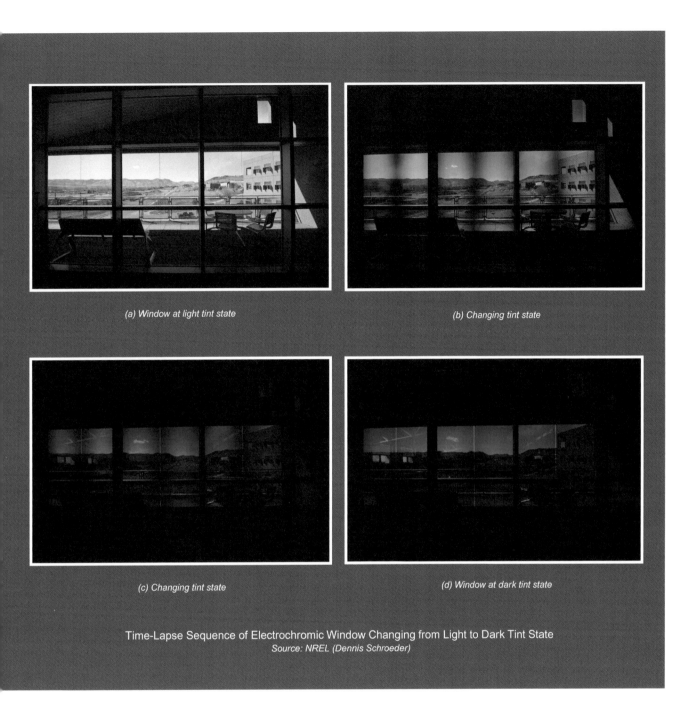

(a) Window at light tint state

(b) Changing tint state

(c) Changing tint state

(d) Window at dark tint state

Time-Lapse Sequence of Electrochromic Window Changing from Light to Dark Tint State
Source: NREL (Dennis Schroeder)

best at peak hours, but work significantly less effectively outside the optimized time range. There are different configurations of exterior shading (see Figure 5-14).

- *Horizontal Devices.* Overhangs and other sunshades, soffits, awnings, and trellises respond well to steep solar angles and work best on south-facing façades. Passive solar gains are possible in winter, however additional interior shading will be required to counter glare. Overhangs should continue beyond the width of the window and should be located directly above the window at the head. If overhangs are located higher than the window head, the horizontal projection must be extended.
- *Vertical Devices.* Vertical screens or horizontal louvers configured in vertical arrays work when oriented south, west, or east.

Dynamic Shading Systems. Dynamic or operable systems are the most effective shading devices available, as they don't have to compromise on one single position to minimize heat

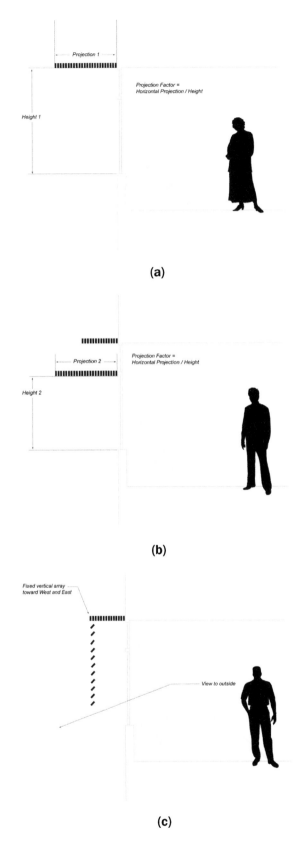

(a)

(b)

(c)

Figure 5-14 (DL14) Fixed External Shading in (a and b) Horizontal Configuration and (c) Vertical Configuration

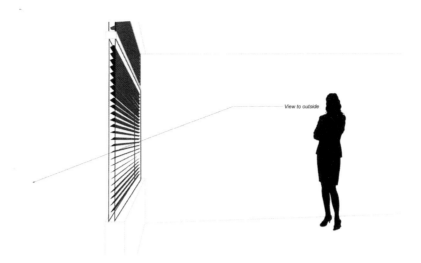

Figure 5-15   (DL14) Operable Louvers Located between Glass Panes

gain and maximize daylight. The most common technologies used are louvered systems and fabric-based roller shades. These systems are able to reduce solar heat gain by as much as 80% to 90%, while concurrently allowing for daylight and views. In addition, these systems can be effective in shading east- and west-oriented glazing, which is difficult for fixed systems. Operable systems are motorized, controlled either manually or automatically, and can be driven by solar tracking technology (see Figure 5-15).

Exterior Systems. On the exterior, operable systems are less commonly used than fixed systems, due to higher maintenance and vulnerability in windy conditions. Ideally, best applications are found in double-skin façade systems, a rapidly emerging technology in which accessibility is easier and weather protection allows for more lightweight solutions.

- *Interstitial Systems* feature operable louvers integrated with the insulated glazing unit (IGU) and located between the glass panes. Louvers are rotated, raised, and lowered electrically. Interstitial systems are a clean, tidy solution with good accessibility for application in healthcare environments. High-performance glass configuration can require coordination to avoid conflicts caused by potential scratching of coating in positions two or three.

- *Dynamic Glazing.* A recent technology in architectural glazing is dynamic glazing, which uses electrochromic or thermochromic film laminated into the glass assembly to allow a variation of LSG in response to solar exposure.

Internal Shading Systems. Fixed interior shades or operable roller shade systems are typically used to filter light to mitigate glare or to ensure thermal comfort against direct solar radiation that escapes the exterior shading devices. Internal shades use fabrics with various levels of transmissivity to reduce heat radiation and provide thermal comfort and glare protection.

Internal shading should not be considered as a strategy for improving energy performance. Since the heat has already entered the space, internal shades do not contribute to reducing cooling loads and are useless for downsizing mechanical systems. Interior light shelves can also act as internal shades, but they are not a recommended choice for healthcare buildings due to cleanability issues.

Automated or Manual Operation. The success of daylighted spaces depends on how occupants interact with the daylighting system. This is particularly true for blinds or shades that are available for adjustment by occupants. Occupants are motivated to close the blinds but not to reopen them. Occupants adjust blinds for the long term. If blinds are left closed, the daylighting potential will not be realized. Automated systems allow user override but can be programmed to reset themselves to their system/performance-based position.

Also, if temporary darkening of a specific space is not functionally required, do not install shades or blinds on the daylighting glass. Unnecessary blinds result in reduced performance, increased first costs, and higher long-term maintenance expenses.

Daylight Shading Control for Special Activities. If a space requires darkening for audio-visual or other functions, consider motorized roller shades or motorized vertical blinds for apertures that are out of reach. This may seem to result in higher maintenance costs, but such controls can have the opposite effect. The mechanical stress placed on manual operators by personnel (because of uneven cranking) limits the effective life of these devices to less than 10 years. The inconvenience associated with the process also results in a number of these shades being left closed. Motorized shades, which cost more up front, provide operators with greater ease of operation and result in a better-performing daylighting design. Some motorized devices can also be programmed to reset in the open position at the beginning of each day.

TV monitors or LCD projectors require that the light level at the specific location of the screen fall in the range of 5 to7 fc for optimum contrast. Slightly higher levels (7 to 15 fc) should still provide acceptable light levels for the visual aids, but the reduced contrast will make them harder to read.

As an option to shading the daylighting apertures, consider locating the screen or monitor in a part of the room that has less daylight and does not produce glare on the screen.

DL17 *Interior Finishes for Daylighting* (Climate Zones: all)

Select light colors for interior walls and ceilings to increase light reflectance and reduce lighting and daylighting requirements. The color of the ceiling, walls, floor, and furniture have a major impact on the effectiveness of the daylighting strategy. When considering finish surfaces, install light colors (white is best) to ensure the daylight is reflected throughout the space.

Consider a ceiling tile or surface that has a high reflectivity. Make sure that the ceiling tile reflectance includes the fissures within the acoustical tiles, as these irregularities affect the amount of light absorbed. Do not assume that the color of a tile alone dictates its reflectance. When selecting a tile, specify a minimum reflectivity. Most manufactures will list the reflectance as if it were the paint color reflectance. The commissioning authority (CxA) should verify the reflectance. See EL1 for additional information on interior finishes.

DL18 *Outdoor Surface Reflectance* (Climate Zones: all)

Consider the reflectance of the roofs, sidewalks, and other surfaces in front of the glazing areas. The use of lighter roofing colors can increase daylighting concentration and, in some cases, can increase indoor illuminance levels to reduce power consumption for electrical lighting.

High-albedo roofs reflect heat instead of absorbing it to lower the heat load and keep the building cooler. Use caution however, when locating light-colored walkways or surfaces in front of floor-to-ceiling glazing. Light-colored surfaces improve daylighting, but can also cause unwanted reflections and glare that impacts interior spaces.

DL19 *Calibration and Commissioning* (Climate Zones: all)

Even a few days of occupancy with poorly calibrated controls can lead to permanent overriding of the system and loss of savings. All lighting controls must be calibrated and commissioned after the finishes are completed and the furnishings are in place. Most photosensors require daytime and nighttime calibration sessions. The photosensor manufacturer and the quality assurance (QA) provider should be involved in calibration. Document the calibration and commissioning (Cx) settings, and plan for future recalibration as part of the maintenance program.

DL20 *Dimming Controls* (Climate Zones: all)

In all regularly-occupied daylighted spaces, such as staff areas, continuously dim rather than switch electric lights in response to daylight to minimize occupant distraction. Specify dimming ballasts that dim to at least 20% of full output, with the ability to turn OFF when daylighting provides sufficient illuminance. Provide a means and a convenient location to override daylighting controls in spaces that are intentionally darkened to use overhead projectors or slides. The daylighting control system and photosensor should include a 15-minute time delay or other means to avoid cycling caused by rapidly changing sky conditions, and a one-minute fade rate to change the light levels by dimming. Automatic multilevel daylight switching may be used in nonregularly occupied environments, such as hallways, storage, restrooms, lounges, and lobbies.

DL21   Photosensor Placement and Lighting Layout (Climate Zones: all)

Correct photosensor placement is essential. Consult daylighting references or work with the photosensor manufacturer for proper location. Mount the photosensors in a location that closely simulates the light level (or can be set by being proportional to the light level) at the work plane. Depending on the daylighting strategy, photosensor controls should be used to dim particular logical groupings of lights. Implement a lighting fixture layout and control wiring plan that complements the daylighting strategy. In sidelighted spaces, locate luminaires in rows parallel to the window wall, and wire each row separately. Because of the strong difference in light that will occur close to the window and away from the window, having this individual control by bank will help balance out the space. In a space that has a skylight, install one photosensor that controls all the perimeter lights and a second that controls all the lights within the skylight well.

DL22   Photosensor Specifications (Climate Zones: all)

Photosensors should be specified for the appropriate illuminance range (indoor or outdoor) and must achieve a slow, smooth linear dimming response from the dimming ballasts.

In a closed-loop system, the interior photocell responds to the combination of daylight and electric light in the daylighted area. The best location for the photocell is above an unobstructed location, such as the middle of the space. If using a lighting system that provides an indirect component, mount the photosensor at the same height as the luminaire or in a location that is not affected by the uplight from the luminaire.

In an open-loop system, the photocell responds only to daylight levels but is still calibrated to the desired light level received on the work surface. The best location for the photosensor is inside the skylight well or adjacent to vertical glazing.

DL23   Select Compatible Light Fixtures (Climate Zones: all)

First consider the use of indirect lighting fixtures that more closely represent the same effect as daylighting. Indirect lighting spreads light over the ceiling surface, which then reflects the light to the task locations; with the ceiling as the light source, indirect lighting is more uniform and has less glare.

In addition, insist on compatibility between ballast, lamps, and controls. Ensure that the lamps can be dimmed and that the dimming ballasts, sensors, and controls will operate as a system.

REFERENCES AND RESOURCES

Burpee, H., J. Loveland, M. Hatten, and S. Price. 2009. High-performance hospital partnerships: Reaching the 2030 challenge and improving the health and healing environment. *ASHE International Conference on Health Facility Planning, Design, and Construction, March 8–11, Phoenix, AZ*.

CEC. 2006. Monitored energy performance of electrochromic windows controlled for daylight and visual comfort. CEC-500-2006-052-AT8. California Energy Commission, Sacramento, CA.

Lee, E.S., M. Yazdanian, and S.E. Selkowitz. 2004. The Energy-Savings Potential of Electrochromic Windows in the U.S. Commercial Buildings Sector. LBNL-54966; Building Technologies Program, Environmental Energy Technologies Division, Lawrence Berkeley National Laboratory, Berkeley, CA.

Pradinuk, R. 2008. Doubling daylight. *Sustainable Healthcare Architecture*. R. Guenther and G. Vittori, eds. Hoboken, NJ: John Wiley & Sons.

Rudolph, S.E., J. Dieckmann, and J. Brodrick. 2009. Technologies for smart windows. *ASHRAE Journal* July:104–6.

ELECTRIC LIGHTING DESIGN

INTERIOR LIGHTING

Quality lighting has been shown in recent studies (Joseph 2006) to improve the health of occupants and staff, and to improve their overall experience within the healthcare facility. It can assist visual acuity and proper photobiological stimulation, reduce risk of fall and injury, and provide a consistently pleasing environment of care.

In addition, interior lighting can comprise between 10%–15% of a healthcare facility's total energy use. Good lighting design costs less to operate and maintain. It can increase energy conservation and contribute to a significant reduction in energy use and internal cooling load.

Good Design Practice

EL1   Electrical Lighting Design for Healthcare Facilities (Climate Zones: all)

The whole-building lighting power density (LPD) metric from ASHRAE/ASHE Standard 90.1 represents an average LPD for the entire building. This metric accommodates individual spaces that have higher power densities if they are offset by lower power densities in other areas. In contrast, the space-by-space method calculates an overall lighting power allowance for the entire project by adding the products of the individual spaces and their respective LPD recommendation by space type. Typical spaces are shown in Table 5-2. For spaces not listed, use the appropriate entry in ASHRAE/ASHE Standard 90.1 Table 9.6.1, "Lighting Power Densities Using the Space-by-Space Method" (ASHRAE 2010). In highly efficient healthcare buildings, the necessary level of energy optimization suggests the use of the space-by-space method in lieu of the whole-building method.

For lighting to be most efficient, spaces must have light-colored finishes. Ceiling reflectance should be at least 85% for direct lighting schemes, and preferably at least 90% for indirect and daylighting schemes. This generally means using high-performance white acoustical tile or high-reflectance white ceiling paint on hard surfaces. For daylighted schemes, the average reflectance of the walls should be at least 50%, and 70% for the portions of the wall adjacent to the daylighting aperture and above 7 ft. This generally means using light tints for the wall surface, as the lower reflectance typical of doors, trim, and other objects on the walls reduces the average. Floor surface reflectance should be at least 20%, for which there are many suitable surface materials.

Not all the space types in a hospital is distributed equally. In fact, a few space types dominate the area distribution in a facility. In the prototype facility, patient rooms, corridors, offices, and operating rooms make up well over 50% of the building area. Focusing the design effort on optimizing the lighting power in these spaces maximizes the savings potential. See Figure 5-16 for an illustration of how the application of lighting power reduction is proportioned in the prototype facility detailed in Chapter 1.

EL2   Linear Fluorescent Lamps and Ballasts (Climate Zones: all)

Linear fluorescent lamps, both T8 and T5 sizes, with electronic ballasts are a commonly specified commercial fluorescent lighting system in the United States. These systems offer excellent energy efficiency. Fluorescent lamps with low-mercury content are available from major lamp manufacturers and are the standard for sustainable design projects.

To evaluate the efficacy of the lighting system, consider the mean, or "design," lamp lumens in the lamp manufacturers' specification data. This value is lower than the initial lumens and reflects the depreciated lumen output occurring at 40% of the lamp's rated life, which better characterizes actual performance.

To determine the lighting source efficacy, which is expressed in mean lumens per watt (MLPW), multiply the lamp mean lumens by the number of lamps and the ballast factor (BF),

Table 5-2 Space-by-Space Lighting Power Density Recommendations

Space	How-to Tips	Recommended LPD, W/ft^2	Control Scheme*
Patient room	EL12	0.7^1	ML/DL
Nurse station	EL13	0.9	ML/DL
Surgery/operating room	EL14	1.7	ML
PACU/noninvasive treatment	EL15	0.8	ML
Treatment/procedure room	EL16	1.5	ML/DL
Exam room	EL17	1.0	ML/OC/DL
LDR/obstetrics	EL18	0.7	ML
Radiology/imaging	EL19	0.8	ML
Work room/supply room	EL13	1.0	ML/OC
Individual office	EL20	0.8	ML/OC/DL
Conference room	EL20	1.0	ML/OC/DL
Corridor (twenty-four-hour care)	EL13	0.7	ML/DL/LS
Corridor (noncare)		0.7	TC/OC/DL/LS
Lab/pharmacy		1.2	SW/OC
Lobby		0.9	TC/OC/DL/LS
Physical therapy		0.9	ML/TC/OC/DL
Laundry		0.6	TC/OC
Lounge/waiting		0.8	TC/OC/DL/LS
Food preparation		1.2	TC/OC

^{1}Includes allowance for decorative lighting, excluding examination light.
*ML = multilevel or dimming, SW = manual switch, TC = astronomic time schedule,
 OC = occupancy/vacancy sensor, DL = daylight harvesting, LS =light level setback

and then divide by the ballast input power (watts). For example, using two (2) standard T8 lamps and a generic instant start ballast, the system efficacy is

$$\frac{2 \text{ lamps} \times 2660 \text{ mean lumens} \times 0.87 \text{ ballast faction}}{59 \text{ watts}} = 77 \text{ MLPW}$$

Generally, the lumen output varies according to the color temperature, color rendering index (CRI), and between standard (RE7##), premium (RE8##), and high-performance (RE8##/HL) lamps. The light source efficacy and lighting power density (LPD) recommendations in Chapter 4 can be achieved by using the high-performance versions of fluorescent lamps and ballasts.

The color rendering index (CRI) is a scale measurement identifying a lamp's ability, generally, to adequately reveal color characteristics. The scale maximizes at 100, which indicates the best color-rendering capability. Lamps specified for ambient lighting should have a CRI of 80 or greater to allow for accurate perception of color characteristics. As shown in Table 5-3, "standard" T-8 lamps have lower CRI values than is recommended.

High-performance T8 lamps are defined, for the purpose of this document, as having a lamp efficacy of 90+ lm/W, based on mean lumens divided by the cataloged lamp input watts. High-performance T8s also have a CRI of 82 or higher and at least 95% lumen maintenance.

T5 lamps may also be used as an alternative to T8 lamps. T5 lamps are now available in standard, premium, and high output (HO) ratings. An advantage of T5s is reduced use of natural resources (glass, metal, phosphors) in the lamp, plus the ability to use smaller luminaires

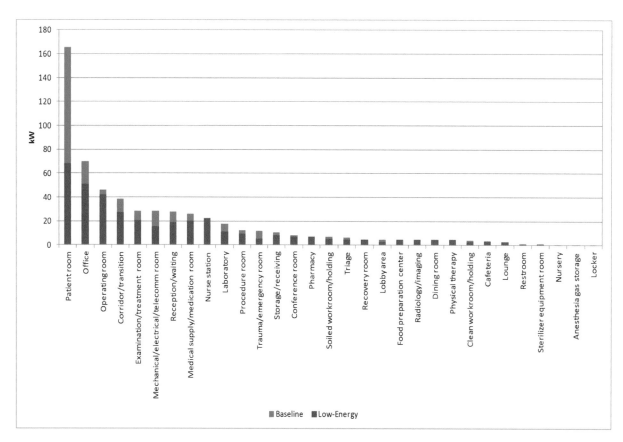

Figure 5-16   Lighting Power Density Weighted by Area

Table 5-3   Typical T8 Lamp Specification Data

Lamp General Description	T8 Lamp Designation	Lumens		CRI	Color Temp, K
		Initial	Mean		
Standard F32T8	F32T8/RE741/ECO	2800	2660	78	4100
Premium F32T8	F32T8/RE841/ECO	2950	2800	85	4100
High Performance F32T8	F32T8/RE841/HL/ECO	3100	3000	85	4100

than those found in comparable T8 systems. The standard and premium versions, nominally 28 W, offer at least 90 MLPW with any available ballast. When used in optimally designed luminaires, they offer very high efficiency. T5HO lamps offer at least 75 MLPW on any ballast, including dimming ballasts. Despite their lower efficacy, their high output may provide better overall performance in some applications (see Table 5-4).

The ballast has significant impact on the energy efficiency of the lighting system. Similar to lamp efficacy, lighting system efficacy is a measure of the energy efficiency of the combined lamp and ballast system.

Standard "Generic" Instant Start Electronic Ballasts. The most common and least expensive ballast; the typical input power for a two-lamp normal light level (0.87 ballast factor) is about 59 W. If you do not specify ballast performance, this is likely what the manufacturer will use in the luminaire.

Table 5-4   Typical T5 Lamp Specification Data

Lamp General Description	T8 Lamp Designation	Lumens		CRI	Color Temp, K
		Initial	Mean		
Standard F28T5	F28T5/RE841/ECO	2900	2700	85	4100
Premium F28T5	F28T5/RE841/HL/ECO	3050	2900	85	4100
High Output F54T5HO	F54T5/RE841/ HO/ECO	5000	4650	85	4100

Low Light Output Version of Standard Ballasts. Similar to the standard ballast, this version operates at 0.78 ballast factor, resulting in a light level about 10% less than the standard ballast, with corresponding reduction in input power, about 54 W for a two-lamp ballast.

High Light Output Version of Standard Ballasts. Similar to the standard ballast, this version operates at 1.15–1.20 ballast factor, resulting in a light level about 32% higher than the standard ballast, with a corresponding increase in ballast input power of 74 to 78 W for a two-lamp ballast.

Program Start Ballasts. Available in low power and normal power models, program start ballasts use an additional circuit to perform programmed starting, which makes lamps last longer when frequently switched.

Dimming Ballasts. Electronic ballasts that provide a continuous range of dimming are available in ranges varying from 100%–20% to 100%–1%. Most dimming ballasts require 60 to 66 W for two lamps. Additional power, compared to fixed output ballasts, is used to heat the lamp cathodes to permit proper dimming operation, but some newer high-performance dimming ballasts do have full output MLPW over 90. (MLPW efficacy is less valuable for evaluating dimming ballasts since the lumen output, ballast factor, and corresponding input power varies over the dimming range of the ballast). Another variation is "stepped dimming," which typically provide 2 or 3 levels, such as 50% and 100%, or 35%, 65%, and 100%. Stepped dimming ballasts are typically less expensive than continuous dimming.

High-Performance Electronic Ballasts. High-performance electronic ballasts are defined, for the purpose of this document, as a two-lamp ballast using 55 W or less with a ballast factor of 0.87 (normal light output) or greater. High-performance ballasts are also available for low light output, high light output, and dimming versions.

Table 5-5 shows combinations of various lamps and ballasts (two-lamp ballasts are shown; values for one-, three-, and four-lamp ballasts are slightly different). Use this table to select fluorescent lamps and ballasts to meet the LPD and efficacy recommendations of Chapter 4. Low-wattage T8 lamps are available (energy-saving 30, 28, or 25 W versions of a 4 ft lamp) but may result in lower light levels or an increased number of fixtures or lamps to achieve recommended light levels. Because of limitations in their use for dimming and other applications, these lower-wattage lamps are not considered for these recommendations. In general, specifying high-performance electronic ballasts and fluorescent lamps is required to meet the energy-efficiency objectives.

EL3   *Compact Fluorescent* **(Climate Zones: all)**

To achieve the LPD recommendations in Chapter 4, compact fluorescent lamps (CFLs) can be used for a variety of applications, such as utility lighting, in small spaces downlighting, and accent lighting and wall-washing. Suitable lamps include twin tube, multiple twin tube, twist tube, and long-twin-tube lamps. Only pin-based CFLs are included in this group, since a screw-based lamp can be replaced with an incandescent lamp and is therefore not compliant with most energy codes. Suitable luminaires have integral hard-wired electronic ballasts.

The efficacy of CFLs is typically less than 60 MLPW and therefore they should not be used for general lighting in most space types. In fact, to meet the 50 MLPW efficacy requirements, some CFL-and-ballast combinations must be avoided (see Table 5-6). Furthermore, the

Table 5-5   Efficacy Values for Different Linear Fluorescent Lamp/Ballast Combinations (with Two Lamps)

Ballast	Lamp Selection				
	F32T8 Standard	F32T8 Premium	F32T8 High Performance	F28T5 Standard	F28T5 Premium
Generic Standard Instant Start (59 W, 0.87 BF-T8/1.0 T5)	77	80	87	NA	NA
Standard Instant Start Low Light Level (54 W, 0.78 BF)	75	78	85	NA	NA
Standard Instant Start High Light Level (74 W, 1.15 BF)	81	84	92	NA	NA
Standard Program Start Normal Light Level (60 W, 0.88 BF)	78	82	88	95	100
Program Start Low Light Level (56 W, 0.78 BF)	73	75	82	NA	NA
Dimming Rapid Start (64 W max, 0.88 BF-T8/1.0 T5)	72	75	81	NA	NA
High-Performance Normal Light Level (55 W, 0.88 BF-T8/1.0 T5)	85	90	95	95	100
High-Performance Low Light Level (48 W, 0.78 BF)	85	88	96	93	98
High-Performance High Light Level (70 W, 1.15 BF)	86	89	97	98	103
High-Performance Dimming, Step and Continuous (54 W, 0.87 BF-T8/1.0 T5)	78	81	97	90	95

▇ Meets 90 MLPW efficacy criteria

Table 5-6   System Efficacy for CFL-Ballast Systems

Lamp Type	Magnetic Ballast and Preheat Lamp (2-Pin Lamps)	Electronic Ballast (4-Pin Lamp) Program Start (Instant Start)	
5–13 W twin tube	All < 50	57 (13 W only)	
13–26 W double twin tube	All < 50	13 W	57
		18 W	52
		26 W	53
18–42 W triple- and quad- twin tube and most twist tube lamps	N/A	18 W	53
		26 W	55
		32 W	55
		42 W	57
2D	28 W < 50	28 W	63
Long twin tube	N/A	18 W	46
		24/27 W	61
		36/39 W	64
		40 W	60

▇ Does not meet efficacy criteria   ▇ Meets 50 MLPW efficacy criteria

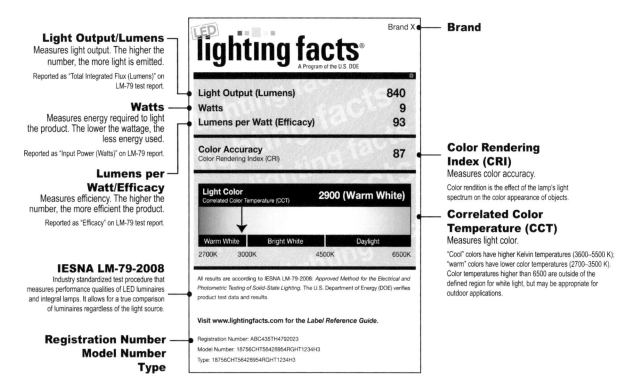

Light Output/Lumens
Measures light output. The higher the number, the more light is emitted.
Reported as "Total Integrated Flux (Lumens)" on LM-79 test report.

Watts
Measures energy required to light the product. The lower the wattage, the less energy used.
Reported as "Input Power (Watts)" on LM-79 report.

Lumens per Watt/Efficacy
Measures efficiency. The higher the number, the more efficient the product.
Reported as "Efficacy" on LM-79 test report.

IESNA LM-79-2008
Industry standardized test procedure that measures performance qualities of LED luminaires and integral lamps. It allows for a true comparison of luminaires regardless of the light source.

Registration Number
Model Number
Type

Brand X — **Brand**

Color Rendering Index (CRI)
Measures color accuracy.
Color rendition is the effect of the lamp's light spectrum on the color appearance of objects.

Correlated Color Temperature (CCT)
Measures light color.
"Cool" colors have higher Kelvin temperatures (3600–5500 K); "warm" colors have lower color temperatures (2700–3500 K). Color temperatures higher than 6500 are outside of the defined region for white light, but may be appropriate for outdoor applications.

Figure 5-17 (EL4) LED Lighting Facts Label
Source: U.S. DOE (www.lightingfacts.com)

photometric efficiency of CFLs in luminaire reflectors is often less than 50%, further degrading the energy performance compared to other alternatives, such as light-emitting diodes.

EL4   Solid-State Light-Emitting Diode (LED)

Although in its infancy as a commercially viable alternative, excellent solid-state light-emitting diode (LED) options are available in all commonly specified sizes, including MR, GU, PAR, 4 in, and 6 in downlights and 1×4, 2×2, and 2×4 recessed luminaires. In addition to the higher efficiency associated with solid-state lighting, other benefits such as dimming, precise control of color, precise photometric control, and reduced radiated heat into the room interior are implicit. Also, solid-state luminaire housings can be more easily sealed at the ceiling to eliminate infiltration from the plenum above, because they have few or no removable or moving parts. This contributes to infection control, which is a benefit in care areas providing for highly immune-suppressed patients.

LED sources differ from discharge light sources, such as fluorescent and metal halide, in that many are completely integral to the luminaire and not simply an interchangeable component in a luminaire assembly. This requires a different methodology for evaluation, one that does not separate the light source from the luminaire. When considering the efficacy in delivering light, the photometric performance of the luminaire must be considered in conjunction with the input power. A luminaire efficacy value can be calculated by dividing the total luminaire-delivered lumens by the luminaire input power. The U.S. Department of Energy and IESNA have developed a standard and labeling system for reporting the efficiency of LED lighting products. IESNA Standard LM-79-2008, *Approved Method for the Electrical and Photometric Testing of Solid-State Lighting Devices* (IESNA 2008), establishes the testing protocols for evaluating LED lighting products. The DOE "LED Lighting Facts" label program is a simple way to read and evaluate the performance of the product under consideration (see Figure 5-17). LED luminaires for use in general lighting should have a luminaire efficacy exceeding 50 lm/W.

In comparison, a similar luminaire with a compact fluorescent source might have a luminaire efficacy of only 35 lm/W.

LEDs offer many other benefits, such as being mercury free and having an extended mean time between failures. This increased life reduces waste and disposal costs and frees up maintenance personnel from routine lamp changes so their time can be spent on more critical tasks.

Although costs continue to decrease as the technology matures, initial costs of LEDs tend to be higher than for previously common solutions. However, the significant wattage reduction of LEDs can reduce the number and size of electrical power feeds to the luminaires. Additionally, fluorescent solutions often require special ballasts and control systems to achieve dimmability that are more expensive than LEDs. As a matter of life-cycle cost, LED can outperform other sources because of their longer life and associated decreased maintenance needs. The cost of a single lamp change can offset the difference in initial cost.

EL5   *Metal Halide* (Climate Zones: all)

To achieve the LPD recommendations in Chapter 4, metal halide lamps may be used for general lighting in large spaces, outdoor lighting, and for accent lighting and wall washing in low wattages. There are two primary types in the metal halide family, ceramic metal halide (CMH) and quartz metal halide (QMH) lamps. Both types are high-intensity discharge lamps in which intense light energy is generated inside an arc tube made either of ceramic or quartz glass. The two types are comparably efficient. CMH lamps have very good color in the warm (3000 K) and neutral (4000 K) ranges; QMH lamps' color-rendering quality is mediocre except in high-color temperature lamps (5000 K and above). In general, only the improved CRI CMH lamps are recommended for interior applications.

Metal halide lamps may be further categorized into low wattage (150 W and lower) and high wattage (higher than 150 W). All low-wattage lamps are pulse start and can be operated on either magnetic ballasts or more efficient electronic ballasts. High-wattage lamps are available as both probe start (less efficient) and pulse start (more efficient). Recently, electronic ballasts have become practical for indoor use of pulse-start metal halide; most ballasts for high-wattage lamps are magnetic. The Energy Independence and Security Act (EISA) of 2007 regulates the type of ballast that may be used in commercial luminaires starting in 2009. The Act sets minimum efficiency performance for ballasts for metal halide lamps greater than 150 W and less than 500 W. The effective result of the legislation is that magnetic probe-start metal halide systems are rendered obsolete in favor of pulse start and electronic ballast systems.

Metal halide lamps' apparent high efficacy (from initial rated lumens) is often offset by their high rate of lumen depreciation. Probe-start metal halide lamps operated on magnetic ballasts will lose more than 45% of their rated lumen output over life; with pulse-start lamps, the losses are about 35% on magnetic ballasts but can be improved to only about 20% by using electronic ballasts. Since mean lumens takes lumen depreciation into account, the type of ballast plays a significant role in the efficacy. As a result, a number of lamps and ballasts do not meet the efficacy criteria, as shown in Table 5-7 (not a comprehensive list).

Caution: Metal halide lamps require a warm up and restrike time of up to 15 minutes if turned off during operations. Therefore, a supplemental emergency source is required that provides light during the restrike time when used in applications requiring emergency standby power. Metal halide lamp performance is affected by the position of the lamp arc tube. When the lamp is operated in a position other than the rated position, the output will be reduced. This is known as the "tilt factor." Lamps applied in a manner where tilt factor reduces output will have reduced efficacy that may fall outside the recommendations. An additional consideration is metal halide lamps' potential for experiencing nonpassive end of life, in which hot gases are discharged under high pressure and can break the lamp-bulb glass envelope. This can lead to a potentially dangerous shower of hot pieces of glass and can damage a luminaire, so the luminaire should be designed to safely contain these events. Luminaires with open apertures or plastic housings, and those located within regularly occupied spaces, should use a version of

Table 5-7 System Efficacy for Metal Halide Lamp-Ballast Systems

Lamp	Type	Magnetic Ballast	Electronic Ballast (Minimum Efficacy; Some Ballasts Will Be Higher)
20 W CMH	Pulse start	N/A	55
35/39 W CMH	Pulse start	43	53
50 W QMH	Pulse start	33	40
70 W CMH	Pulse start	45	51
100 W CMH	Pulse start	51	60
150 W CMH	Pulse start	59	67
175 W QMH	Probe start	N/A	N/A
320 W QMH	Pulse start	67	72
350 W QMH	Pulse start	71	76
	Pulse start	73	77
400 W QMH	Probe start	N/A	N/A
	Pulse Start	71	82
400 W CMH	Pulse Start	72	87

Does not meet efficacy criteria   Meets efficacy criteria

metal halide lamp rated for use in open fixtures (i.e., "O" rated). These lamps incorporate special measures to contain nonpassive lamp failure.

EL6   *General Lighting Control Strategies* (Climate Zones: all)

To maximize the energy performance of your facility, lighting control strategies should be adopted to optimize how your lights are turned on, when and how your lights are turned off, and the output level of your lights whenever they are operating. The optimum electric light level in a given space is dependent on the task or activity in the space, the user's personal preference or desired aesthetic, or the amount of daylight in the space. Typically, to obtain the highest lighting energy savings in a hospital, lighting should be adjusted to optimum levels whenever the lights are turned on.

An example of this approach is the common need for relatively high illuminance levels in a space for housekeeping and maintenance, where lower light levels are appropriate for typical operation or patient care. In this situation, separately controlling the higher level of illumination with a manual-ON time interval OFF switch, instead of setting the room lighting at the higher level all the time, will save energy. Another prime lighting control strategy for most public spaces, corridors, waiting rooms, etc. is "daylighting" control, where electric light levels are automatically adjusted to supplement the available daylight in a space throughout the day.

EL7   *Occupancy-Based Control* (Climate Zones: all)

Use occupancy sensors in all exam and treatment rooms; staff support spaces, such as for nutrition and medication; clean and soiled utility rooms; offices; mechanical rooms; restrooms; and storage rooms. The greatest energy savings and occupancy satisfaction is achieved with a manual-ON/automatic-OFF occupancy sensor scheme (also referred to as "vacancy" sensing). This avoids unnecessary operation when electric lights are not needed, reduces the frequency of switching, and maximizes lamp life compared to automatic-ON schemes. In every application, the occupant should not be able to override the automatic off setting, even if it is set for manual ON. A manual OFF or separate switching capability is also useful for multilevel lighting schemes where a higher light level is only needed periodically. Unless otherwise recommended, occupancy sensors should be set for medium-to-high sensitivity and a 15-minute time delay (the optimum time to achieve energy savings without excessive loss of lamp life). Review the manufacturer's data for proper placement and coverage.

In high-performance integrated lighting control systems, motion sensors can also be used in spaces that see little if any traffic during late-night hours. If light levels are automatically set back late at night, motion sensors can be used to raise light levels in public corridors, waiting rooms, and other spaces whenever someone approaches and occupies the space.

The two primary types of occupancy sensor technology are passive infrared (PIR) and ultrasonic. PIR sensors can see only in a line of sight and should not be used in rooms where the user cannot see the sensor (e.g., storage areas with multiple aisles or restrooms with stalls). Ultrasonic sensors can be disrupted by high airflow and should not be used near air duct outlets. Dual-technology sensors combine sensor technologies; these should be considered for spaces larger than 150 ft^2 or those with objects or partitions that could affect the performance of PIR. Sensors can also incorporate auxiliary relays that interface between lighting and other building systems.

Cautions: Occupancy sensors should not be used with high-intensity discharge (HID) lamps because of warmup and restrike times.

Fluorescent lamps and CFLs should use programmed-start ballasts if frequent ON-OFF cycles are expected. (Some standard ballasts and all dimming ballasts are programmed-start.)

EL8   *Occupant Manual Control—Dimming and Switching* (Climate Zones: all)

In patient care spaces, controls for switching and dimming the lighting system (and motorized window shades if provided) should be readily accessible by staff, patients, and visitors. In spaces with several lighting zones, where multiple control locations are desired, the number of conventional 120V/277V switches and multigang switch locations can become cumbersome and confusing to patients, visitors, and caregivers. In these applications, low-voltage multifunction wall controls with appropriate labeling should be considered.

In other than patient-care areas, controls should be located where they are easily accessible and understandable by the caregiving staff. In general use spaces, lighting should be controlled by a time of day scheduling system or occupancy sensors. Wall controls should be provided for manual override. These manual controls should be placed in remote locations for use only by staff.

EL9   *Patient Control* (Climate Zones: all)

Practical patient control of lighting and window shades should be integrated into the patient's pillow speaker or other bed-side remote control. In most areas, giving the patient the capability to control electric light levels and window shades to enhance their comfort is beneficial. It also reduces patients' dependency on nurses to make adjustments to the room environment, which can improve nurses' productivity.

Recent studies of lighting patterns in patient rooms indicate that providing the patient a granular level of manual control of lighting in room spaces results in lights being turned off a significant portion of the time the patient is in the room (Burpee et al. 2011).

EL10   *Time Clock Control* (Climate Zones: all)

Interior Lighting. In some general purpose, retail, and dining spaces, and even administration office areas, time-of-day scheduling controls can be used to assure that lights are turned on when desired and reduced or turned off after hours when not required. (Refer to section EL8 for information on how occupancy sensors can be used with time clock controls to raise light levels when someone approaches or occupies the space.)

In spaces that have significant daylighting, such as entry lobbies, time-of-day scheduling can be used to reduce the output or turn off some interior lights during the day.

Exterior Lighting. Use an astronomical time switch with an exterior photocell for all exterior lighting. Turn off exterior lighting not designated for security purposes when the building is unoccupied. This system can be programmed to control lighting related to the daily sunrise and sunset for the geographic location of your building, which not only eliminates the need to make seasonal adjustments to your time clock controls but also maximizes the energy saved with time clock control (lights are never turned on too early or left on longer than is needed). Astronomical time switches can retain programming and the time setting during loss of power for at least 10 hours. If a building energy-management system is being used to control and monitor mechanical and electrical energy use, it can also be used to schedule and manage outdoor lighting energy use.

EL11   *Daylight Harvesting Control* (Climate Zones: all)

In atriums, lobbies, waiting rooms, corridors, open office administration areas, and other appropriate spaces, automated daylight harvesting controls can be used to regulate the output of electric lights to optimize the quality of the visual environment while conserving significant amounts of energy. Step-dimming systems can be applied where abrupt incremental changes in ambient electric light levels will not be a distraction to the occupants in the space; otherwise, continuous-dimming systems should be applied.

Daylight harvesting controls may be considered in patient rooms, especially in lighting zones nearest the windows. Lighting power reduction during daylight hours is shown to be as high as 87% (Brown 2005). However, patients' control of the environment is a priority, and automatic controls should not override the patients' ability to manually control the lights.

EL12   *Lighting for the Patient Room (Climate Zones: all)*

The private patient room must accommodate a multitude of medical tasks. Patient room lighting design must reconcile multiple lighting needs as simply and economically as possible. The patient, visitors, doctor, nurse, and housekeeping personnel may each require different illuminance levels. Furthermore, in most large hospitals, patient rooms comprise a large percentage of the total space area and connected lighting power (see Figure 5-16 in EL1) and therefore present one of the best opportunities to reduce total energy consumption.

A long-term design trend is to give the patient room the aura of a home or hotel bedroom, so it is desired that the luminaires are not overly "institutional" in appearance. Decorative luminaires, such as wall sconces, are welcome but should be controlled separately from other lighting for the patient and examination. Use luminaires with high-efficacy sources and limited power and light output (see Figure 5-18). Note that the recommended LPD for the patient room includes power for any decorative or accent lighting.

The room lighting should accommodate reading, at the normal reading position, for a patient sitting up in bed, as well as for visitors. Consideration should be given to a patient lying prone on the bed, exposed to the luminance of ceiling lights, and thus vulnerable to glare. A wall-mounted indirect light located at the head of the patient bed is a proven approach for low-glare general lighting.

Lighting for staff examination of patients should be as shadow-free as possible and have a color quality that enables accurate observation of all tissue surfaces. Whether fixed or portable, examination lighting should be confined to the bed area and intuitively controlled by the nursing staff, separate from other room lighting. Power for the examination light is not included in the recommended LPD as long as it is controlled separately from and not needed for general room lighting.

A source of local low-level illuminance is needed in the room during the night to allow nurses and patients to navigate during normal sleeping hours. There is a potential conflict between the nursing staff's need for light for observation and the patient's need for darkness at night to accommodate sleep. A low-wattage shielded LED night light located between bed and door is a good choice. The effects of lighting on natural circadian rhythms should be considered, and lighting should be designed to avoid disruption of the patient's sleep cycle. The use of warm- or amber-colored light during the night may better accommodate sleep than would some other light. These lights should also be considered in the design of the corridor immediately outside the patient room.

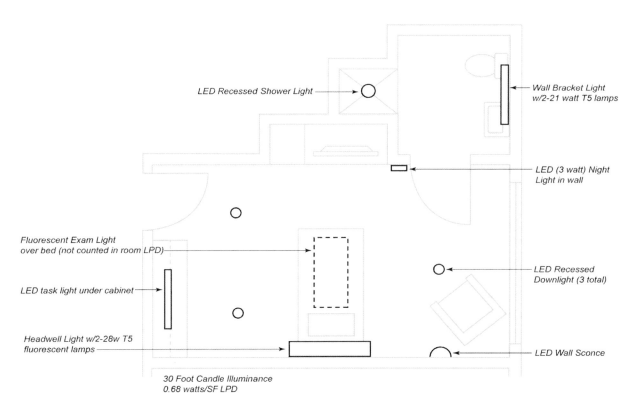

Figure 5-18 (EL11) Patient Room Lighting

The patient bathroom should be adequately illuminated to prevent falls caused by wet floors. The vanity area should be illuminated so the face is properly modeled. This is often accomplished by a luminaire mounted to the wall either flanking or above the mirror. The patient bathroom should be controlled with a vacancy sensor.

The preferred strategy for lighting control is to separate control by lighting function and location, creating multiple choices for zones and levels of lighting. Lighting controls should be located for the convenience of the patient, visitors, and nursing staff. Switching or dimming controls positioned at the entrance to the patient's room are convenient for nursing staff and visitors. An all-OFF function switch should also be provided at the room entry if there are more than three zones of control or switches. In addition, in a private single-patient room, controls for general room lights should be accessible to the patient in the bed.

In patient rooms with three or more lighting zones, the number of switches and control locations can be cumbersome and confusing to users. In these applications, low-voltage multifunction controls with appropriate labeling can make control functions more intuitive and user-friendly, as well as simplify installation. Integration of the control system with an ergonomically friendly patient control, such as the nurse-call remote or bedside control panel, can also be implemented. These systems can even incorporate control of room amenities such as the TV and window shades. Convenient controls empower the patient, which can reduce his or her dependency on a nurse to make adjustments to the environment. This positively influences the patient comfort and also can improve nurses' productivity.

Patient room designs should provide the patient and staff access to daylight and views. To further optimize energy performance, lighting controls should take advantage of daylight provided by allowing dimming or turning off of lights in the daylighted zone when ample daylight is present. Manual dimming controls are appropriate for the area immediately around the patient bed, while automated controls might be considered for the lighting zone nearest the window.

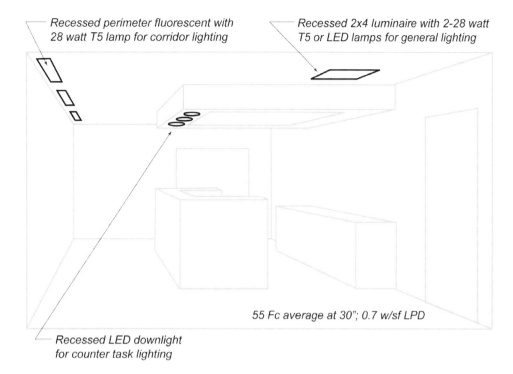

Recessed perimeter fluorescent with 28 watt T5 lamp for corridor lighting

Recessed 2x4 luminaire with 2-28 watt T5 or LED lamps for general lighting

55 Fc average at 30"; 0.7 w/sf LPD

Recessed LED downlight for counter task lighting

Figure 5-19   (EL12) Nurse Station Lighting

EL13   *Lighting for Nurses' Stations and Care Area Corridor* (Climate Zones: all)

In most cases, patient care is coordinated from a nursing station. Reading, writing, filing, monitoring, communications, dispensing of medication, and many other care-related functions take place here. Data entry and charting using a computer means that low glare illuminance should be considered to mitigate reflected glare on the monitor screen. In addition, digital record processes are creating a trend where data entry occurs throughout the care area, with distributed workstations located in the corridor outside the patient rooms in addition to the nursing station.

Other than patient rooms, corridors represent the best opportunity to save energy from lighting in a large hospital. The nursing station is used continuously night and day. Consider the lighting transitions to and from corridors and patient rooms so that they are fully coordinated under both day and nighttime conditions to avoid continuous retinal readaptation (Figure 5-19).

During sleeping hours, high levels of illumination in the corridor may trespass into a patient's room when the nurse periodically enters. Therefore, it is suggested that corridor lighting be adjustable to allow a "night" setting with reduced illuminance.

Cautions: In general, recessed downlights are too inefficient to provide the necessary illumination in corridors. However, recessed downlights that use CFLs or LEDs may be appropriate for supplemental light in applications where a low-brightness appearance is desired or as a task light in a specific area.

Corridors should have an emergency lighting system that can produce at least 1 fc, on average, along the path of egress. The controls must operate the intended lights during a power outage regardless of normal control setting. This may require an automatic transfer relay that bypasses normal controls.

Switching of the lighting system in corridors should be readily accessible only to the staff.

Avoid overlighting with inefficient task lighting at work counters. Typical linear fluorescent luminaires may overlight the task area when mounted less than 36 in. from the surface. Lights mounted under wall cabinets and transaction counters are often obstructed by objects in the work area.

Lighting level transitions from nursing stations, corridors, and patient rooms should be coordinated under both daytime and nighttime conditions. Wall control dimming or multiple-level switching control should be provided to balance near- and far-field luminance levels.

Corridor lighting should be equipped with manual dimming or multilevel switches to allow a "night" setting with reduced illuminance. In corridors, lighting controls should *not* be readily accessible to the general public.

Adjacent medication areas should have multiple level switching control to provide at least two light levels, one for general work and one for medication preparation. This space is also a prime candidate for occupancy-based controls.

In general, switching in twenty-four-hour patient care areas should not use an automatic time-of-day control system; however, controls using occupancy sensors may be effective. In other than twenty-four-hour care settings, automatic time-of-day control with local manual override is appropriate. In addition, provide automatic daylight harvesting controls with dimming or multilevel switching in corridors having windows, skylights, or other forms of natural lighting.

EL14 *Lighting for Surgical Suites* (Climate Zones: all)

Operating room lighting is perhaps the most important lighting in the hospital. Various tasks take place there, and lighting needs differ for the surgical team, nurses, anesthesiologists, and other staff. Because of the variety of surgical procedures, the general lighting should suit the varying visual requirements of the surgeon and staff. A uniformly distributed, multilevel, adjustable illuminance should be provided using recessed shielded luminaires, with a quality prismatic lens that gives diffused, low-glare light. The general room lighting should be able to provide at least 100 fc uniformly throughout the surgical field.

Color appearance should not noticeably change when viewed under the surgical task light or the general room illuminance. This is best achieved by matching the spectral power distributions of these two light sources, but usually it is only practical to match their color temperatures. For example, if the main surgical light has a color temperature of 4100 K, then the general room illuminance should be provided by sources with a similar color temperature.

The proliferation of minimally invasive surgical techniques using a variety of different remote vision scopes, as well as implementation of digital imaging and patient telemetry, has led to greater use of heads-up video display monitors, usually LCD flat panels. It is not uncommon to have several display monitors viewable from the surgical table. The combination of heads-up-and-down tasks creates challenges for maintaining a glare-free and comfortable visual environment. It is important to properly balance the room surface's reflectance and luminance to prevent disrupting veiling reflections on the monitors and visual discomfort from high-contrast ratios. The capability to control the luminance of perimeter wall surfaces by varying the general ambient light during the surgical procedure is an important feature.

The surgical task light must provide a variable range with high levels of illuminance, more than 1000 fc, in a small area with little or no shadows. It must also be adjustable, both in beam size and position, to accommodate the multiple viewing needs and positions of the various members of the surgical team. The task lighting system normally is composed of two to three specialty luminaires suspended from the ceiling over the surgical table. These lights commonly use high-output quartz halogen sources with special dichroic reflectors to manage the color temperature and radiated energy of the light. The latest solid state LED lighting technology offers promise of more energy efficiency and even better shadow-free light distribution, with less radiated heat (see Figure 5-20).

General and ambient lighting fixtures should incorporate dimmers or multilevel switching controls. High light levels are required to clean and set up these spaces. During procedures, especially when video screens or microscopes are introduced, physicians and technicians desire lower ambient light levels for a clear view of video images. Controls should be conveniently provided to make adjustments to the perimeter and ambient light that match the specific requirements of each procedure and the preferences of the surgical team.

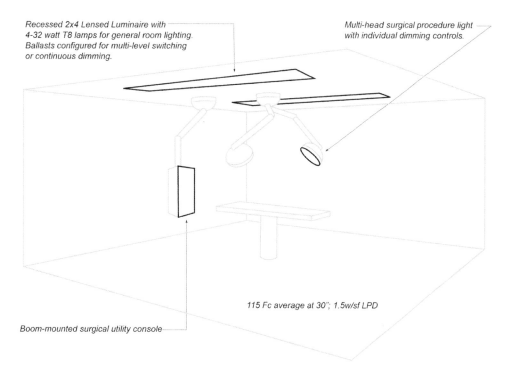

Recessed 2x4 Lensed Luminaire with
4-32 watt T8 lamps for general room lighting.
Ballasts configured for multi-level switching
or continuous dimming.

Multi-head surgical procedure light
with individual dimming controls.

115 Fc average at 30"; 1.5w/sf LPD

Boom-mounted surgical utility console

Figure 5-20   (EL13) Operating Room Lighting

EL15   *Lighting for PACU/Recovery Rooms* (Climate Zones: all)

The postanesthetic care unit (PACU) recovery room is where the patient is placed after a surgery. Its lighting needs are also applicable to preoperative holding and induction rooms. This space has to accommodate careful examination and monitoring of the patient and, on occasion, an emergency procedure if the patient deteriorates.

As patients regains consciousness, they are sensitive to intense brightness, especially since they are typically supine in the bed. Therefore, the general lighting approach should be subdued, with the capability of quickly raising illuminance in case staff need to work. A multilevel scheme with dimming, stepped switching, or multiple light sources should be considered.

The presence of daylight in the area, while not necessary, can enhance the patient's comfort as long as direct glare from glazing is avoided (see Figure 5-21).

Wallbox dimming or dual-level controls should be adopted so that lights can be dimmed for patient comfort and increased for critical tasks when needed. Lowered ambient light levels also may be desired for some emergency procedures (such as when using a laryngoscope). Individual light controls should be provided at locations that are convenient for the staff to use.

EL16   *Lighting for Nonsurgical Treatment Procedure Rooms* (Climate Zones: all)

Rooms for noninvasive treatments and procedures, commonly seen in the emergency department as well as in other outpatient care environments, pose complex demands on lighting because of the wide variety of activities that may take place there. General lighting for examining patients should be as free of shadows as practical and have a color quality that enables accurate diagnosis of all tissue surfaces. When the patient is being examined, uniformity and level of illuminance are important. The ability to reduce general illuminance to a subdued level is also desirable for patient comfort in some common situations.

Repair of lacerations and treatment of wounds is frequently performed. This meticulous work has similar illumination needs as surgery. Although these tasks are typically smaller, and procedures are not quite as long and demanding as surgery, they still require the use of specialized task lighting similar to that used in the operating room. Whether fixed or portable,

Surgical Task Lighting

Lighting that provides directed contrast is crucial during surgery—particularly for deep incisions—and is usually provided by overhead task lights in conjunction with headband lights worn by the surgeons. The task lights in a conventional operating room are about 2 ft in diameter and use halogen bulbs. The lights radiate tremendous amounts of heat along the path of the lighting beam, making the doctors, who wear full personal protective equipment (masks, gowns, etc.), overheat quickly. To combat the effect, the air-conditioning setpoint is lowered. It is common for operating rooms to be designed with the capability to maintain 60°F at less than 60% rh.

This cold temperature, in turn, makes patients undergoing surgery essentially hypothermic. This condition causes blood to drain away from the skin, which then makes them much more vulnerable to post-operative infection. To mitigate this risk, doctors wrap patients in an electric blanket called a "bair hugger." The bair hugger is often the largest electrical draw in the room.

Replacing traditional halogen lights with LED surgical lamps provides multiple benefits, including the following:

- High light output with adjustable light characteristics to match the needs of the situation, leading to enhanced visual acuity.
- Low, infrared-free heat generation that dissipates by convection upward and doesn't overheat the doctors performing surgeries. As a result, surgeons don't need to cool the operating room, and patients don't require heating blankets.
- Savings of 60% of the energy used for lighting while significantly reducing the energy demands of cooling the surgeons and warming their patients.
- Enhanced mitigation of shadows cast by surgical staff (shadow dilution).

Furthermore, while halogen lamps are typically rated for just 1000 to 3000 hours and fail catastrophically (suddenly and without warning), LED surgical task lights are generally rated for 25,000 to 40,000 hours and are expected to "fail" by gradually fading in brightness. Some of the primary benefits of LED surgical task lights include the following:

- LEDs require less wattage to produce equivalent light levels (efficacy).
- Substantial thermal energy must be conducted away from LEDs, but they radiate relatively little ultraviolet (UV) or infrared (IR) energy (heat in beam).
- Dimming without color shift or flicker, which also has potential benefits related to patient outcomes (system compatibility must be verified on a case-by-case basis).
- Enhanced mitigation of shadows cast by surgical staff.
- Improved maintenance through significantly longer life and a noncatastrophic failure mechanism.

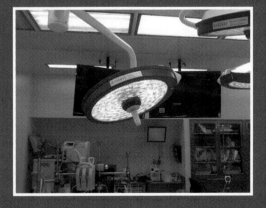 

(Left) LED Surgical Task Lamp and (Right) Shadow Dilution Demonstration
Source: John D'Angelo, Cleveland Clinic

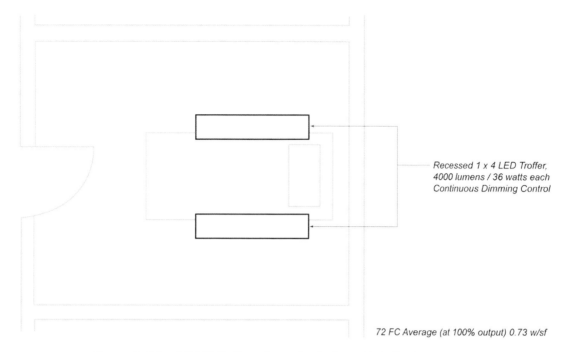

Recessed 1 x 4 LED Troffer,
4000 lumens / 36 watts each
Continuous Dimming Control

72 FC Average (at 100% output) 0.73 w/sf

Figure 5-21 (EL14) Patient Anesthetic Care Unit (PACU) Lighting

specialized task lighting should be located in the bed area and controllable by the nursing staff (see Figure 5-22).

In nonsurgical treatment areas, such as dialysis, chemotherapy, and other infusion treatment units, manual dimming or multilevel switching light controls should be provided for staff to adjust light levels to relax patients before and during these procedures. When possible, the patient should able to control their lights and window shades according to their personal preference to reduce stress and make them as comfortable as possible. Handheld remote controls or infrared controls integrated into a television remote control are options that allow the patients to control their environment during long procedures.

EL17 *Lighting for Exam Rooms* (Climate Zones: all)

Exam rooms are spaces for general examination and diagnosis. General lighting for examining patients should be as free of shadows as practical and have a color quality that enables accurate diagnosis of all tissue surfaces. The uniformity and level of illuminance are also important (see Figure 5-23).

When in the room waiting to be examined, patients may be suffering from migraine headaches and other conditions that make them very sensitive to light. Multilevel switching or dimming to reduce the general illuminance to a subdued level is desirable for their comfort. Occupancy/vacancy sensors are also ideal in this application. In exam rooms with windows, automatic daylighting controls with dimming or step-dimming capabilities also reduce energy consumption.

EL18 *Lighting for the Obstetrics Suite* (Climate Zones: all)

A recent trend has been the use of multipurpose rooms for observation, labor, and delivery during routine births. Sometimes, the newborn is even kept in the same room as the mother after delivery instead of in a separate nursery. These rooms are commonly referred to as labor, delivery, and recovery (LDR) rooms and may also include post-partum stay. Such rooms frequently have a home or hotel-like atmosphere and use a specially designed "birthing bed."

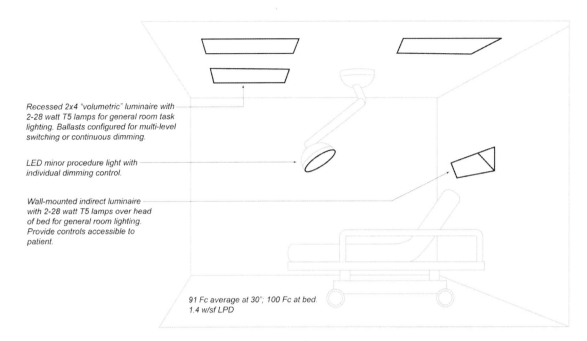

Recessed 2x4 "volumetric" luminaire with 2-28 watt T5 lamps for general room task lighting. Ballasts configured for multi-level switching or continuous dimming.

LED minor procedure light with individual dimming control.

Wall-mounted indirect luminaire with 2-28 watt T5 lamps over head of bed for general room lighting. Provide controls accessible to patient.

91 Fc average at 30"; 100 Fc at bed. 1.4 w/sf LPD

Figure 5-22 (EL15) Nonsurgical Treatment Room Lighting

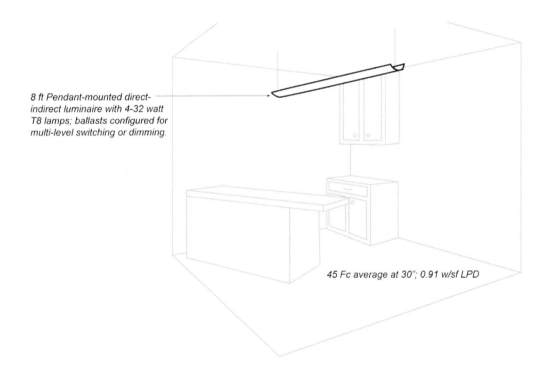

8 ft Pendant-mounted direct-indirect luminaire with 4-32 watt T8 lamps; ballasts configured for multi-level switching or dimming.

45 Fc average at 30"; 0.91 w/sf LPD

Figure 5-23 (EL16) Exam Room Lighting

After birth, the infant is typically kept in a nursery for observation. Nursery lighting should allow for easy examination of infants in cribs and incubators. The general lighting should not be kept at high levels because infants may be vulnerable to retinopathy—damage to the retina from overexposure to light. Luminaires for general lighting should be selected and/or installed so that the luminance, as seen from the normal bassinet position, is not uncomfortable or harmful to the infant patient. Variable indirect ambient lighting is desirable for this type of space.

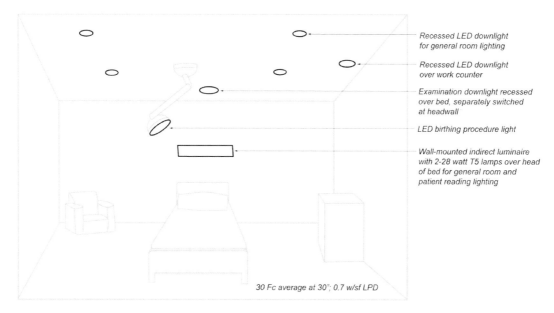

Recessed LED downlight
for general room lighting

Recessed LED downlight
over work counter

Examination downlight recessed
over bed, separately switched
at headwall

LED birthing procedure light

Wall-mounted indirect luminaire
with 2-28 watt T5 lamps over head
of bed for general room and
patient reading lighting

30 Fc average at 30"; 0.7 w/sf LPD

Figure 5-24   (EL17) Labor, Deliver, and Recovery (LDR) Lighting Plan

Special care nurseries (SCNs) or neonatal intensive care units (NICUs) are used for premature or ailing infants. Flexible lighting levels are needed for these spaces. Staff may prefer subdued light for some periods yet need high levels during emergencies or treatment. Parents often visit the room to feed or hold their infants. Dimming or zones of individualized control should be provided. Also, spaces exposed to daylight may improve healing time and deter depression (see Figure 5-24).

Today's birthing rooms are intended to have a home-like atmosphere. To compliment the furnishing and room finishes, manual wallbox dimming controls should be provided for patients, visitors, and staff to adjust general ambient lighting to create an environment that is as comfortable and relaxed as possible. Wall controls should be conveniently located at the newborn's crib so that staff may adjust lights to low levels to protect infants from retinal overexposure and bring lights to full output in the event of an emergency.

As in standard patient rooms, manual or automated daylight harvesting controls should be considered for the lighting zone nearest the windows so that electric lights may be dimmed or turned off when ample daylight is present.

EL19   *Lighting for Radiology and Diagnostic Imaging* (Climate Zones: all)

The modern radiographic suite involves a wide variety of visual tasks performed with complex equipment, such as x-ray, fluoroscopy, or ultrasound. Lighting must be planned with care, taking into consideration personnel and the need to minimize glare that can disturb patients. Since radiology personnel frequently view video screens or may need to view the patient from an adjacent space through a window, an emphasis should be placed on minimizing glare (Figure 5-25).

Special types of diagnostic imaging, including computed tomography (CT), magnetic resonance imaging (MRI), and positron emission tomography (PET) typically require three spaces: a control room, an equipment room, and the scanning room where the patient is treated. The patient is typically observed during the procedure through a window by a staff operator in the adjacent control room. This requires careful balancing of illuminance in the two spaces to maintain visibility, so the lighting in both rooms should be variable or dimmable.

The scanning equipment can be intimidating, and some patients experience claustrophobia during CT and, especially, MRI scans. It helps if the scanning area is visually relaxing. Also,

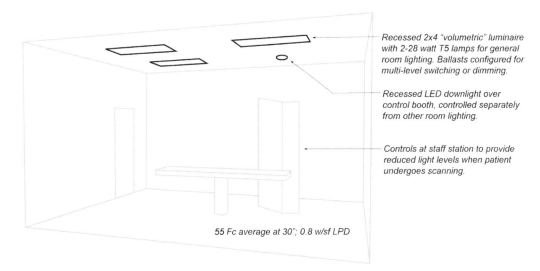

Recessed 2x4 "volumetric" luminaire with 2-28 watt T5 lamps for general room lighting. Ballasts configured for multi-level switching or dimming.

Recessed LED downlight over control booth, controlled separately from other room lighting.

Controls at staff station to provide reduced light levels when patient undergoes scanning.

55 Fc average at 30"; 0.8 w/sf LPD

Figure 5-25 (EL18) Imaging Suite Lighting

the general lighting should be capable of being subdued to produce an environment comfortable and calming to the patient. Since the patient typically is in a supine position on a gantry, his or her field of view should be kept free from uncomfortably high luminance or glare.

Radiation therapy uses clinical linear accelerators, tomotherapy, and radiosurgery to treat tumors and cancer. The type of space used for these is similar to that for other types of diagnositc imaging, but because high doses of radiation are applied, the treatment area is enclosed in special concrete vaults. The visual tasks and conditions are also similar to those for other kinds of imaging, but given the setting, more emphasis should be placed on creating a comfortable environment for the patient.

Because radiologists and technicians frequently view video and image intensifier screens during radiology procedures, desired illuminance values in these areas range from 20 to 2000 lux. Dimming controls should provide convenient control of the general lighting to enable the medical staff to clearly see fine details in these video images.

In diagnostic imaging rooms, general lighting should also be adjustable with a dimming system to create an environment comfortable and calming for the patient.

Lighting control systems may require special direct-current output to prevent interference with the imaging equipment and the controls located outside the scanning area.

EL20   *Lighting for Individual Offices and Conference Rooms* (Climate Zones: all)

Private offices for administrators, doctors, nursing department heads, etc., are located throughout a healthcare facility. These rooms should be designed the same as offices in any other building. A target lighting power density of 0.8 W/ft^2 is achievable with average illuminance of at least 30 fc and local task illuminance of 50 fc on desks. This can be achieved with pendant-mounted indirect/direct luminaires or recessed fluorescent lighting. Luminaires should be selected to mitigate glare, especially glare reflected on computer monitor screens (Figure 5-26).

Conference and meeting rooms are also located in different areas of the facility, both in administrative and nursing areas. The visual tasks in a conference room are not unlike those in an enclosed office but may also include the need for audio-visual presentation. This capability invites the use of variable illumination and multiple sets of luminaires to highlight a presentation wall. The target average illuminance is in the range of 30 to 40 fc (see Figure 5-27).

To assure that lights are on only when needed, occupancy-based controls should be applied to individual private offices. The best performance is achieved with vacancy mode (manual ON/ automatic OFF) occupancy sensors. For highest employee comfort and productivity and energy efficiency, multilevel switching or dimming controls allow each staff person to set his or her

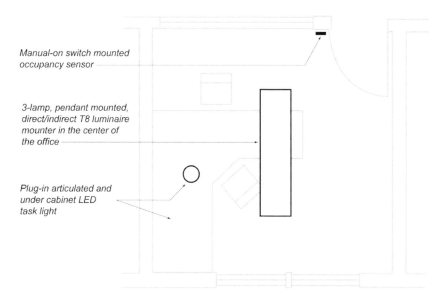

Manual-on switch mounted occupancy sensor

3-lamp, pendant mounted, direct/indirect T8 luminaire mounter in the center of the office

Plug-in articulated and under cabinet LED task light

Figure 5-26 (EL19) Small Office Lighting Plan

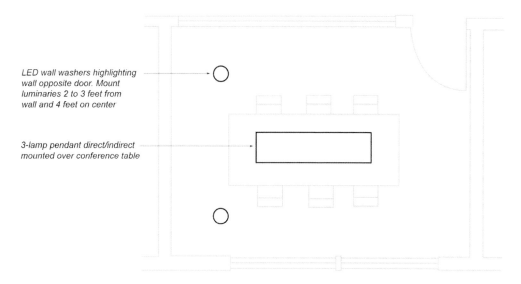

LED wall washers highlighting wall opposite door. Mount luminaries 2 to 3 feet from wall and 4 feet on center

3-lamp pendant direct/indirect mounted over conference table

Figure 5-27 (EL19) Conference Room Lighting Plan

lights according personal preference. Energy savings from personal controls can range from 15% to 50%.

EL21 *Lighting Control for General Public Spaces— Lobbies, Waiting Rooms, Public Corridors, and Atriums* (Climate Zones: all)

In atriums, lobbies, waiting rooms, corridors, and other spaces in which daylight is used, daylight harvesting controls should be considered to regulate the output of electric lights to automatically optimize the quality of the visual environment while saving significant amounts of energy. Step-dimming systems can be applied where abrupt incremental changes in ambient electric light levels will not be a distraction to occupants. In spaces where it is desired that adjustments in ambient electric light be transparent to the occupants, continuous-dimming systems should be applied.

Where appropriate, time clock controls should be applied to optimize the ON/OFF times of the lighting in select public areas. Areas should also be identified where a night setback light level is appropriate, where motion sensors can be used to override the setback status if staff or visitors enter the space.

EL22 *Electroluminescent Signage (LEC)* (Climate Zones: all)

Incandescent exit signage draws an average of 40 W per sign. LED exit signs draw an average of 4 W per sign. Electroluminescent exit signs draw less than 0.2 W and can last for 20 years with no maintenance. For a large hospital, it is not unusual to have over a thousand exit signs, which means a savings of 70,080 kWh/yr over incandescent signs and 7008 kWh/yr over LED signs. At roughly the same initial cost as an LED sign, LEC has an instant economic payback. Because they have no lamp strings or waste heat, LEC signs have extremely long lives compared to other kinds of incandescent signs.

EXTERIOR LIGHTING

Large hospitals can generally be expected to have a combination of surface and structured parking in addition to walkway and green-space lighting. Because of their constant operation and need to ensure patient and employee security, hospitals tend to both overlight these spaces and to keep lights turned on around the clock instead of taking advantage of daylighting and sensor opportunities.

The Commercial Building Energy Alliance (CBEA) has published free specifications for both site and structured parking that are completely adaptable or usable as-is and can achieve required lighting performance for as little as 0.18 W/ft^2. The specifications are available for free download:

LED Site (Parking Lot) Lighting Specification
http://www1.eere.energy.gov/buildings/alliances/parking_lot_lighting.html

High Efficiency Parking Structure Lighting
http://www1.eere.energy.gov/buildings/alliances/parking_structure_spec.html

The following recommendations are provided for design of parking lots, building exteriors, and grounds.

EL23 *Exterior Lighting Power* (Climate Zones: all)

Exterior LPD allowances in ASHRAE/IESNA Standard 90.1-2004 (ASHRAE 2004) are broken into two categories: tradable and nontradable. The only nontradable area for a large hospital is for the ambulance and emergency vehicle loading area. Many facility operators may be reluctant to significantly reduce lighting below standard levels due to concerns for safety, security, and community presence, which in many situations, are valid. However, most of the exterior areas are in the tradable category and located in portions of the hospital site appropriate for lighting power reduction and should be implemented there.

The recommended limit of exterior lighting power for lighting parking lots, driveways, and paved grounds is 0.10 W/ft^2. Design lighting to keep light limited to paved areas and off of grounds that do not require lighting. Design walkways and sidewalks to use less than 0.8 W per lineal foot, and areas under drop-off canopies should use less than 1.0 W/ft^2.

Parking lot lighting should not be significantly brighter than lighting of the adjacent street. Follow IESNA RP-33-1999 (IESNA 1999) for uniformity and illuminance recommendations. Further savings are available by reducing parking lighting levels by 50% between midnight and 6:00 a.m.

Caution: carefully design parking lot and grounds lighting so that luminaire wattage is not increased in an attempt to use fewer lights and poles. Increased contrast reduces visibility at

Cleveland Clinic 100th Street Garage

Cleveland Clinic is a large, multispecialty, not-for-profit, academic medical center whose main campus is located in Cleveland, Ohio. In 2011, Cleveland Clinic used the CBEA high-efficiency parking structure lighting specification as the basis of award for conversion of their 100th Street garage from high-pressure sodium to LED. The garage is 970,250 ft^2 with over 1500 parking spaces on six partially closed floors and a rooftop level. There are 830 main garage fixtures, 28 site lighting fixtures on the roof, and 65 stairwell fixtures. In addition to being a lower wattage source, LED allowed step dimming not possible with the existing lights. 620 of the replacement lights used occupancy sensors to toggle between a high and low power setting, and the 218 fixtures closest to the perimeter used photo and occupancy sensors.

The energy savings per year is 1,276,583 kWh per year, yielding a 4.2 year simple payback. With utility incentives, the payback was reduced to 3.2 years. In addition to the energy savings, the higher quality light allowed a better performance for existing security cameras and an overall "safer" feeling for patients and staff.

night beyond the immediate fixture location. Do not use floodlights and noncutoff wall-packs, as they can cause glare and light trespass onto neighboring properties.

Façade lighting can improve safety and security, but limit it to 0.15 W/ft^2 or 3 W per lineal foot of illuminated surface. This does not include lighting of walkways or entry areas that may also light the building. To control unwanted glare from patient-room windows, keep the lighting equipment mounting locations on the building and do not install floodlights onto nearby parking lot lighting standards. Use downward-facing lighting to mitigate light trespass and light pollution concerns.

EL24　*Sources* **(Climate Zones: all)**

All general lighting luminaires should use pulse-start metal halide, induction, solid-state LED, linear fluorescent, or compact fluorescent amalgam lamps with electronic ballasts. These sources should have an initial efficacy of at least 60 lm/W. In addition, consider the following:

- Standard high-pressure sodium lamps are not recommended because of their reduced visibility and poor color-rendering characteristics.
- Incandescent lamps are not recommended.
- For colder climates (Climate Zones 6, 7, and 8), fluorescent lamps and CFLs are subject to reduced light output and starting complications. If used in these climates, they should be in enclosed luminaires and provided with cold-temperature ballasts. Use CFL lamps with amalgam to maintain light output.

REFERENCES AND RESOURCES

ASHRAE. 2004. ANSI/ASHRAE/IESNA Standard 90.1-2004, *Energy Standard for Buildings Except Low-Rise Residential Buildings*. Atlanta: ASHRAE.

ASHRAE. 2007. ASHRAE/IESNA Standard 90.1-2007, *Energy Standard for Buildings Except Low-Rise Residential Buildings*. Atlanta: ASHRAE.

ASHRAE. 2010. ASHRAE/IES Standard 90.1-2010, *Energy Standard for Buildings Except Low-Rise Residential Buildings*. Atlanta: ASHRAE.

Brown, G.Z., J. Kline, G. Livingston, B. McDonald, C. Smith, M. Wilkerson, J. Brickman, and D. Staczek. 2005. Daylighting hospital patient rooms in Northwest hospitals. A joint study of the University of Oregon's Energy Studies in Buildings Laboratory and Zimmmer,

Gunsul, and Frasca Architects LLP. (Summary located at Betterbricks: http://www.better-bricks.com/graphics/assets/documents/Daylighting_Patient_Rooms_brochure_final.pdf).

Burpee, H., A. Helmers, K. Feliciano. 2011. Targeting 100! Legacy Salmon Creek Medical Center, Patient Room Lighting Report. University of Washington, College of Built Environments, Integrated Design Lab, Seattle, WA. http://idlseattle.com/Health/study_hospital.html.

IESNA. 1998. IESNA RP-20-1998, *Recommended Practice on Lighting for Parking Facilities.* New York: Illuminating Engineering Society of North America.

IESNA. 1999. IESNA RP-33-99, *Recommended Practice on Lighting for Exterior Environments.* New York: Illuminating Engineering Society of North America.

IESNA. 1994. IESNA DG-5-94, *Lighting for Walkways and Class I Bikeways.* New York: Illuminating Engineering Society of North America.

IESNA. 2000. *IESNA Handbook,* 9th ed. New York: Illuminating Engineering Society of North America.

IESNA. 2003. *IES G-1-03, Guideline on Security Lighting for People, Property, and Public Spaces.* New York: Illuminating Engineering Society of North America

IESNA. 2006. ANSI/IESNA RP-29-2006, *Lighting for Hospitals and Healthcare Facilities.* New York: Illuminating Engineering Society of North America.

IESNA. 2008. IESNA Standard LM-79-2008, *Approved Method for the Electrical and Photometric Testing of Solid-State Lighting Devices.* New York: Illuminating Engineering Society of North America.

Joseph, A. 2006. The Impact of Light on Outcomes in Healthcare Settings. Paper funded by a grant from the Robert Wood Johnson Foundation. The Center for Health Design, Concord, CA.

U.S. Congress. 2007. *Energy Independence and Security Act of 2007*, SEC. 324. Metal Halide Lamp Fixtures. Bill H.R.6, Public Law:110–140.

PLUG AND PROCESS LOADS

EQUIPMENT AND CONTROL

PL1 *General Guidance* (Climate Zones: all)

Plug and process loads (PPL) in a hospital are diverse and represent many different types of energy consumption loads. They can be typical "plug in" equipment, such as copy machines, vending machines, refrigerators, coffee machines, etc. These loads also include office and medical technology, such as computers, printers, interactive whiteboards, and coffee makers, as well as infusion pumps, monitors, and anesthesia carts. PPL also include low-voltage systems and miscellaneous building loads, such as elevators, security cameras and monitors, portable heaters, fire alarm systems, temperature control systems, and ejection pumps. It is important to understand, minimize, and account for all plug loads when designing a hospital.

PPL provide a significant opportunity for energy savings. Without accounting for kitchen loads, they consume a significant portion of the hospital's energy, depending on climate zone and the relative efficiencies of other building systems. As the HVAC and lighting systems become more energy efficient, the PPL percentage of total building energy increases unless energy reduction strategies are addressed. Many PPLs constitute a continuous energy load. These may include servers, refrigeration equipment, security, etc. that cannot be avoided. Other PPL can be deactivated to conserve energy when not in use.

PL2 *Computer (Information Technology) Equipment* (Climate Zones: all)

Hospital computer equipment considerations need to include the main distribution frame (MDF) room; intermediate distribution frame (IDF) rooms; individual workstations; and television, intercom, and security systems. The MDF and IDF room energy consumption can be significant, and the energy use there is relatively constant. More and more individual devices are mobile and

Computer Power Management
Saving Millions while Computers Sleep

University of Pittsburgh Medical Center (UPMC) is an $8 billion integrated global health enterprise headquartered in Pittsburgh, PA. The 450 clinical facilities and 20 hospitals cover approximately 15 million ft^2 and contain roughly 49,000 desktop computers.

Rather than rely on standard sleep or shutdown systems, UPMC chose to employ an IT energy-management platform from an outside vendor. This software centrally administers power settings for approximately 30,000 PCs across the health system's network. The software places PCs in lower power states or "sleep mode" without interfering with end-user productivity, desktop maintenance, or upgrades. Start up of the system was staged in two phases (nonclinical and clinical) and deployment was phased by building and user group. Full deployment required approximately one year due to conflicting operating priorities, but the system start up went smoothly with few or no problems.

Based on 2011 statistics, UPMC's annual energy consumption per desktop prior to the energy management platform was 710 kWh per year. After the installation of the platform, the annual kWh per machine dropped 28% to 514 kWh, resulting in 5.5 million fewer kWh/year and producing an annual savings of $382,000.

- Software purchase $390,000
- Vendor services $30,000
- Total project cost $420,000
- Yearly savings $382,000
- Simple payback   1.1 years

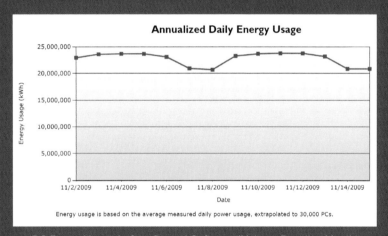

PC Power Usage before Central Software (Using a Baseline Month)

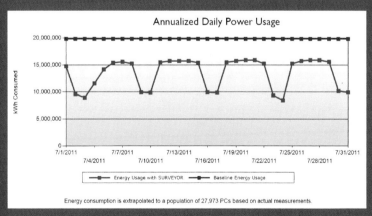

PC Power Usage after Central Software (Compared to the Baseline Month)
Figures reprinted with permission from UPMC

not plugged in except for recharging, but the rapid proliferation of electronic devices of all types must be taken into account. To reduce energy consumption by this equipment in off-peak hours, the hospital's technology coordinator should be included in the design process.

Eliminate unnecessary equipment and consolidate printing equipment to minimize the number of required devices. Use of multifunction devices that provide printing, copying, and fax operations reduce power demand from multiple devices.

Server equipment should also be selected with energy consumption as a priority. The use of laptops (or tablets) in lieu of workstation computers should be considered to minimize energy use. A laptop computer uses significantly less power than a workstation computer.

Computer systems should have network control with power-saving modes and be controlled during unoccupied hours. Despite the predominance of ENERGY STAR® features built into modern desktops, most organizations either turn these features off or use programs as marketing "screensavers" that negate the efficiency potential. Shutting down desktop computers when not in use can save significant energy. Software is commercially available that will shut off computers that remain inactive for a preprogrammable period of time. Depending on the sophistication of the software, it can also be programmed to exclude classes of computers, allow the user to remotely wake a desktop computer for remote login, and allow the IT department to wake classes of computers for periodic uploads and put them back to sleep when finished.

PL3 *Staff and Occupant Equipment Control* (Climate Zones: all)

Copiers, vending machines, fax machines, coffee makers, and drinking fountains consume power constantly when left unregulated. To reduce this load potential, consider controlling the top outlet of each duplex outlet to deactivate the power on a set schedule or via occupancy sensor. The occupancy sensor may be the same used to control the lighting in the room.

Vending machines, especially soda machines, can be a large consumer of energy if left uncontrolled. Vending machines should be delamped and equipped with occupancy sensor controls for cooling operation if applicable. ENERGY STAR rated vending machines include this type of control or can be retrofitted with add-on equipment. The soda vending machine efficiency can be improved by limiting the refrigeration compressor starts/stops to a maximum of one every three hours. This provides greater compressor run time and improves efficiency.

Power circuits for vending machines and drinking fountains without refrigeration, copy machines, coffee machines, water coolers, and other similar equipment can be controlled through a contactor interfaced to the buildings occupied/unoccupied schedule. A local override switch can activate the circuit if operation is needed outside of occupied hours.

A personal appliance policy should be created for the hospital, and constant energy-awareness training for equipment and appliances should be conducted. A hospital energy team consisting of administrators, faculty, and facility staff is an effective way of educating occupants via participation.

PL4 *Phantom/Parasitic Loads* (Climate Zones: all)

A wireless router with flashing lights is a common example of an electronic device that consumes energy when not in use. This use of electrical energy is classified as a phantom or parasitic load, and is also known as standby power or leaking electricity. Almost all electronic or electrical devices today consume phantom-levels of energy. Equipment with electronic clocks or timers or remote controls, portable equipment and office equipment with in-line transformers all have phantom loads. Phantom loads can consume up to 5% of an electrical plug load.

The best, most direct way to control phantom loads is to unplug electrically powered items when they are not in use. In lieu of directly unplugging these items, they can be plugged into a switched power strip. Occupancy sensor-controlled plug strips can also be used to power down these devices. Items can also be plugged into the occupancy-controlled outlet (See PL3). Occupants can be taught with proper instruction to plug the majority of their appliances into the power-controlled plugs.

Table 5-8   Recommendations for Efficient Plug Load Equipment

Equipment/Appliance Type	Purchase Recommendation	Operating Recommendation
Desktop computer	ENERGY STAR only	Implement sleep mode software
Laptop computer or tablet —use where practical to minimize energy consumption	ENERGY STAR only	Implement sleep mode software
Computer monitors	ENERGY STAR flat screen monitors only	Implement sleep mode software
Printer	Consider multifunction devise, ENERGY STAR only	Implement sleep mode software
Copy machine	Consider multifunction devise, ENERGY STAR only	Implement sleep mode software
Fax machine	Consider multifunction devise, ENERGY STAR only	Implement sleep mode software
Water Cooler	ENERGY STAR only	N/A
Refrigerator	ENERGY STAR only	N/A
Vending machines	ENERGY STAR only	De-lamp display lighting
TV, VCR, DVD, DVR	ENERGY STAR with flat screens and sleep modes	Many of these items are only used during peak times and should be unplugged with occupancy sensors

PL5   *ENERGY STAR Appliances/Equipment* (Climate Zones: all)

Hospital policy should require all electrical equipment and appliances placed in the facility to carry the ENERGY STAR label. See the ENERGY STAR Qualified Products page for a list of qualified ENERGY STAR products (DOE 2011a).

The recommendations presented in Table 5-8 for the purchase and operation of plug load equipment is an integral part of this Guide.

PL6   *Low-Voltage System Plug Load Specification* (Climate Zones: all)

The rapid deployment of various low-voltage systems such as fire alarms, security, building monitoring, and physiological monitoring loads can be significant and should not be overlooked when seeking to reduce overall plug-load energy consumption. Specify only high-efficiency monitors and devices when possible. Where available, use systems that distribute their power over low-voltage cabling (often referred to as power over ethernet [POE]) instead of systems that power their remote devices using local 120V plugs. POE systems are generally more efficient and consume less energy than 120V systems that use in-line transformers. Also, pay careful attention to energy consumption of various end-use devices.

PL7   *Unnecessary Equipment* (Climate Zones: all)

Identify and eliminate equipment that is not fundamental to the core function of the facility. Some evidence suggests that equipping moveable medical equipment that is commonly in short supply with radio-frequency identification (RFID) reduces the necessary quantities of such equipment by making them easier to track. Also, more and more equipment is battery powered, rather than directly connected to a power source, and should be considered (though the environmental impact of discarded batteries should also be taken into account).

KITCHEN EQUIPMENT AND DESIGN

PL8   *General Guidance* (Climate Zones: all)

Most large hospitals are designed with a complete cooking kitchen and a full cafeteria. A typical hospital kitchen includes significant refrigeration equipment, such as a walk-in freezer, walk-in cooler, ice machine, and pass-through refrigerators.

Despite the wide range of appliances in the kitchens and cafeterias and the resulting energy intensity of a particular building, the appliance selection process and best practices design strategies apply to all food service facilities. To impact the energy consumption of the kitchen, it is best to include the food service manager in the design process. Opportunities to conserve energy include the following:

- Select cooking appliances that reduce radiant heat loss to the kitchen by eliminating high-heat producing appliances, such as broilers, griddles, and ranges, and replacing them with combination oven-steamers (combi ovens), tilting skillets, convection ovens, microwaves, or appropriate lighter-duty appliances.
- Select appliances that minimize idle energy use.
- Select exhaust-hood styles that reduce exhaust air and makeup airflow.
- Select walk-in freezers and coolers with high-performance thermal envelopes and refrigeration systems. The refrigeration system should comply with Section 312 of the Energy Independence and Security Act of 2007 (DOE 2011b).
- Select ENERGY STAR equipment as a minimum standard for designs that include any of the eight appliance categories currently available. For other categories, refer to publications from the Consortium for Energy Efficiency (CEE 2011) and the Food Service Technology Center (FSTC 2011).

PL9 *Energy-Efficient Kitchen Equipment* (Climate Zones: all)

Select energy-efficient appliances, including dishwashers, solid-door freezers, fryers, hot-food holding cabinets, ice machines, refrigerators (solid and glass door), and steamers. In addition, select low-flow hot-water fixtures to minimize both water use and energy use.

The Commercial Kitchens Initiative (CKI) and ENERGY STAR Web sites provide good lists of efficiency strategies and ENERGY STAR rated commercial kitchen equipment (CEE 2011; DOE 2011a). The goal of the CKI is to provide clear and credible definitions in the marketplace as to what constitutes highly efficient energy and water performance in cooking, refrigeration, and sanitation equipment and to help streamline the selection of products through a targeted market strategy.

A number of resources are available from the Food Service Technology Center (FSTC 2011) with links and guidance on efficient design for commercial kitchens. FSTC is the industry leader in commercial kitchen energy efficiency and appliance performance testing, and has developed over 35 standard test methods for evaluating commercial kitchen appliance performance.

Note that there are only eight categories of commercial kitchen equipment in the ENERGY STAR program. There are over 35 ASTM standard performance test methods that provide a recognized method to test the capacity, performance, and energy use of appliances. Using a specification that requires the manufacturer to provide test results from an ASTM test method assures that appliances submitted for approval during construction meet the project's design energy goals. Table 5-9 lists appliances with ASTM performance test method standards (ASTM 2011).

PL10 *Exhaust and Ventilation Energy Use* (Climate Zones: all)

Design exhaust ventilation systems with proper layout of cooking equipment and proper hood design to minimize total airflow while still providing sufficient exhaust flow. After minimizing ventilation needs, consider variable-speed exhaust hood flow systems. The design and specifications of a kitchen hood system, including the exhaust hood, ductwork, exhaust fan, and makeup air need to be addressed by the food service consultant and/or the mechanical engineer, which requires sufficient collaboration and communication between these two disciplines. Additional opportunities include makeup air energy recovery using dedicated makeup air units with desiccant or flat plate heat exchangers. Energy recovery from grease-laden

Table 5-9 Commercial Food Service Appliance ASTM Standard Test Methods

ASTM #	Appliance Type
F1275-03	Griddles
F1361-05	Open deep-fat fryers
F1484-05	Steam cookers
F1496-99(2005)	Convection ovens
F1521-03	Standard test methods for performance of range tops
F1605-95(2001)	Double-sided griddles
F1639-05	Combination ovens
F1695-03	Underfired broilers
F1696-96(2003)	Energy performance of single-rack hot-water sanitizing, door-type commercial dishwashing machines
F1704-05	Capture and containment performance of commercial kitchen exhaust ventilation systems
F1784-97(2003)	Pasta cookers
F1785-97(2003)	Steam kettles
F1786-97(2004)	Braising pans
F1787-98(2003)	Rotisserie ovens
F1817-97	Conveyor ovens
F1920-98(2003)	Rack conveyor, hot water sanitizing, commercial dishwashing machines
F1964-99(2005)	Pressure and kettle fryers
F1965-99(2005)	Deck ovens
F1991-99(2005)	Chinese (wok) ranges
F2022-00	Booster heaters
F2093-01	Rack ovens
F2140-01	Hot-food holding cabinets
F2141-05	Self-serve hot deli cases
F2142-01	Drawer warmers
F2143-04	Refrigerated buffet and preparation tables
F2144-05	Large open-vat fryers
F2237-03	Upright overfired broilers
F2238-03	Rapid cook ovens
F2239-03	Conveyor broilers
F2324-03	Prerinse spray valves
F2379-04	Powered open warewashing sinks
F2380-04	Conveyor toasters
F2472-05	Staff-served hot-deli cases
F2473-05	Water bath rethermalizers
F2474-05	Heat gain to space performance of commercial kitchen ventilation/appliance systems
F2519-05	Grease particle capture efficiency of commercial kitchen filters and extractors
F2644-07	Commercial patio heaters

exhaust air is usually too expensive, especially if the exhaust and makeup air designs have been optimized.

The following commercial kitchen ventilation design guides provide additional guidance for energy efficiency:

- *Design Guide 1: Selecting and Sizing Exhaust Hoods* (SCE 2004) covers the fundamentals of kitchen exhaust and provides design guidance and examples.
- *Design Guide 2: Optimizing Makeup Air* (CEC 2002) augments Design Guide 1, with an emphasis on the makeup air side of the equation.
- *Design Guide 3: Integrating Kitchen Exhaust Systems with Building HVAC* (SCE 2009) provides information that may help achieve optimum performance and energy efficiency in commercial kitchen ventilation systems by integrating kitchen exhaust with building HVAC.
- *Design Guide 4: Optimizing Appliance Positioning and Hood Performance* (PG&E 2011) discusses the influence of appliance positions under a hood on the exhaust requirements.

PL11 *Minimize Hot-Water Use* (Climate Zones: all)

FSTC publishes a hot-water system design guide for commercial kitchens that provides key information to restaurant designers and engineers on how to achieve superior performance and energy efficiency with their systems. The design guide, *Improving Commercial Kitchen Hot Water System Performance: Energy Efficient Water Heating, Delivery and Use* (Fisher-Nickel 2010), reviews the fundamentals of commercial water heating and describes the design process, including the following topics:

- Reducing hot-water use of equipment while maintaining performance
- Increasing the efficiency of water heaters and distribution systems
- Improving hot-water delivery performance
- Incorporating "free heating" technologies, such as waste heat recovery and solar preheating

PL12 *High-Efficiency Walk-in Refrigeration Systems* (Climate Zones: all)

Energy-efficiency improvements for walk-in refrigeration systems were included in the 2007 amendments to the Energy Policy and Conservation Act. Walk-in boxes that have 3000 ft^2 or less of floor area are subject to the regulations. The important improvements for all walk-ins manufactured after January 1, 2009, are as follows:

- Automatic door closers (to ensure complete closure when the door is within 1 in. of full closure)
- Strip curtains or spring-hinged doors (to minimize infiltration whiles doors are open)
- Insulation ratings of at least
  a. R-25 for walk-in cooler walls, ceiling, and doors
  b. R-32 for walk-in freezer walls, ceiling, and doors
  c. R-28 for walk-in freezer floors
- Electronically commuted motors (ECM) or three-phase motors for evaporator fans rated at 1 hp or less
- Permanent-split capacitor (PSC), ECM, or three-phase motors for condenser fans rated at 1 hp or less
- High-efficacy internal lighting sources (e.g., 40 lm/W or less, including ballast, unless on a timer that shuts lights off after 15 minutes)

Energy performance metrics are still being defined and may be published by the Department of Energy in 2012.

Energy efficiency improvements on the refrigeration side include variable volume compressors, staged compressors, floating-head pressure controls, liquid pressure amplifiers, subcooling liquid refrigerant, and evaporative condensers. Consider the following system technologies, as

Table 5-10   Refrigeration Technology Savings Estimates and Applications

Technology	Estimated Savings Potential (NRC 2011)	Applicable To New Construction?	Applicable To Retrofit?
Floating head pressure controls	3% to 10%	Yes	Yes
Liquid pressure amplifier	Up to 20%	Yes	Yes
Subcooled liquid refrigerant			
Oversized condenser	5% to 9%	Yes	No
Mechanical subcooler	Up to 25%	Yes	Yes
Evaporative condensers	3% to 9%	Yes	Yes

recommended by National Resources Canada (NRC 2011), but note that they may not have additive effects on reducing energy use if combined. Estimated savings for these technologies are shown in Table 5-10.

- *Floating-head pressure controls* applied to systems with outdoor air-cooled condensers take advantage of low air temperatures to reduce the amount of work for the compressor by allowing the head pressure to vary with outdoor conditions. This reduces compressor load and energy consumption and can extend compressor life. The technology is standard on many new systems and can be added to existing systems.
- *Liquid pressure amplifiers* are small refrigerant pumps that reduce capacity loss at low head pressures when outdoor temperatures are cool by raising the liquid line pressure. Using liquid pressure amplifiers on air-cooled systems increases efficiency as ambient temperature drops.
- *Subcooled liquid refrigerant* results in a lower evaporator temperature and reduces load on the compressor. There are two ways to accomplish this:
  a. Using an oversized condenser or an additional heat exchanger that increases the heat exchange area to the liquid-filled portion of a condenser can provide additional natural cooling to the condensed refrigerant.
  b. Using a relatively small-capacity mechanical-cooling system or a refrigerant line from a central system, the liquid refrigerant can be cooled further, which increases total system efficiency and cooling capacity.
- *Evaporative condensers* use wetted pads to cool ambient air as it enters an air-cooled condenser, which increases the condenser capacity and cools the liquid refrigerant, thus reducing compressor load compared to air-cooled equipment. Note that evaporative media require regular periodic maintenance to assure savings. Ensure this maintenance is done properly. This technology works in climates with a large wet-bulb depression. Evaporative condensers, where a tubular coil is directly wetted by the spray water, can also be used to achieve substantial energy savings on the order of 50% or more over air-cooled systems. These units operate similarly to closed-circuit cooling towers, except that the system refrigerant is condensed directly in the tubes. Note that in such installations, the refrigerant charge is increased over a typical water-cooled system.

PL13   Position Hooded Appliances to Achieve Lower Exhaust Rates (Climate Zones: all)

Research sponsored in part by ASHRAE (2005) shows that the position of appliances under a hood can make a significant difference in the required exhaust rate—up to 30%. Some key recommendations are as follows:

- Position heavy-duty equipment in the middle of the cook line.
- If a heavy-duty appliance is on the end, a side panel or end wall is imperative.
- Fryers and broilers should not be placed at the end of a cook line. Ranges can be located at the end of cook line because, under typical operating conditions, the plume strength is not as high as that of broilers.

- Locate double-stacked ovens or steamers at the end of the hood. This has a plume-control effect that tends to assist capture and containment.

Positioning of appliances requires approval of the kitchen manager and kitchen consultant. If these recommendations are followed, let the kitchen hood manufacturer and design mechanical engineers know why these decisions were made, and reference the ASHRAE research or the Food Service Technology Design Guide 4 (PG&E 2011). The resulting design exhaust and makeup air rates should be less than those of a conventional design.

PROCESS LOADS

PL14   *Large Medical Equipment* (Climate Zones: all)

Healthcare facilities can include various kinds of equipment that contribute to different processes within the building either directly (as in an imaging machine) or indirectly (as in a sterilizer). In healthcare facilities, there is an overlap between process loads and plug loads (infusion pumps, otoscopes, blood pressure cuffs, monitoring equipment, and computers used for electronic health records that also plug into 120V receptacles).

Most large imaging equipment consume significantly lower electricity during periods of nonuse (CTs and MRIs). Savings can be achieved by reviewing equipment power use and coordinating needed cooling loads during unoccupied periods. Reducing airflow to only that needed to keep the equipment in the desired temperature and humidity range can eliminate reheat and excess air. Imaging equipment can have a variable-air-volume (VAV) system with minimum airflow set to zero during unoccupied times. The heat of the equipment will be offset by cooling to keep the equipment in the proper temperature range.

If imaging or radiation equipment requires a supplemental cooling loop, it may be more efficient to create a separate equipment loop. This loop may be able to operate at higher temperatures and be less susceptible to variations that commonly occur in larger cooling loops due to normal space temperature control fluctuations. This allows the larger cooling loop to take advantage of temperature and or pressure reset strategies that may otherwise be limited by imaging equipment support.

PL15   *High-Performance Laundry Equipment* (Climate Zones: all)

The size of textile care operations can vary greatly between the types and sizes of healthcare facilities they are designed to support. With the exception of some physical therapy centers, typically, outpatient facilities do not have an on-premise laundry. Hospitals have significant laundering needs that usually run about 2% of their total operating budget. In some cases they have an on-premise laundry, but otherwise they contract with outside or off-site resources for their textile care needs. There are examples where competitive hospital organizations have come together to help fund a centralized laundry facility because it was the most economical solution for all of them. Large laundries can take advantage of economies of scale and realize greater efficiencies throughout their operations. Tunnel washers, ironers with feeders and folders, washers with high-speed extract, ozone laundry systems, water reuse systems, and improved linen management systems can all significantly lower water, energy, labor, and linen replacement costs. New technology, better management, and larger state-of-the-art equipment can use far less water and energy to clean linen, as compared to older, traditional laundering methods. Conventional commercial washers consume approximately 1.2 gal of hot water per pound of laundry processed. New water-conserving commercial washers consume approximately 0.9 gal of hot water per pound of laundry. These improvements in washer efficiency add up to sizable water and energy savings over time.

Ozone laundry washing systems can dramatically reduce the amount of water and energy used for textile care each day. Ozone and its derivatives are powerful oxidizers that replace many of the chemicals normally used in traditional laundering methods. Water must be cold for ozone to dissolve into it, and the colder the water is, the more efficiently it works. Ozone will absolutely not dissolve into water that is above 95°F. These rules are what provide the exceptional energy savings that can be delivered by an effective ozone laundry system. All light- to medium-soiled linen and most medium- to heavily-soiled linen can be very effectively cleaned and sanitized with cold water and a proper, uniform dose of dissolved ozone. In a traditional laundry, 70% of the water used is heated by as much as 100°F or more. This can be reduced to 10% or less with a good ozone laundry system.

Another important characteristic of commercial washers is the amount of water removed or extracted during the spin cycle. Extraction efficiency is a function of the gravitational force (g-force) generated in the washer drum. Standard washers generate a g-force of only about 85 g. High-performance washers generate g-forces over 350 g. Water retained after extraction in a traditional slow-speed (85 g) machine is roughly 87.5% of the dry weight of the laundry. Washers with high-speed extract can reduce water remaining in the linen to around 50% of the dry weight of the linen. The use of ozone and the elimination of many of the traditional chemicals in the wash can enhance extraction efficiency and reduce water weight retention even further. All linen must be dry when it leaves the laundry. Therefore, all of the water remaining in the linen after extraction must be evaporated using heat in the dryers or ironers. It takes approximately 2000 Btu to evaporate one pound of water. Therefore, the more water removed from the linen before it goes into the ironer or dryer, the more energy saved drying the linen. Shorter dryer cycles equate to substantial energy savings. On average, high-performance washers use about 25% more electricity than standard slow-speed extract washers but more than make up for this increased electricity use by offsetting hot water and drying energy use.

In general, because dryers are direct-fired appliances, sending both heated air and products of combustion through the bin containing the clothes to be dried, there are very few efficiency differences among them. Adding insulation to a dryer will help retain heat and lower energy consumption, and microprocessor-controlled timers and moisture sensors can prevent overdrying and save a substantial amount of energy over time. The key to reducing dryer energy consumption the most is to reduce the retained moisture content of the linen before it is put through the dryer cycle.

PL16 *Elevators* (Climate Zones: all)

Elevators use energy to move people, to provide light, and to provide ventilation. The light and fan energy consumption for low-use elevators can exceed the movement energy consumption. ASHRAE/IES Standard 90.1-2010 (ASHRAE 2010) requires efficient (35 LPW) lighting systems and moderately efficient (0.33W/cfm) ventilation. ASHRAE/IES Standard 90.1-2010 also requires that "When stopped and unoccupied with doors closed for over 15 minutes, cab interior lighting and ventilation shall be de-energized until required for operation."

In general, traction elevators consume less energy to transport people than do hydraulic elevators. This is because traction elevators use a counterweight typically equal to the weight of the elevator cab plus 60% of the elevator's weight capacity. For example, when the cab contains enough people to equal the weight of the counterweight, the only energy required is for acceleration and deceleration. In rough figures, a traction elevator may use half the movement energy that would be consumed by a hydraulic elevator. Today, regenerative traction elevators are also available. These elevators generate power when a lightly loaded cab goes up or a heavily loaded cab goes down. As a rule of thumb, these consume 50%–60% of the energy that a standard traction elevator consumes. Traction elevators are recommended for all elevators, and regenerative traction elevators are recommended for all high-use elevators.

Elevator energy use can be furthered lowered with the following measures:

- Use regenerative technology for all elevators, not just high-use elevators.
- Specify or program lower acceleration and deceleration rates. This reduces energy use, but also increases average waiting and travel times.
- Delay the door opening by a few seconds for one- or two-stop elevators, which may result in people taking the stairs.
- Specify both higher efficacy and lower lighting levels. LED lighting offers an excellent opportunity for elevator energy savings, because LED lights are not adversely affected by

frequent switching on and off, which makes it possible to shorten switching recommendation below 15 minutes.

- Reduce fan energy from 0.33 W/cfm, which is a target that is not difficult to comply with for most elevators.
- Employ more advanced dispatching systems to minimize instances where multiple cabs respond to the same call or to decide which cab to send to which calls.

PL17   *Escalators* (Climate Zones: all)

Escalators used to be constant-speed devices. An older version of ASME A17.1/CSA B44, *Safety Code for Elevators and Escalators*, required that escalators and fast walks be slowed or stopped only manually from a position within sight of the treads, which made it difficult to conserve elevator and escalator energy. This requirement was revised in the 2007 edition of the code (ASME 2007). In response, ASHRAE/IES Standard 90.1-2010 requires that escalators and fast walks be slowed (not stopped) to the minimum speed permitted by the ASME safety code when unoccupied. Another option applicable only to downward traveling escalators that are used heavily is to include regenerative technology so that escalators generate electricity when people descend to lower floors.

REFERENCES AND RESOURCES

ASHRAE. 2005. Effect of appliance diversity and position on commercial kitchen hood performance. ASHRAE Research Project RP-1202. ASHRAE, Atlanta, GA.

ASHRAE. 2010. ANSI/ASHRAE/IES Standard 90.1-2010, *Energy Standard for Buildings Except Low-Rise Residential Buildings*. Atlanta: ASHRAE.

ASME. 2007. ASME A17.1/CSA B44-2010, *Safety Code for Elevators and Escalators*. New York: American Society of Mechanical Engineers.

ASTM. 2011. Standards. ASTM International, West Conshohocken, PA. http://www.astm.org/Standard/index.shtml.

CEC. 2002. Design Guide 2: Optimizing Makeup Air. California Energy Commission, Sacramento, CA. http://www.fishnick.com/ventilation/designguides.

CEE. 2011. Commercial kitchen initiative. Consortium for Energy Efficiency, Boston, MA. http://www.cee1.org/com/com-kit/com-kit-equip.php3.

DOE. 2011a. Find ENERGY STAR products. U.S. Department of Energy, Washington, D.C. http://www.energystar.gov/index.cfm?c=products.pr_find_es_products.

DOE. 2011b. Energy Independence and Security Act of 2007 prescribed standards. Appliances and Commercial Equipment Standards. U.S. Department of Energy, Washington, DC. http://www1.eere.energy.gov/buildings/appliance_standards/eisa2007.html.

Fisher-Nickel. 2010. Improving Commercial Kitchen Hot Water System Performance: Energy Efficient Water Heating, Delivery and Use. Fisher-Nickel, Inc., San Ramon, CA. http://www.fishnick.com/design/waterheating/.

FSTC. 2011. Food service technology center. San Ramon, CA. http://www.fishnick.com/.

NEMA. 2002. NEMA TP-1-2002, Guide for Determining Energy Efficiency for Distribution Transformers. Rosslyn, VA: National Electrical Manufacturers Association.

NRC. 2011. Business: Industrial walk-in commercial refrigeration introduction. Natural Resources Canada, Ottawa, Ontario, Canada. http://oee.nrcan.gc.ca/industrial/equipment/commercial-refrigeration/index.cfm?attr=24.

PG&E. 2011. Design Guide 4: Improving Commercial Kitchen Ventilation System Performance by Optimizing Appliance Positioning and Hood Performance. Pacific Gas and Electric Company, San Francisco, CA. http://www.fishnick.com/ventilation/designguides/CKV_Design_Guide_4_091911.pdf.

SCE. 2004. Design Guide 1: Selecting and Sizing Exhaust Hoods. Southern California Edison, Rosemead, CA. http://www.fishnick.com/ventilation/designguides.

SCE. 2009. Design Guide 3: Integrating Kitchen Exhaust Systems with Building HVAC. Southern California Edison, Rosemead, CA. http://www.fishnick.com/ventilation/designguides.

SERVICE WATER HEATING

GENERAL RECOMMENDATIONS

WH1 *Water Use Reduction* **(Climate Zones: all)**

All fixtures should be low flow for sinks and showers. Consider sensors for sinks used predominately for hand washing. Ensure that recirculation loops for hot water are close to the faucet to minimize the time needed for water to reach tempered conditions. Minimizing hot-water dead legs also reduces the risk of Legionella.

WH2 *Service Water Heating (SWH) Types* **(Climate Zones: all)**

This Guide does not cover systems that use oil, hot water, steam, or purchased steam for generating service water heating (SWH). The use of solar (RE2) and recovering energy from condenser water systems (HV38) are addressed. These systems are alternative means that may be used to achieve 50% (or greater) energy savings over ASHRAE/IESNA Standard 90.1-2004 (ASHRAE 2004) and, where used, the basic principles of this Guide would apply.

The SWH equipment found in this Guide includes high-efficiency gas-fired water heaters and heat pump or condenser heat recovery water heaters. Natural gas and propane fuel sources are available options for gas-fired units.

Many factors must be considered when deciding whether to use gas or electricity, including availability of service, installation cost, utility costs, operator familiarity, and the impact of source energy use. Efficiency recommendations for both types of equipment are provided to allow for choice.

WH3 *System Descriptions* **(Climate Zones: all)**

Gas-Fired Storage Water Heater. A water heater with a vertical or horizontal water storage tank. A thermostat controls the delivery of gas to the heater's burner. The heater requires a vent to exhaust the combustion products. An electronic ignition is recommended to avoid the energy losses from a standing pilot. Either fan-forced combustion or a flue damper should be provided. Standard heater efficiency is typically 80%, but heaters included in this Guide's recommendations have rated efficiencies of at least 95%.

Gas-Fired Instantaneous Water Heater. A water heater with minimal water storage capacity. The heater requires a vent to exhaust the combustion products. An electronic ignition and either a flue gas damper or fan-forced combustion are recommended to avoid the energy losses from a standing pilot and exfiltration due to stack effect. Using an instantaneous water heater requires increased peak input but eliminates the typical storage tank jacket heat losses for a net increase in water heating efficiency. This guide recommends heaters with a minimum rated efficiency of 95%.

Electric Resistance Instantaneous Water Heater. A compact undercabinet or wall-mounted-type water heater with insulated enclosure and minimal water storage capacity. A thermostat controls the heating element, which may be of the immersion or surface-mounted type. Instantaneous, point-of-use water heaters should provide water at a constant temperature regardless of input water temperature. The use of this type of water heater may not be advisable for patient rooms because of the considerable increase in cost of the large electrical feeders that may be required based on the large number of heaters required. They may, however, be advantageous for public restrooms and other small, remote toilet rooms. These units should be located close enough to the point of use that recirculation piping is not required downstream of each heater.

Caution: Careful attention should be paid to water chemistry and suspended solids. Instantaneous heaters are susceptible to fouling.

Heat Pump Water Heater. These units use a heat pump to heat water and simultaneously cool either the air around the heater or the fluid in a piping system (e.g., a water-to-water heat pump coupled with a storage tank that is used to heat water). Air-cooled units are usually only available in small sizes and include a storage tank. Water-cooled units are available in large sizes but must be field assembled, and many plumbing codes will require a special double-wall heat exchanger to prevent refrigerant from contaminating the potable water. If electricity is used for water heating, either centralized heat-pump-type heaters or small instantaneous electric resistance heaters located at the points of water use should be used. Air-cooled heat-pump water heaters should be located in rooms where the cooling produced is either not objectionable or a desirable feature. The energy factor for packaged air-cooled units and the coefficient of performance (COP) for water-to-water units should be at least 2.3. Another recommended option is to use recovered condenser energy to generate heating water and then transfer heat from the heating water to the domestic water. The advantage of this option is that both the heat and the cooling are beneficial. Depending on the heating water reset schedule, it is usually most efficient to preheat the domestic water to a temperature somewhat below the heating water temperature and complete the heating process with a gas-fired heater.

WH4   Sizing (Climate Zones: all)

The water heating system should be sized to meet the anticipated peak hot-water load, stated both in gallons per minute (gpm) and gallons per hour (gph). Plumbing codes include a supply fixture unit (SFU) sizing method that yields peak building gpm. In the SFU method, each hot-water-using fixture or appliance is assigned an SFU value. The SFU values are totaled for the entire building, and then a diversity factor is applied to arrive at expected peak gpm.

Where instantaneous water heaters are used, sizing is based on peak gpm. If peak gpm can be met, instantaneous water heaters will have excess capacity at all other lower demand periods.

Storage-type water heaters are sized using manufacturer-published first-hour delivery capacity, which is a combination of storage capacity and recovery capacity. If a storage water heater system can meet the largest hourly demand, the storage water heaters will have excess capacity at all other lower demand periods.

Hourly hot-water demand is calculated by assigning each hot-water-using fixture an expected hourly use then applying a diversity factor. For both instantaneous- and storage-type systems, timing of peak functional area use should be analyzed. For example, peak kitchen or laundry hot-water use may not coincide with peak shower demand. Water heater capacity may be reduced based on this analysis.

Healthcare facilities cannot operate without hot water. Should a healthcare facility be forced to close because of a lack of hot water, unacceptably high losses of both revenue and reputation would be incurred. For this reason, at least two water heaters should be included in the base design. Common diversity factors would be 50%, 100%, or N+1.

WH5   Equipment Efficiency (Climate Zones: all)

Efficiency levels are provided in the climate-specific tables in Chapter 4 for the four types of water heaters listed in WH2.

The gas-fired storage water heater efficiency levels correspond to condensing storage water heaters. High-efficiency condensing gas storage water heaters (energy factor [EF] higher than 0.90 or thermal efficiency [E_t] higher than 0.90) are alternatives to the use of gas-fired instantaneous water heaters.

For gas-fired instantaneous water heaters, the EF and E_t levels correspond to commonly available instantaneous water heaters. Gas-fired instantaneous water heaters have historically proved difficult to incorporate into a recirculating service hot-water system at periods of low or no system demand. Also, in a recirculating system, the benefit of lower standby losses with an instantaneous water heater are easily overwhelmed by the recirculating hot-water piping losses, further reducing the appeal of an instantaneous unit.

A point-of-use version of the electric instantaneous water heater is a good solution for smaller demands at remote locations. In healthcare facilities, this might occur at imaging equipment, such as a linear particle accelerator (LINAC), where a single cold-water line can be routed to the remote sink.

WH6   *Location* (**Climate Zones: all**)

Plumbing codes require that the maximum noncirculated distance from water heater to point-of-use must not exceed 100 ft. Good design limits the noncirculated distance to approximately 25 ft or less, minimizing unacceptable delays for users to receive hot water.

Healthcare facilities have a relatively high density of hot-water-using plumbing fixtures located throughout the building, so it is usually not possible to locate the water heater satisfactorily close to all hot-water demand points. Because of high service hot-water use and many demand points, healthcare facilities typically use a recirculating service hot-water system.

If a recirculating service hot-water system is used, the optimum water heater location is at the building water service entrance near the water softeners (if required) to minimize overall piping costs. Due to the premium cost for space at a water entrance room, another common location is in a remote mechanical room (a penthouse for example). Combustion air and flue gas exhaust venting requirements for gas water heaters need to be reviewed and, for aesthetic reasons, may dictate the location.

Heat tracing on hot-water supply piping may be used to satisfy code or user requirements, and advantages are noted for future remodeling projects. Disadvantages of heat tracing include maintenance and limited product lifetime. Heat tracing lends itself to longer "dead-legs" and, where waterborne bacterial control is an issue, heat tracing applications should be carefully reviewed.

WH7   *Pipe Insulation* (**Climate Zones: all**)

All SWH piping should be installed in accordance with accepted industry standards. Insulation thicknesses should be in accordance with the recommendation tables in Chapter 4, and the insulation should be protected from damage.

REFERENCES AND RESOURCES

ASHRAE. 2004. ANSI/ASHRAE/IESNA Standard 90.1-2004, *Energy Standard for Buildings Except Low-Rise Residential Buildings*. Atlanta: ASHRAE.

ASHRAE. 2011. *ASHRAE Handbook—HVAC Applications*. Atlanta: American Society of Heating, Refrigerating and Air-Conditioning Engineers, Inc.

HVAC SYSTEMS AND EQUIPMENT

SPACE PLANNING—CRITICAL VS. NONCRITICAL SPACES

HV1   *Thermal Zoning* (**Climate Zones: all**)

Thermal zoning should consider outdoor exposure, minimum airflow requirements, pressure relationship requirements, space layout and function, and occupancy scheduling. Areas that have required air exchange rates add complexity to thermal zoning. Combining dissimilar rooms can cause excessive supply airflow and ventilation airflow, both resulting in the use of unnecessary energy.

Coordinate the location of nonclinical spaces so that they can be served by HVAC systems that can be setback or shut down when their locations are unoccupied (with temperature setback control and optimized start up). Typical examples are administration and finance offices, dining, outpatient services, and occupational/physical therapy areas.

In other spaces, such as operating and procedure rooms and pharmacies, pressure relationships must be maintained. These require that the system be operated twenty-four hours a day. Such spaces should also be grouped together. Consider using an airflow setback strategy (see HV31) in constant-use spaces that are not usually occupied during off hours (nights and weekends), such as surgical suites, PACUs, procedure rooms, and nonemergency department treatment and exam rooms. The setback control can be handled automatically through occupancy sensors or timed schedules with occupant override.

Some data/information technology rooms and equipment and control rooms for diagnostic systems (e.g., MRI, CT, and linear accelerators) may need constant cooling. In outpatient facilities, this usually results in the use of dedicated HVAC systems. In-patient facilities' central systems usually operate constantly and can potentially serve these spaces as well. Redundancy is sometimes a consideration for these applications. Consider serving these spaces with a combination of both a dedicated system and connection to the central system. Operate the most efficient system as the primary and the other as the redundant (backup) system. Typically, energy efficiency is a second-level priority for these systems. This means that the designer should determine how to deliver the highest efficiency without compromising reliability.

HVAC SYSTEM TYPES

HV2   *Water-Source Heat Pumps (WSHP) System with Dedicated Outdoor Air and Boiler/Tower* (Climate Zones: all)

Typically, a separate water-source heat pump (WSHP) is used for each thermal zone for which that system type is practical. This includes office space, patient rooms, and most common areas. There are, however, limitations to this system type that make other systems preferable in some areas.

- It is difficult to provide low dew-point space conditions (e.g., 60% relative humidity [rh] in operating rooms intended for low-temperature operation).
- It is difficult to filter recirculated air beyond about MERV 10.
- Recirculated air is not permitted in some rooms, so this system is not practical.

For healthcare owners, these systems achieve large savings because of the nearly total elimination of reheat energy, reduction of energy used to dehumidify air more than is needed to satisfy the sensible loads, and fan power savings. In addition, heat recovery within the building is inherent.

This type of equipment is available in preestablished increments of capacity. The components are factory designed and assembled and include a filter, a fan, a refrigerant-to-air heat exchanger, a compressor, a refrigerant-to-water heat exchanger, and controls. The refrigeration cycle is reversible, allowing the same components to provide cooling or heating.

Individual WSHPs are typically mounted in the ceiling plenum over the corridor (or some other noncritical space), as shown in Figure 5-28, or in a closet next to the occupied space. The equipment should be located to meet the acoustic goals of the space and minimize fan power, ducting, and wiring. This may require that the WSHPs be located outside of the space.

In traditional WSHP systems, all the heat pumps are connected to a common water loop. A closed-circuit cooling tower and a water boiler are also installed in this loop to maintain the temperature of the water within a desired range, typically between 60°F and 90°F. The circulation loop should have a variable-speed pump. The circulating loop may include a controller to reset circulating-loop temperature according to exterior and operating conditions.

See HV3 for variations of heat rejection and extraction available using ground or lake sources.

Packaged WSHPs 4 tons and above should incorporate a two-stage or variable-capacity compressor with variable-speed fans and a multistage thermostat. For additional energy savings, smaller units could have similar performance. The unit should be controlled by varying fan speed so that airflow will reduce with compressor staging.

The cooling, heating, and fan performance of the heat-pump unit should meet or exceed the levels listed below.

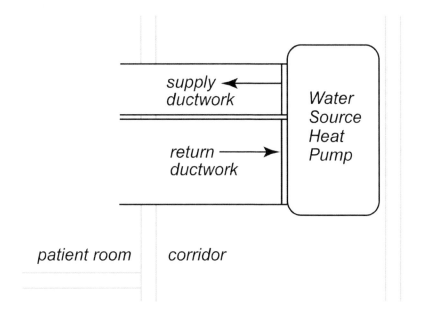

Figure 5-28   Water-Source Heat-Pump Location
Diagram courtesy of Trane, a division of Ingersoll Rand

Refrigeration. Reducing compressor energy can be accomplished in a number of ways, including, but not limited to the following:

- Two stage—lower stage at 70% and lower load, full-load greater than 70%
- Cooling energy efficiency ratio (EER), part load/full load 17.6/15.0, heating COP 5.7/5.0
- Single stage with variable-speed motor, cooling EER 16.4, heating COP 5.2

Air Delivery. The fan energy is included in the calculation for the EER for WSHP equipment based on standard rating procedures (ASHRAE 2005) that include an assumed external air delivery pressure drop. Pressure drop in the air delivery system, including ductwork, diffusers, and grilles, should not exceed 0.5 in. w.g.

Per ASHRAE/IES Standard 90.1 (ASHRAE 2010c), the WSHP unit should incorporate a solenoid valve to shut off flow of circulating loop water through the unit when the compressors are deenergized. The unit should also cycle fans when no conditioning is called for.

Outdoor air (OA) is conditioned and delivered by a separate dedicated ventilation system. This may involve ducting the OA directly to each heat pump, delivering it in close proximity to the heat-pump intakes, or ducting it directly to the occupied spaces. Depending on the climate, the dedicated OA unit may include components to filter, cool, heat, dehumidify, or humidify the OA (see HV9).

Dehumidification for Systems Serving Areas that Must only Comply with ASHRAE Standard 62.1. Basic constant-volume systems (such as most heat pumps) match sensible capacity to the sensible load, and dehumidification is coincidental. As the load diminishes, the compressor runs for shorter periods and is off for longer periods. The compressors may not run long enough for the majority of the accumulated condensate to fall into the drain pan, and the compressor stays off for longer periods of time, which may allow the remaining moisture on the coil surface to reevaporate while the fan continues to run. Some dehumidification may occur, but only if the sensible load is high enough. Space rh tends to increase under part-load conditions, unless the dedicated outdoor air system (DOAS) provides sufficiently dehumidified air to satisfy the latent loads.

For WSHPs, the DOAS should be designed to dehumidify the outdoor air so that it is dry enough (has a low enough dew point) to offset the latent loads in the spaces to maintain indoor humidity levels to comply with the 65% maximum rh recommended by ASHRAE Standard

62.1 (ASHRAE 2010b) (see HV9). This helps avoid high indoor humidity levels without additional dehumidification enhancements in the WSHP units.

Alternatively, some WSHP units could be equipped with hot gas reheat for direct control of space humidity.

Dehumidification for Systems Serving Areas with Mandatory 60% Maximum Relative Humidity. To comply with ASHRAE/ASHE Standard 170 requirements, many areas of healthcare facilities require humidity levels to be maintained below 60% rh (ASHRAE 2008). This is difficult for systems with cycling compressors, including many WSHPs. Most HVAC systems dehumidify by cooling. The 60% rh limit equates to a 54°F dew point if the space has a 90% sensible heat ratio and is maintained at 70°F, which is typical for healthcare facilities where clothing levels are relatively high (refer to ANSI/ASHRAE Standard 55 [ASHRAE 2010a] for detailed information about thermal comfort). For WSHP systems, this means a supply air temperature (SAT) of no more than 55°F (after supply fan heat is included) or that air with a lower humidity ratio must be supplied from the DOAS (see HV9). Since the heat-pump compressors normally run only in response to space temperature, they normally will not dehumidify adequately in cool, humid weather, and the DOAS should be the primary dehumidification system. If the OA requirement is low and/or the space latent loads are high, the DOAS may be required to supply air at a lower dew point than traditional systems, either by overcooling and using recovered energy for reheat (if needed) or by employing desiccant technology (HV18). The largest energy savings from WSHP systems is the elimination of the need for reheat.

HV3   *Ground Source or Lake-Source Heat Pump*

Water-source heat-pump systems are applied in four common configurations:

- Closed-circuit cooling tower and boiler systems (described in HV2)
- Ground-loop systems with tubing located in vertical wells (ground-source heat pump [GSHP])
- Lake systems with tubing at the bottom of a lake (lake-source heat pump [LSHP])
- Hybrid systems that use a closed-circuit cooling tower to minimize the cost of the well field

All the heat pumps are connected by a water piping loop. The loop temperature is kept within limits by exchanging heat with a boiler and closed-circuit cooling tower (WSHP), with the earth (GSHP), or with a lake or pond (LSHP) (ASHRAE 1997; ASHRAE 2011b). WSHP systems usually keep the water temperature within narrower limits than GSHP or LSHP systems but consume boiler energy and closed-circuit cooling-tower fan energy. Both GSHP and LSHP systems use extended temperature range heat pumps.

GSHP systems primarily do not reject heat; they store it in the ground for use at a different time. During the summer, the heat pumps extract heat from the building and transfer it to the ground. When the building requires heating, this stored heat is transferred from the ground to the building. In a perfectly balanced system, the amount of heat stored over a given period of time equals the amount of heat retrieved. This offers the potential to reduce (or often eliminate) the energy used by a closed-circuit cooling tower and/or boiler, but installation costs are higher because of the geothermal heat exchanger, and the pumping energy may be higher because of the pressure loss of the heat exchanger. Well systems have limitations if the net heat gain or loss is too unequal, because all of the net energy transfer must be through the perimeter of the well field, which is limited by the relatively low conductivity of the ground. Larger hospitals that require cooling during most hours of the year may be better served by lake systems that reject heat well and absorb it poorly. Geothermal heat pumps can be transitioned to a hybrid system with the addition of a closed-circuit cooling tower and/or a boiler at a future date should the cooling needs increase or the field become saturated and additional heating or cooling capacity is required.

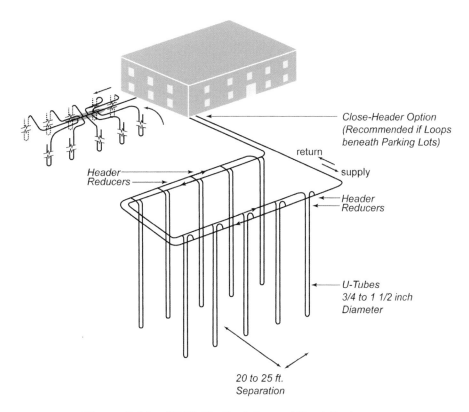

Close-Header Option
(Recommended if Loops
beneath Parking Lots)

return

supply

Header
Reducers

Header
Reducers

U-Tubes
3/4 to 1 1/2 inch
Diameter

20 to 25 ft.
Separation

Figure 5-29 (HV3) Vertical Ground Heat Exchanger
Source: Figure 10, Chapter 32 (Geothermal Energy) of the
2011 ASHRAE Handbook—HVAC Applications

LSHP systems are very similar to GSHP systems but have much greater heat rejection capability per acre of property covered by the heat exchanger and much lower cost per ton of heat rejection capacity. The greater heat rejection can be attributed to the evaporation effect from the lake's surface. Large healthcare facilities tend to need much more cooling than heating on an annual basis. The large imbalance of heat rejected and extracted poses a problem for GSHP systems, which may increase the ground temperature excessively if there is too much imbalance. Lakes, however, have more heat rejection capacity than heat extraction capacity and are generally best matched to buildings that are usually in cooling mode.

GSHP and LSHP systems both offer other advantages compared to conventional WSHP systems and conventional system. The central plant is substantially reduced in size, which lowers building construction costs. The sizes of boilers and cooling towers are reduced greatly because they condition much less of the facility. The noise and legionella potential from the cooling towers is reduced greatly. These advantages must be weighed against the added cost of the ground or lake heat exchanger.

A typical ground heat exchanger includes many vertical pipe bores, typically 200 to 600 ft deep. An example is shown in Figure 5-29. Multiple vertical pipe bores are circuited together with horizontal piping and typically ganged together in a piping vault. From the vault, supply and return pipe mains are routed to the building and all the heat pumps. The water may be recirculated via a central pumping system or a distributed pumping system where individual pumps are located at each heat pump.

For large healthcare facilities with large internal loads, GSHP systems are most appropriate in climate zones 5, 6, and 7 where cooler climates tend to balance the heating and cooling. LSHP systems are most appropriate in climate zones 1 through 6. Designers should carefully consider the annual and daily heat balance and heat exchanger size and design to avoid exceeding the allowable ground or lake temperature limits (e.g., freezing the lake).

Lake-Coupled Geothermal System

Located in Elgin, IL, Sherman Hospital's new greenfield facility replaced a 100-year-old building in the downtown area when it opened in September 2009. Included in the 255-bed facility is a six-floor inpatient bed tower, private patient rooms, Level II trauma center, emergency department, cancer center, cardiac care center, radiology, women's diagnostic center, kitchen, and cafeteria.

Built with a $200,000,000 budget and constructed on a former 154-acre farmstead, the 650,000 ft2 building sits next to a 15-acre man-made lake and features the largest lake-coupled geothermal system in the world today. The lake serves as the energy source for the geothermal system. It is estimated to save 30% to 40% of Sherman's space conditioning costs and upwards of a million dollars a year. The system qualified Sherman for a $400,000 grant from the Illinois Clean Energy Community Foundation.

The use of geothermal technology provides clean, reliable, renewable, environmentally friendly energy that replaces fossil fuel consumption. It offers significant operational savings and eliminates the need for cooling towers. The mechanical plant size is reduced, and shaft sizes are 10% smaller compared to conventional ducted heating and cooling systems, because a portion of the energy is supplied hydronically. The geothermal system's constant, steady supply of energy is well-suited to a hospital that is occupied 24 hours a day. In addition to its role as an efficient energy source, the lake provides therapeutic value, connecting a healthy campus with personal health.

The 18 ft-deep lake provides 2400 tons of cooling, with room to expand to 3400 tons as the campus grows. Loops of piping structured in 30 x 8 ft preassembled grids are floated to the bottom of the lake. The system features 177 miles of polyethylene pipe, 175 heat exchangers, and 757 water-to-air heat pumps to circulate energy throughout the facility.

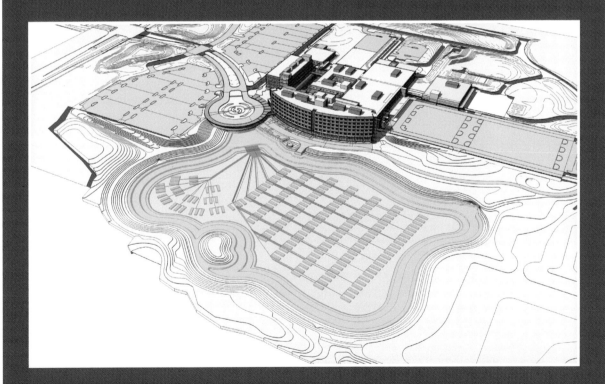

Lake-Coupled Geothermal System
Source: KJWW Engineering Consultants

A hybrid system can be used to account for the imbalance between heat stored and heat extracted in the extreme climate zones. For example, in a cooling-dominated climate such as climate zones 1 or 2, a large amount of heat must be rejected to the ground during the cooling season, but a much smaller amount of heat is extracted from the ground during the heating season. This imbalance can cause the temperature of the ground surrounding the ground heat exchanger to increase over time. Conversely, in a heating-dominated climate such as climate zones 6 or 7, a relatively small amount of heat is rejected to the ground during the cooling season, but a much larger amount of heat must be extracted from the ground during the heating season. In this case, the ground temperature can decrease over time. A hybrid approach involves adding a closed-circuit cooling tower to the loop for a system that is installed in a cooling-dominated climate or adding a boiler to a system in a heating-dominated climate. Hybrid systems can also significantly reduce the first cost of the system by reducing the size of the well fields or lake-source heat exchangers. This can make the system much more cost effective while still saving a great deal of energy. Hybrid systems reduce risk by providing an additional means of heat rejection should the ground become saturated or the site experience well failures.

HV4 *Mixed-Air VAV System with Separate OA Treatment* (Climate Zones: all)

In this system, a central VAV air-handling unit cools recirculated air to serve several individually controlled zones. OA is pretreated prior to being mixed with return air.

The components of the VAV air-handling unit include OA dampers and return air dampers (to allow for air-side economizing, when used), filters (see HV26), fans, cooling coil, and controls.

The components of the VAV terminal units include two airflow modulation devices and controls. VAV terminal units are typically installed in the ceiling plenum above the occupied space or above an adjacent corridor. However, the equipment should be located to meet the acoustic goals of the space, permit access for maintenance, and minimize fan power, ducting, and wiring.

For each healthcare space in which ASHRAE/ASHE Standard 170 (ASHRAE 2008c) requires a minimum air change rate, the VAV terminal unit in the supply duct modulates supply airflow to maintain space temperature but not below the minimum air change rate required. This minimum air change rate is reduced during unoccupied periods, but any required space-to-space pressure relationships must still be maintained (see HV31). Note that if the minimum air change rate required for a zone is higher than the design airflow needed for cooling or heating, the supply airflow to that zone is constant during occupied periods (see HV10).

For each healthcare space in which ASHRAE/ASHE Standard 170 requires either positive or negative pressure with respect to adjacent spaces, a motorized damper or VAV terminal unit is also included in the return duct from that space. The VAV terminal unit in the supply duct modulates supply airflow to maintain space temperature and/or maintain the minimum air change rate required, and the VAV terminal unit in the return duct modulates to maintain either a positive or negative pressure in the space (through direct pressure measurement or by controlling to an offset from supply airflow rate (see HV31 for additional information). Use caution when selecting return air VAV terminals to minimize air-side pressure loss.

All VAV terminal units served by each air-handling unit are connected to a common air distribution system for which supply air temperature is reset aggressively. The amount of outdoor air varies according to ASHRAE Standard 62.1 multiple space equation (see HV10). ASHRAE/ASHE Standard 170 could be modified by an addendum that could change the application of this method; please consult the most current addenda of Standard 170. All air-handling units are connected to a common water distribution system (see HV35). Cooling is provided by the centralized water chillers using condenser water heat recovery to reduce new energy used for reheat (HV38). Heating in the dedicated OA unit is typically provided by an indirect-fired gas burner, a hot-water coil, or an electric resistance heater.

Kosair Children's Medical Center

Kosair Children's Medical Center is located in Louisville, KY, and was built as a satellite pediatric medical center for the existing downtown hospital. The facility was occupied in 2009 and was constructed to meet current hospital design standards. It is a 70,000 ft^2 building that includes a surgery department, emergency room, radiology area, laboratory, and central sterile and support spaces. The emergency and radiology departments are in constant operation.

Geothermal System

A project priority was to construct a sustainable facility with emphasis on minimizing energy consumption. A geothermal heat pump system was chosen to achieve this energy goal. It is the first healthcare facility in Kentucky to be 100% geothermal, utilizing all individual heat pump units for room temperature and humidity control. The heat pump units are generally located in mechanical rooms or penthouses to allow good service access. All heat pump units three tons and greater are provided with dual compressors piped to a single refrigerant circuit to improve part-load efficiency.

A dedicated outdoor air system (DOAS) is provided to supply conditioned outdoor air to all rooms. The unit has an integral heat recovery wheel and supplemental cooling/heating water coil to provide final tempering of the discharge air. Water-to-water geothermal heat pump chillers supply either chilled or hot water to the coil as dictated by outdoor air conditions. The air-distribution system includes constant-air-volume (CAV) boxes to deliver code-required outdoor airflow to all rooms. Time schedules are programmed so the outdoor airflow is reduced when areas are unoccupied.

The geothermal bore field supports 220 tons of installed HVAC equipment tonnage. The geothermal field is comprised of 84 vertical bores, each 400 ft deep. The bore field supply water temperature varies from the mid 80s in August to the mid 50s in February. A distributed water-pumping system recirculates the water between the geothermal bores and building heat pump units. Each heat pump unit has an individual water recirculating pump that runs only when its respective heat pump compressor is operating.

Heat pump units that serve patient treatment areas have prefilters and final filters to meet hospital air-filtration guidelines. Low pressure drop air filters were specified, and special attention was paid to duct layout to allow the heat pump fan to deliver proper room airflow.

(continued next page)

Kosair Children's Medical Center
Reprinted with permission of CMTA Engineers

Energy Performance

The medical center is currently operating at 116 kBtu/ft^2 annually. To control energy consumption, heat pump systems offer several advantages over traditional healthcare HVAC systems. First, reheat energy waste, which occurs in all variable- and constant-volume air-handling systems is eliminated. The compressors only operate when room cooling or heating is necessary. Second, fan energy is reduced because system total static pressure is significantly lower than the standard healthcare VAV system. In addition, geothermal heat pump systems allow for distributed energy generation. Central steam boilers are eliminated along with the inefficiency of central steam production. Domestic hot water is generated via geothermal domestic water heaters. Central sterile equipment and HVAC humidifiers have point-of-use steam production. The exterior wall system is an insulated concrete form assembly.

Life-Cycle Costs

Energy performance of this facility, while great, must be balanced with the system first cost and maintenance costs. The healthcare organization that built this facility also built a full-service hospital a year earlier on the same campus. That facility used a traditional VAV system with central boilers and chillers. The geothermal heat pump system proved to be approximately the same cost to construct on a per-square-foot basis.

A walk-through of the building was performed with the maintenance staff. Since the staff services both facilities, they have experienced the time it takes to maintain each facility during the first two years of operation. The heat pump units have required only minimal service since installation, and the original concern over filter maintenance has proven unwarranted. The geothermal system has required extra time to retrain the staff, which would not have been required if a traditional system was installed. Integrating the heat pump factory controls into the healthcare systems direct digital controls has been more difficult than expected. A detailed analysis of maintenance requirements is warranted to provide factual data and a true comparison.

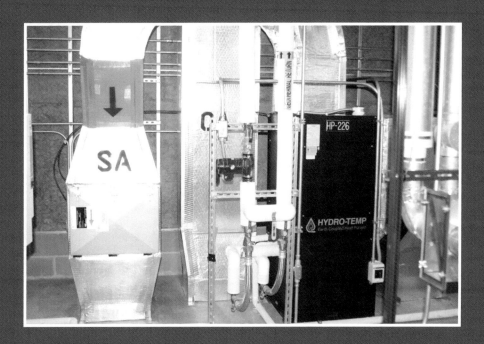

Example Patient Room Layouts
Copyright HOK. Reprinted with permission

Space heating is typically provided by terminal heating coils and perhaps supplemented by baseboard or ceiling radiant heating. System controls should minimize reheat. When hot water is used for heating, all the heating coils, along with the water boiler(s), are connected to a common water distribution system.

Cooling equipment, heating equipment, and fans should meet or exceed the efficiency levels listed in the climate-specific tables in Chapter 4. The cooling equipment should also meet or exceed the part-load efficiency level where shown.

Dehumidification for Systems Serving Areas that Must Only Comply with ASHRAE Standard 62.1. In a typical chilled-water system, a modulating valve reduces cooling capacity by throttling the water flow through the cooling coil. In VAV systems, with a controlled cooling coil discharge temperature that is maintained low enough to satisfy the zone requiring the most cooling or a maximum dew-point temperature, the dehumidification requirement is satisfied. Resetting coil discharge temperature to minimize reheat saves energy, as noted in HV20.

VAV systems typically dehumidify effectively over a wide range of indoor loads because they generally limit the maximum discharge air temperature at part-load conditions. As noted in HV17, include one or more zone humidity sensors to limit the reset if the rh within the space exceeds 65%, or limit the reset based on outdoor temperature or dew point.

Dehumidification for Systems Serving Areas with Mandatory 60% Maximum Relative Humidity. To comply with ASHRAE/ASHE Standard 170 requirements, many areas of healthcare facilities require humidity levels to be maintained below 60% rh. This is difficult for direct expansion (DX) systems with cycling compressors, especially if they have only a few stages of capacity control. Most HVAC systems dehumidify by cooling. The 60% rh limit equates to a 54°F dew point if the space is maintained at 70°F and has a typical space sensible heat ratio of 90%. For the baseline system serving noncritical care areas, this means a SAT of no more than 56°F after supply fan heat is included. The dew point required may be as low as 45°F when serving surgery rooms that are intended to operate at 60°F dry bulb. Grouping spaces on a centralized air-handling unit requires careful attention to avoid overventilating space with lower requirements (see HV1).

VAV systems typically dehumidify effectively over a wide range of indoor loads, as long as the VAV system continues to provide cool, dry air at part-load conditions (discharge air temperature control). Resetting coil discharge temperatures and mixed supply air temperatures to minimize reheat saves energy, as noted in HV20.

This system also provides the benefits and issues associated with an air-side economizer (see HV19).

HV5   *Fan-Coils with Dedicated Outdoor Air System (DOAS)* (Climate Zones: all)

In fan-coil systems, a separate fan-coil unit is used for each thermal zone. The components are factory designed and assembled and include filters, a fan, heating and cooling coils, controls, and possibly OA and return air dampers. OA supply is provided by a DOAS.

Fan coils are typically installed in each conditioned space, in the ceiling plenum above the corridor (or some other noncritical space), or in a closet adjacent to the space (see the WSHP figure in HV2 as an example). However, the equipment should be located to meet the acoustic goals of the space; this may require that the fan coils be located outside of the space while also attempting to minimize fan power, ducting, and wiring. Fan coils should be equipped with a variable-speed fan to automatically enable VAV operation and enhance motor efficiency.

All the fan coils are connected to a common water distribution system. Cooling is provided by a centralized water chiller. Heating is provided by either a centralized boiler (or by electric resistance heat in climates with very small heating requirements) located inside each fan coil.

OA is conditioned and delivered by a DOAS that may involve ducting the OA directly to each fan coil or ducting it directly to the occupied spaces. Depending on the climate, the dedicated OA unit may include a heat recovery device (see HV14 and HV15.)

Dehumidification for Systems Serving Areas that Must only Comply with ASHRAE Standard 62.1. In a typical chilled-water fan-coil system, a modulating valve reduces system capacity by throttling the water flow through the cooling coil. The warmer coil surface that results provides less sensible cooling (raising the supply air dry-bulb temperature from the fan coil), but it also removes less moisture from the passing airstream (raising the supply-air dew point). The DOAS must provide sufficiently dehumidified air to satisfy the latent loads; otherwise, this type of control may fail to comply with the 65% rh limits of ASHRAE Standard 62.1 during humid weather.

For fan-coil units, the DOAS should be designed to dehumidify the outdoor air so that it is dry enough (has a low enough dew point) to offset the latent loads in the spaces (see HV9). This helps avoid high indoor humidity levels without additional dehumidification enhancements in the fan-coil units. Alternatively, fan coils could be equipped with multiple-speed or variable-speed fans for improved humidity control and part-load energy reduction.

Dehumidification for Systems Serving Areas with Mandatory 60% Maximum Relative Humidity. To comply with ASHRAE/ASHE Standard 170 requirements, many areas of healthcare facilities require humidity levels to be maintained below 60% rh. The 60% rh limit equates to a 54°F dew point if the space is maintained at 70°F and has a 90% space sensible heat ratio. For the baseline system serving noncritical care areas, this means a SAT of no more than 55°F for draw-through fan-coils (after supply fan heat is included).

For fan-coil units, the DOAS should be designed to dehumidify the outdoor air enough to offset the latent loads (see HV9). This helps avoid high indoor humidity levels without additional dehumidification enhancements in the fan-coil units. If the outdoor air requirement is low and/or the space latent loads are high, the DOAS may be required to supply air at a lower dew point than traditional systems, either by overcooling and using recovered energy for reheat (if needed) or by employing desiccant technology (HV18).

The cooling equipment, heating equipment, and fans should meet or exceed the efficiency levels listed in the recommendation tables in Chapter 4 or listed in this chapter (HV8). The cooling equipment should also meet or exceed the part-load efficiency level, where shown. Performance requirements for ducted fan coils are (1) 0.30 W/cfm design supply air to a space with VAV operation and (2) coil chilled-water ΔTs of at least 14°F.

HV6   ***Mixed-Mode Ventilation for Nonclinical Spaces*** (Climate Zones: ❷B, ❸B, ❸C, ❹C, ❺B, **and as appropriate elsewhere)**

Compared to buildings with fixed-position windows, buildings with properly applied and properly used operable windows can provide advantages in energy conservation.

Natural ventilation involves the use of operable elements in the façade of a building to bring in OA. ASHRAE Standard 62.1 requires either engineering analysis to confirm adequate ventilation or compliance with prescriptive requirements that govern the size and spacing of the openings and as the permanent accessibility of the controls by the occupants.

Occupant-controlled naturally conditioned spaces, as defined by ASHRAE Standard 55, are "those spaces where the thermal conditions of the space are regulated primarily by the opening and closing of windows by the occupants." ASHRAE Standard 55 allows an adaptive comfort standard to be used under a limited set of conditions.

When considering either natural ventilation or naturally conditioned spaces, one must first consider the climate and the number of hours when an occupant might want to open the windows and evaluate whether a natural scheme is possible for the range of outdoor temperature and humidity. If the climate supports natural ventilation/conditioning, then the design team should also investigate the OA quality (to determine the acceptability of introducing it directly into the occupied spaces); noise impacts from adjacent streets, railways, or airports; and building security concerns. Cooling tower locations should also be taken into account when natural ventilation is considered.

A mixed-mode, or hybrid, approach uses a combination of natural ventilation from operable windows (either manually or automatically controlled) and a mechanical system that includes air distribution equipment. A mixed-mode system usually falls into one of three categories:

- *Zoned Use:* Some areas of the building are provided with natural ventilation and a mechanical ventilation/conditioning system for times when natural ventilation is not effective. The remainder of the building is served by only a mechanical ventilation system.
- *Change-Over Use:* An area of the building is naturally ventilated/conditioned for part of the year but is fully heated or cooled during extreme weather.
- *Concurrent Use:* An area of the building is naturally ventilated but artificially cooled (often via a passive radiant system).

It is important to evaluate the frequency of natural ventilation use because in mixed-mode systems, the owner is often purchasing two systems: a mechanical air-conditioning system and the operable windows in the façade.

In mixed-mode systems, the mechanical ventilation system should be shut off when windows are opened. Operable window systems can be controlled manually or by electrical interlock.

HV7   Certification of HVAC Equipment (Climate Zones: all)

Rating and certification by industry organizations is available for various types of HVAC equipment. In general, the certification is provided by industry-wide bodies that develop specific procedures to test the equipment to verify performance. Units for which certification programs exist should be certified. Certifications that incorporate published testing procedures and transparency of results are much more reliable for predicting actual performance than are certifications that are less transparent. For types of equipment for which certification is available, selection of products that have been certified is highly recommended. AHRI is one body that provides such certification.

For products for which certification is not available or that have not been subjected to certification available for their type of equipment, the products should be rigorously researched for backup for performance claims made by the supplier. The project team should determine by what procedure the performance data was developed and account for any limitations or differences between the testing procedure and the actual use. Examples of equipment types that have recognized certifications include packaged heat pumps, packaged air-conditioning units, water chillers, gas furnaces and boilers, cooling towers, and water heaters.

HVAC EQUIPMENT CONSIDERATIONS

HV8   Cooling and Heating Equipment Efficiencies (Climate Zones: all)

The cooling and heating equipment should meet or exceed the efficiency levels (both full load and part load) listed in the recommendation tables in Chapter 4. In some cases, recommended equipment efficiencies are based on system size (capacity).

A few individual zones in a healthcare facility may be served by single-zone equipment (such as packaged or split DX units). In this case, this equipment must meet the more stringent of either the requirements of local code or the current version of ASHRAE/IESNA Standard 90.1.

There are many factors in making a decision whether to use gas or electricity, such as availability of service, utility costs, operator familiarity, and impact on source energy use. Efficiency recommendations for both types of equipment are listed in the recommendation tables in Chapter 4 to allow the user to choose.

HV9   Dedicated Outdoor Air Systems (100% OA Systems) (Climate Zones: all)

DOAS can reduce energy use by decoupling the dehumidification and conditioning of OA ventilation from sensible cooling and heating in the zone. Please note that this Guide uses "DOAS" and "100% OA system" interchangeably.

The OA is conditioned by a separate DOAS that is designed to filter (see HV26), heat, cool, and humidify/dehumidify the OA and deliver it dry enough (at a low enough dew point)

Delivering Conditioned OA in Series
or in Parallel with Local HVAC Units

While no one configuration is best for all situations, every effort should be made to deliver the conditioned OA in parallel with the local units rather than in series. The parallel configuration typically results in smaller local HVAC units and less overall energy use (Mumma 2008). Parallel configurations also avoid the possibility of the supply air temperature being over 15°F above space temperature, in which case ASHRAE Standard 62.1 requires 25% more OA.

to offset space latent loads (Mumma 2001; Morris 2003). The DOAS can be equipped with high-efficiency filtration systems with static pressure requirements above the capability of some terminal equipment (e.g., fan coils and heat pumps). Terminal HVAC equipment heats or cools recirculated air to maintain space temperature. Terminal equipment may include fan-coil units, WSHPs, or radiant panels.

DOAS can also be used in conjunction with multiple-zone recirculating systems, such as centralized VAV air handlers, but most often VAV systems do not use separate ventilation systems. Separate treatment of outdoor air is recommended for the central VAV system to gain benefit of air economizer.

DOAS can primarily reduce energy use in three ways:

1. They often avoid the high OA intake airflows at central air handlers needed to satisfy the multiple-spaces equation of ASHRAE Standard 62.1 (ASHRAE 2010b).
2. they eliminate (or nearly eliminate) simultaneous cooling and reheat that would otherwise be needed to provide adequate dehumidification in humid climates.
3. with constant-volume zone units (heat pumps, fan coils), they allow the unit to cycle with load without interrupting ventilation airflow. A drawback of many DOAS is that they cannot provide air-side economizing. This is more significant in drier climates where 100% OA can be used for economizing without concern of raising indoor humidity levels.

In addition, population diversity and use of unused OA are not allowed when ventilation is provided separately.

Consider delivering the conditioned OA cold (not reheated to neutral) whenever many zones are in cooling mode and reheat only when needed. Providing cold (rather than neutral) air from the DOAS offsets a portion of the space sensible cooling loads, allowing the terminal HVAC equipment to be downsized and use less energy (Shank and Mumma 2001; Murphy 2006). Reheating the dehumidified air (to a temperature above the required dew point) may be warranted if the following apply:

• Reheat consumes very little energy (using energy recovery, solar thermal source, etc.) and few of the zones are in the cooling mode.
• All of the zones are in the heating mode.
• For those zones in the cooling mode, the extra cooling energy needed (to offset the loss of cooling due to delivering neutral-temperature ventilation air) is offset by higher-efficiency cooling equipment and the reduction in heating energy needed for those zones in the heating mode (more likely to be true on an annual basis if the reheat in the DOAS is accomplished via air-to-air or condenser heat recovery).

In addition, implementing reset control strategies and exhaust air energy recovery (see HV15) can help minimize energy use.

There are many possible 100% OA system configurations. Figure 5-30 illustrates the configuration used in this Guide, where one unit supplies conditioned outdoor air to multiple spaces, and each space has an additional unit that provides space conditioning. The salient

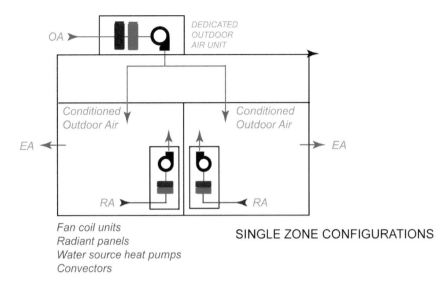

Fan coil units
Radiant panels
Water source heat pumps
Convectors

SINGLE ZONE CONFIGURATIONS

Figure 5-30   (HV9) Examples of DOAS Configurations

energy-saving features of DOAS are the separation of ventilation air conditioning from zone air conditioning and the ease of implementation of energy recovery.

When used with a WSHP system, the DOAS can be served by a water-to-water heat-pump system with performance as specified in the Chapter 4 climate-specific recommendation tables.

DOAS can also be used in conjunction with multiple-zone, air-handling systems, using a dual-path configuration that separates and treats the ventilation air upstream of mixing it with the return air. This requires use of the multiple space equation in ASHRAE Standard 62.1.

Split Dehumidification Unit. The horizontal split dehumidification unit (SDU) is a dual-path, return-air-bypass air handler. It consists of two units stacked together in a draw-thru arrangement and that share one supply fan (see Figure 5-31). All of the ventilation air (OA) is ducted to the upper unit where it is dehumidified. Dehumidification of outdoor air is accomplished through the use of subcooling, desiccant drying, heat recovery, or a combination of these. A typical leaving wet-bulb temperature (LWBT) reset control strategy is to monitor space humidities and reset the dehumidification LWBT to maintain no more than 60% rh in the maximum demand space.

The lower unit is sized to handle the return air needed to achieve the desired air-change rate in the space. The warmer return air in the lower unit mixes with the cooler, drier air from the upper unit.

The resulting mixed air provides humidity control by achieving a sensible heat ratio (SHR) of down to 0.4, but also provides sensible reheat without using new energy. The mixed leaving air temperature is controlled by modulating the cooling coil in the return air unit, with temperature reset to meet the demands of the warmest zone. In most instances, the cooling coil in the return air unit will be doing sensible cooling only and will be dry. Maximizing the temperature supplied to the room further reduces the need for zone reheat.

A vertical unit stacks the supply fan on top of a vertical coil module, and OA enters the back of the fan module. This unit is shorter than the horizontal SDU.

Outdoor air economizers can also be used with an SDU. Simply add a mixing module to the return air unit and bring OA into this mixing module when conditions permit economizing.

It is important to balance outside and exhaust/relief airflows within an air-handler zone to avoid pressure imbalances (see HV14).

Cooling equipment, heating equipment, and fans should meet or exceed the efficiency levels listed in Table 5-11. The cooling equipment should also meet or exceed the part-load efficiency levels, where shown. Presently there is no energy performance rating standard for 100% OA systems. In order to meet the 50% energy savings of this Guide, all 100% OA systems must

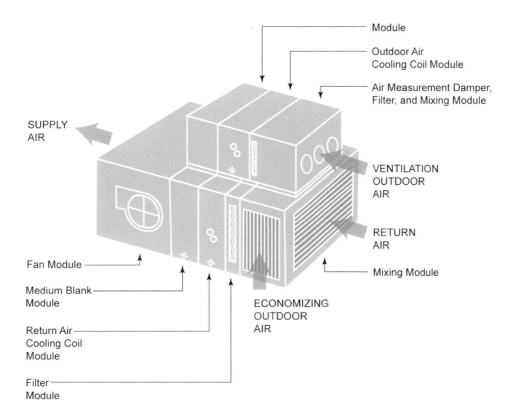

Figure 5-31 Horizontal Split Dehumidification Unit (SDU)
Source: Trane - A division of Ingersoll Rand

Table 5-11 Recommended Efficiency Levels

Item	Efficiency	Rating Standard
Fans	FEG ≥ 71	AMCA-205
Cooling-only chillers	≤ 0.55 kW/ton	AHRI 550/590
Heat recovery chillers	≤ 1.7kW/ton with 42/56 evaporator and 115/135 condenser	AHRI 550
Energy *recovery systems*	≥ 75% energy recovery effectiveness with ≤ 0.75 in. air pressure drop for each airstream	AHRI 1060

incorporate energy recovery systems so that the incoming air condition is similar to the condition of incoming mixed air in a conventional system. This Guide specifies 100% OA system performance (with heat recovery) at the standard AHRI conditions used to determine EERs and heating seasonal performance factors (HSPFs) for conventional mixed-air systems. Gas furnaces should be condensing.

Exhaust-air energy recovery is recommended on many OA systems. Systems delivering 100% OA have many different configurations. In general, energy recovery systems should be configured for no more than 1.5 in. w.g. total static pressure drop. For units that do not have EER ratings per AHRI, fans should be selected for a minimum 65% mechanical efficiency with motors at no less than 93% efficiency.

HV10 *Ventilation Air* (Climate Zones: all)

Ventilation air assists in maintaining acceptable indoor air quality (IAQ) and offsets the amount of exhausted air in order to maintain building pressure. It is air introduced into the building either naturally (via open windows) or by mechanical means. Ventilation improves IAQ by

ASHRAE Standard 62.1 and the International Mechanical Code

Many states reference ASHRAE Standard 62-2001. In May 2007, the International Code Council (ICC) approved an ASHRAE proposal to incorporate the prescriptive ventilation rate procedure from ASHRAE Standard 62.1-2004 into the International Mechanical Code (IMC). The new requirements were first included in the 2007 IMC supplement. Understand that this method generally reduces the amount of ventilation and associated energy. It may prove beneficial to check with local code officials and suggest a variance requesting to use this method since the ICC has approved it.

diluting the concentration of contaminants. In general, the more OA ventilation is used, the higher the energy use is, especially in the extreme climate zones. Project teams and healthcare organizations need to select an appropriate balance between ventilation and energy that best aligns with the goals of the project.

A first step is determining the ventilation code or set of criteria that will be used for the design. Outpatient diagnostic and treatment facilities have different ventilation criteria and standards than surgical suites and hospitals. In general, unlicensed outpatient facilities follow the building code requirements that typically reference a version of ASHRAE Standard 62.1.

Licensed facilities (e.g., outpatient surgery centers, nursing homes, etc.) and hospitals most often reference federal and state health regulations. In most states, the health departments reference the Facility Guidelines Institute (FGI) *Guidelines for the Design and Construction of Healthcare Facilities* (AIA 2010). The remaining states have developed their own ventilation requirements. The FGI Guidelines incorporate ASHRAE/ASHE Standard 170 in its entirety, including all published addenda. The code ventilation rates are the minimum requirements.

Implement strategies that minimize the energy needed to condition ventilation air. Following are some ideas.

General Strategies for Reducing Energy Associated with Conditioning Ventilation Air.

- Be sure to test unoccupied sequences to prevent unnecessary ventilation during off hours.
- Carefully group rooms on air handlers to minimize overventilation.
- Do not base the occupant density on that used for egress design.
- Typically, ventilation can be reduced if based on designed occupant densities.
- Refer to HV19 for DOAS and economizer strategies.

Strategies to Avoid Overventilation when Using ASHRAE Standard 62.1. One approach to optimizing ventilation in a multiple-zone VAV system is to combine the various demand-controlled ventilation (DCV) strategies (HV11) at the zone level (using each where it best fits) with ventilation reset at the system level.

Install carbon dioxide (CO_2) sensors only in large, densely occupied zones and those experiencing widely varying patterns of occupancy. These sensors reset the ventilation requirement for their respective zones based on measured CO_2. Zones that are less densely occupied or have a population that varies only a little (such as private offices, open-plan office spaces, or many classrooms) are probably better suited for occupancy sensors. When unoccupied, the controller lowers the ventilation requirement for the zone. Finally, zones that are sparsely occupied or have predictable occupancy patterns may be best controlled using a time-of-day schedule. This schedule can either indicate when the zone will normally be occupied/unoccupied or can be used to vary the zone ventilation requirement based on anticipated population.

These various zone-level DCV strategies can be used to reset the ventilation requirement for their respective zones for any given hour. This zone-level control is then tied together using ventilation reset at the system level, which resets intake airflow based on variations in system ventilation efficiency.

In addition to resetting the zone ventilation requirement, the controller on each VAV terminal continuously monitors primary airflow being delivered to the zone. The building automation system (BAS) periodically gathers this data from all VAV terminals and solves the equations prescribed by ASHRAE Standard 62.1 to determine how much outdoor air must be brought in at the air-handing unit to satisfy all zones served. Finally, the BAS sends this outdoor airflow setpoint to the air-handing unit that modulates a flow-measuring OA damper to maintain this new setpoint.

Strategies to Avoid Overventilation when Using ASHRAE/ASHE Standard 170. Reduce airflow rates during unoccupied periods in surgery rooms and other spaces with minimum air-change rate requirements. Systems must maintain pressure relationships at all times, even during unoccupied periods. This requires being able to control the supply and return air from these zones.

HV11   *Demand-Controlled Ventilation (DCV)* (Climate Zones: all)

DCV can reduce the energy required to condition OA for ventilation. To address IAQ, the setpoints (limits) and control sequence must comply with ASHRAE Standard 62.1 (refer to the *Standard 62.1 User's Manual* [ASHRAE 2010a] for specific guidance). If DCV in one space affects clinical spaces, ensure that this is taken into account.

Controls should vary the amount of OA in response to a zone's needs. The amount of OA could be controlled by (1) a time-of-day schedule in the BAS; (2) an occupancy sensor (such as a motion detector) that indicates when a zone is occupied or unoccupied; or (3) a CO_2 sensor, as a proxy for ventilation airflow per person, which measures the change in CO_2 levels in a zone. Employing DCV in a DOAS requires an automatic damper and sensor for each DCV zone. A controller then modulates the damper to maintain proper ventilation. This needs to be coordinated with the air-side energy recovery device as well as the air economizer (if installed).

CO_2 sensing should be used in zones that are densely occupied, such as conference and break rooms, cafeterias, physical therapy gyms, and educational spaces, with highly variable occupancy patterns during the occupied period. Consult other AEDGs if your facility contains other space types. For the other zones, occupancy sensors can be used to reduce ventilation when a zone is temporarily unoccupied. For all zones, time-of-day schedules in the BAS should be used to introduce ventilation air only when a zone is expected to be occupied.

The two primary approaches to CO_2 sensing are distributed sensors and centralized sensors. The distributed approach involves installing a CO_2 sensor in each zone where DCV is desired. The centralized approach involves sampling points in each zone but relies on a centralized set of sensors. Both approaches require scheduled maintenance and calibration, otherwise IAQ or energy efficiency may be compromised.

A CO_2 sensor should test air from the breathing zone of the room. Ventilation is controlled by comparing the measured zone CO_2 concentration to the outdoor CO_2 concentration (measured or assumed) and then modulating the ventilation control damper for that zone (refer to the *Standard 62.1 User's Manual* for specific guidance on controls and setpoints). The difference between OA CO_2 and indoor CO_2 shows how much CO_2 is being added. Therefore, both levels are required, although OA CO_2 level is sometimes assumed to be constant.

Selection of the CO_2 sensors is critical in both accuracy and response ranges. Inaccurate CO_2 sensors can cause excessive energy use or poor IAQ, so they need to be calibrated as recommended by the manufacturer (see HV12).

Finally, when DCV is used, the system controls should prevent negative building pressure. If the amount of air exhausted remains constant while the intake airflow decreases, the building may be under a negative pressure relative to outdoors. When air is exhausted directly from the zone, as required by ASHRAE/ASHE Standard 170, the DCV control strategy must avoid reducing intake airflow below the amount required to replace the air being exhausted.

HV12 *Carbon Dioxide (CO₂) Sensors* (Climate Zones: all)

This sensing strategy may have limited application in hospitals. The number and location of CO_2 sensors for DCV can affect the ability of the system to accurately determine the building or zone occupancy. Multiple sensors may be necessary if the ventilation system serves spaces with significantly different occupancy expectations. Where multiple sensors are used, the ventilation should be based on the sensor recording the highest concentration of CO_2.

Sensors used in individual spaces should be installed on walls within the space. Multiple spaces with similar occupancies may be represented by a sensor appropriately located in one of the spaces. The number and location of sensors should take into account the sensor manufacturer's recommendations for it's particular products as well as the projected usages of the spaces. Sensors should be located so that they provide a representative sampling of the air within the occupied zone of the space. For example, locating a CO_2 sensor directly in the flow path from an air diffuser provides a misleading reading concerning actual CO_2 levels (and corresponding ventilation rates) experienced by the occupants.

The OA CO_2 concentration can have significant fluctuation in urban areas. OA CO_2 concentration should be monitored using a CO_2 sensor located near the position of the OA intake. CO_2 sensors should be certified by the manufacturer to have accuracy to within ±50 ppm, factory calibrated, and calibrated periodically as recommended by the manufacturer. CO_2 sensors should be calibrated on a regular basis per the manufacturer's recommendations or every six months (per ASHRAE Standard 62.1 [ASHRAE 2010b]).

HV13 *Indirect Evaporative Cooling* (Climate Zones: **2**B, **3**B, ☀B, **5**B)

In dry climates, incoming ventilation air can be precooled using indirect evaporative cooling. For this strategy, the incoming ventilation air (the primary airstream) is not humidified; instead, a separate stream of air (the secondary or heat rejection stream) is humidified, dropping its temperature, and is used as a heat sink to reduce the temperature of the incoming ventilation air.

The source of the heat rejection stream of air can be either OA or exhaust air from the building. If the air source is exhaust air, this system becomes an alternative for HV15.

Sensible heat transfer between the ventilation airstream and the evaporatively cooled secondary airstream can be accomplished using plate or tubular air-to-air heat exchangers, heat pipes, or a pumped loop between air coils in each stream (often called a "runaround loop"). For indirect evaporative coolers that use exhaust air as the secondary stream, the evaporative cooler can also function for sensible heat recovery during the heating season. If a runaround loop is used for heat transfer both for indirect evaporative cooling and heat recovery, the circulating fluid should incorporate antifreeze levels appropriate to the design heating temperature for that location.

Indirect evaporative cooling has the advantage that IAQ is not affected, as the evaporative cooling process is not in the indoor airstream. Air quality is not as critical for the exhausted secondary airstream as it is for the ventilation stream entering the occupied space.

Indirect evaporative coolers should be selected for at least 90% evaporative effectiveness for the evaporatively cooled airstream and for at least 65% heat transfer efficiency between the two airstreams. They should also be selected to minimize air pressure drop through the heat exchangers.

AIR-SIDE HEAT RECOVERY

HV14 *Exhaust Air Systems* (Climate Zones: all)

Exhaust air systems in healthcare facilities are typically more extensive than those in other types of facilities. They not only provide odor control but also play an important role in infection control. In many cases, the amount of air exhausted from a room is chosen to create negative air pressure relative to the adjacent rooms, lowering the potential for airborne transmission of odor and contaminants. In some cases, the potential contaminants are dangerous enough that fume hoods are required or other capture scenarios are applied. The mechanical system designer should be experienced and collaborate with the healthcare organization's infection control officer and industrial hygienist.

Exhaust airflow rates and relative air pressure criteria will be listed in the ventilation standard being used. As for ventilation requirements (see HV10), outpatient treatment and diagnostic clinics or medical office buildings are likely to use a different standard for exhaust airflow rates and air pressure differences than that used by surgical or hospitals facilities. Clinics often reference local building code requirements, while surgery facilities and hospitals often reference local or state health department regulations. In many states, health departments reference the FGI *Guidelines for the Design and Construction of Healthcare Facilities* (AIA 2010) for ventilation, exhaust, and pressure requirements. In addition, ASHRAE/ASHE Standard 170 is incorporated into the FGI Guidelines. Once the applicable standard is determined, apply it to determine the exhaust flow rates and whether the exhaust systems can be cycled based on occupancy or must operate continuously.

Central exhaust systems do not typically exist in healthcare facilities, or at least are only a portion of the total exhaust. The rooms requiring exhaust tend to be numerous and spread throughout the floor plans, making it difficult to centralize exhaust air from them. They typically are combined based on location and whether they are cycled based on occupancy or must operate continuously. Care should be taken when dealing with exhaust systems that are cycled, since coordination is required to maintain required pressurization relationships. Medical terminology (such as that used for room names) varies from organization to organization, and some terms differ from one geographic region to another. It is important that the mechanical designer understand what the room name actually implies for each specific project. This allows the designer to apply the most appropriate room type listed in the reference, regardless of the room name used. For example, one of the most comprehensive lists of room types can be found in ASHRAE/ASHE Standard 170. The following from Standard 170 lists rooms that require exhaust:

- ER waiting*
- Triage*
- ER decontamination*
- Radiology waiting*
- Toilet room
- Airborne infection isolation (AII) room*
- Physical therapy
- Bathing room
- Locker room
- Darkroom
- Bronchoscopy*
- Sputum collection*
- Medical gas storage
- Pentamidine administration
- Laboratory
- Endoscope cleaning
- Hydrotherapy
- Sterilizer equipment room
- Soiled or decontamination areas
- Ware washing
- Laundry
- Soiled linen sorting storage
- Linen and trash chute room
- Janitor closet or room
- Hazardous material storage*

Following are some tips on how to save energy in exhaust systems.

- Provide motorized dampers that open and close with operation of the fan.
- Locate the damper as close as possible to the duct penetration of the building envelope to minimize conductive heat transfer through the duct wall and avoid having to insulate the entire duct.
- In climate zones 4–8, consider insulating 10–20 ft of duct that is connected to the exterior exhaust fan to avoid condensation.
- For fans that are interlocked with air-handling units, be sure to keep the exhaust fans off and dampers closed during unoccupied periods, even if the HVAC system is operating to maintain setback or setup temperatures.
- Consider designing exhaust ductwork to facilitate recovery of energy (see HV15). Avoid using exhaust from the spaces listed above that are marked with an asterisk or from lab or fume hoods or nuclear medicine, vivaria, and autopsy spaces. Use risk assessment and detailed discussions with operations personnel when considering energy recovery from air sourced from wet labs or pathology.

Food service kitchens and laundry functions may exist in healthcare facilities. However, the trend for many organizations is to outsource these services when possible. If the facility does have food service, the kitchen will generally have separate exhaust and makeup air systems (see PL3 and PL4).

Exhaust system design must ensure that there is enough makeup air to avoid placing the facility under a negative pressure. Existing hospitals are notorious for operating under a negative pressure. This results in infiltration and can lead to moisture control problems. Designers of hospital additions or connections to new facilities should be aware that new facilities often become the sources of makeup air for the original facilities. This can create problems for the new HVAC systems and cause excessive infiltration at new entries.

Provide enough treated OA to a system to equal the exhaust flow from the spaces served by that system plus some additional air for pressurization. One method for determining the amount of pressurization air is to have air in excess of the exhaust airflow equal to 4 cfm per linear foot of exterior door perimeter (e.g., 76 cfm for a 3 ft wide, 6.5 ft tall door) plus 0.038 cfm/ft^2 of exterior wall area served by the system.

HV15   *Exhaust Air Energy Recovery* (Climate Zones: all)

Exhaust air energy recovery can provide an energy-efficient means of reducing the latent and sensible OA cooling loads during peak summer conditions. In hospitals, it is recommended that HVAC system cooling and heating coils be sized for the design loads, without recovery. Upon the failure of an energy recovery device, it may not be feasible to restrict operation or shut down a healthcare facility because of the inability of the heating and cooling systems to make up for loss of the energy recovery capacity.

The climate-specific recommendation tables in Chapter 4 recommend exhaust-air energy recovery and DCV. This energy recovery device should have a total effectiveness as shown in Table 5-12.

The performance levels in Table 5-12 should be achieved with no more than 0.85 in. w.c. static pressure drop on the supply side and 0.65 in. w.c. static pressure drop on the exhaust side. See HV16 for energy recovery device information.

For maximum benefit, the system should provide as close to balanced outdoor and exhaust airflows as is practical, taking into account the need for building pressurization and any exhaust that cannot be ducted back to the energy recovery device (see HV14).

Ducting all exhaust airflows to a single energy recovery device can be difficult and costly in a healthcare facility, because locations of the rooms requiring exhaust are typically remote from each other. This first-cost impact of ducting these remotely located rooms to a central location should be investigated (see also HV14).

Table 5-12   Total System Effectiveness with Energy Recovery

Condition	Effectiveness		
	Sensible	Latent	Total
Heating at 100% airflow	78	70	75
Heating at 75% airflow	83	77	82
Cooling at 100% airflow	80	71	75
Cooling at 75% airflow	84	78	82

Where an air-side economizer is used along with an ERV, add bypass dampers (or a separate OA path) to reduce the air-side pressure drop during economizer mode. In addition, the ERV should be turned off during economizer mode to avoid adding heat to the outdoor airstream. Where energy recovery is used without an air-side economizer, the ERV should be bypassed to prevent the transfer of unwanted heat to the outdoor airstream during mild outdoor conditions.

In cold climates, follow the manufacturer's recommendations for frost prevention, and design AHUs with adequate air mixing and/or coil circulating pumps to avoid freezing coils due to stratification. Coil runaround loops also require the circulation of a water/glycol mixture to avoid freezing.

Caution: Caution should be exercised when applying rotating-wheel type recovery devices to critical care spaces because of the controversial concern about the possibility of cross-contamination of dirty exhaust air to the clean-air side of the device. Consult ASHRAE/ASHE Standard 170 (ASHRAE 2008) for guidance on which exhaust cannot be used for energy recovery.

HV16   *Exhaust-Air Energy Recovery Devices*

Sensible energy recovery devices transfer only sensible heat. Common examples include coil loops (runaround loops), fixed-plate heat exchangers, heat pipes, and sensible energy rotary heat exchangers or sensible energy wheels. Total energy recovery devices not only transfer sensible heat but also moisture (or latent heat)—that is, energy stored in water vapor in the airstream. Common examples include total energy rotary heat exchangers (also known as total energy wheels or enthalpy wheels) and total energy fixed-plate heat exchangers (Figure 5-32). Energy recovery devices should be selected to avoid cross-contamination of the intake and exhaust airstreams. For rotary heat exchangers, avoidance of cross-contamination typically includes provision of a purge cycle in the wheel rotation and maintenance of the intake system pressure higher than the exhaust system pressure. As an example, a cross-flow fixed-plate heat exchanger can have a sensible effectiveness of 50% to 70%. If the exhaust air is 70°F and the outdoor air is 0°F, this device can reduce the required energy to heat the entering outdoor airstream by 37 to 52 Btu/h per cfm of outdoor air. Consult ASHRAE/ASHE Standard 170 (ASHRAE 2008) for guidance on which exhaust cannot be used for energy recovery.

HV17   *Part-Load Dehumidification* (Climate Zones: all)

Basic constant-volume systems match sensible capacity to the sensible load; dehumidification capacity is coincidental. As the load diminishes, the system delivers ever-warmer supply air. Some dehumidification may occur but only if the sensible load is high enough. As a result, the space rh tends to increase under part-load conditions. Therefore this Guide recommends separate treatment of OA to satisfy the space humidity requirements.

Heat Pumps (see HV2, HV3) or Fan-Coil Units (see HV5). The dedicated OA system (see HV9) should be designed to dehumidify the OA so that it is dry enough (low enough dew point) to offset the latent loads in the spaces. This helps avoid high indoor humidity levels without additional dehumidification enhancements in the GSHP or fan-coil units. Care should be taken with space terminal units to minimize the chance for condensation, since condensation that is not removed via the drain pan gives the potential for microbial growth.

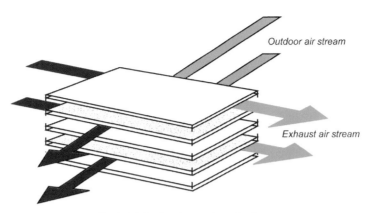

Fixed-plate heat exchanger (crossflow)

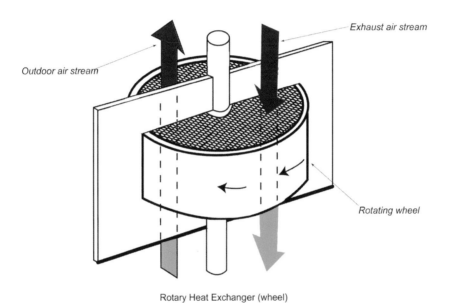

Rotary Heat Exchanger (wheel)

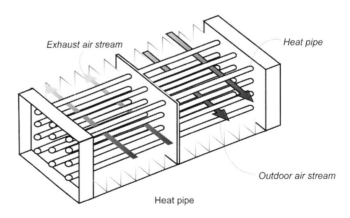

Figure 5-32   (HV16) Examples of Exhaust-Air Energy Recovery Devices

Mixed-Air VAV Air Handlers (see HV4). VAV systems typically dehumidify effectively over a wide range of indoor loads as long as the VAV air-handling unit continues to provide cool, dry air at part-load conditions. Use caution when resetting the SAT or chilled-water temperature during the cooling season. Warmer supply air (or water) means less dehumidification at the coil and higher humidity in the space. If SAT or chilled-water reset is used in a climate with humid seasons, include one or more zone humidity sensors to disable reset if the rh within the space exceeds 60% for clinical spaces and 65% for nonclinical spaces.

HV18   ***Desiccant Systems*** (Climate Zones: all)

Indoor temperature and humidity ranges for healthcare facilities are usually prescribed by local codes or by industry-accepted guidelines. But, particularly in surgery rooms, surgeons often demand lower temperatures than are stated in the guidelines. The need to control humidity at lower room temperatures can challenge conventional dehumidification approaches. Many spaces in healthcare facilities have a maximum rh limit of 60%. ASHRAE Standard 62.1 places a limit of 65% for even non-healthcare spaces.

Desiccant-based dehumidification relies on adsorption (or absorption) to remove water vapor from an airstream. These systems can deliver air at very low dew points without needing to overcool the air.

There are two situations under which desiccant systems have advantages over traditional systems that use cooling coils for all of their dehumidification.

Normal Temperature Spaces. For most spaces that maintain temperatures above about 70°F, it is not difficult to maintain 60% rh, even in humid climates, as long as the cooling coil discharge air temperature is maintained below about 55°F. On the other hand, even for these spaces this method is not necessarily the most energy-efficient option. This is because most zones in healthcare facilities have relatively high minimum air change rates. When HVAC systems deliver cold air at high air changes to spaces that don't have high cooling loads, air must be reheated to prevent overcooling. Reheat is one of the top energy uses in healthcare facilities.

One way of reducing reheat energy consumption is by using desiccant systems to reduce the dew point of the supply air below the discharge temperature from the cooling coil. This allows resetting the supply air temperature higher, which reduces the need for reheat energy. This strategy is especially useful in humid climate zones (e.g., the A and C climate zones in ASHRAE/IES Standard 90.1). In low-humidity climates, there is little advantage over traditional systems.

Low Temperature Spaces. Some zones, such as operating rooms, often need much lower space temperatures than other zones. In these zones, keeping the humidity below 60% rh is difficult with traditional systems, often requiring special features. Those features generally include either a very low chilled-water temperature for the central system (which increases chiller energy use), and/or low-temperature glycol chillers to supplement the central chilled water with a second cooling coil (which adds to the fan energy needs, low-temperature chiller energy, and maintenance costs for an additional chiller).

Desiccant systems usually also have the disadvantage of increasing air pressure drop but often reduce cooling energy substantially by not requiring low chilled-water temperatures. Another advantage is that desiccant systems can reach dew-point temperatures that conventional systems cannot reach.

Types of Desiccant Systems. There are a few methods of drying the air.

- Active desiccant systems that use heat to regenerate a liquid or solid desiccant
- Active desiccants that use condenser heat to regenerate the desiccant
- Systems that use desiccants to transfer moisture from downstream of the cooling coil to the air upstream or the coil, some of which may be exhausted, depending on the wheel configuration

All of these system types have been used successfully in healthcare applications; however, the latter two systems usually provide the lowest energy use, unless extremely low dew-point

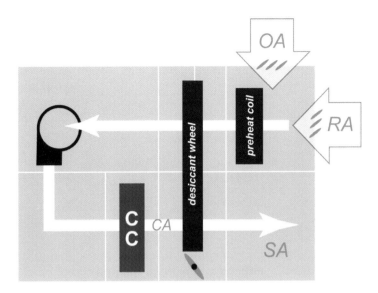

Figure 5-33 (HV18) Examples of Desiccant-Based Dehumidification Systems

temperatures are needed. In some applications, the series coil desiccant-based dehumidification system (Figure 5-33) can save energy compared to the conventional cool and reheat dehumidification approach (Murphy 2006a).

HV19 *Economizer* (Climate Zones: all)

Economizers save energy by providing free cooling when ambient conditions are suitable to meet all or part of the cooling load. Theoretically, enthalpy controls are superior to dry-bulb (sensible) controls in many situations, but practically speaking, they are less accurate and reliable. The designer of each project should consider the relative merits of fixed dry bulb, differential dry bulb, fixed enthalpy, differential enthalpy, and dew-point controls. A detailed comparison of these options is included in the *Standard 90.1 User's Manual* (ASHRAE 2007e).

Guidelines for the Design and Construction of Healthcare Facilities (AIA 2010) defines humidity requirements for individual spaces. Especially in cold and in cool-dry weather, this results in the use of energy to humidify outdoor air that is being used to conserve cooling energy by the economizer controls. ASHRAE/IES Standard 90.1 does not require economizers for systems "[w]here more than 25% of the air designed to be supplied by the system is to spaces that are designed to be humidified above 35°F dew-point temperature to satisfy process needs" (ASHRAE 2010c). This exempts healthcare spaces that are required to maintain 30% rh (unless they are always maintained below 66°F).

One way to provide the free cooling of an economizer cycle without the excessive humidification caused by the introduction of more dry outdoor air is to use a water-side economizer. This involves providing chilled water or a water/glycol mixture to a cooling coil using cooling towers coupled with heat exchangers, closed-circuit cooling towers, or dry coolers. One method is to use cold tower water to cause refrigerant migration in a water chiller to produce chilled water without operating the compressor. Water-side economizers conserve energy by minimizing humidification requirements because excessively dry outdoor air is introduced only at the minimum required outdoor airflow rate. In some climates with extended hours of low wet-bulb temperatures, this savings greatly exceeds the added energy use for additional pumps and heat rejection fans. The main disadvantage is that because of the low (approximately 54°F) indoor dew-point temperatures needed to satisfy the requirements of ASHRAE/ASHE Standard 170, it is difficult to provide 100% economizer cooling unless the outdoor temperature is below 45°F and/or the wet-bulb temperature is below 40°F.

Example of Energy Use with no Economizer, Air Economizer, or Water Economizer. The following points provide an example of an economizer energy comparison:

- An air-handling system humidifies 72°F zones to 30% rh. This is 32 grains (0.0046 lb.) of water per pound of dry air. Outdoor air is 30°F and 60% rh, which is 14.4 grains (0.0021 lb.).
- The air-handling system discharge air setpoint is 54°F, with 2°F of added fan heat, so that the economizer will be operating to provide 52°F mixed air (assuming there is no heat gain from other components in the unit).
- Supply airflow rate is 10,000 cfm.
- The minimum outdoor air requirement is 2000 cfm.
- The mixed air consists of 48% outdoor air and 52% return air. Mixed-air temperatures are 64°F with no economizer and 52°F with either economizer type.
- Cooling energy savings are 10,000 × (63.6 – 52) × 1.09 = 126,440 Btu/h.
- Humidification energy costs for the air economizer system are 10,000 × (0.0046–0.0021) × 1000 × 60/13.5 = 112,000 Btu/h.
- Pump energy for the water economizer will be approximately 1 hp (2545 Btu/h).
- Cooling tower fan energy for the water economizer may be zero or very small at this outdoor air temperature but will not exceed 1 hp (2545 Btu/h) if the tower complies with ASHRAE/IES Standard 90.1 and has variable-frequency drive (VFD) control.
- Totals
  - No economizer = 1418,828 Btu/h
  - Air economizer = 53,305 Btu/h
  - Water economizer = 27,478 Btu/h
  - Condenser reheat = –104,052 Btu/h
  (heating is reduced more than the compressor input energy)

Another method to minimize the impact of economizers on humidification energy in cold climates is to eliminate the economizer and use condenser reheat. In the example above, this option has energy consumption of –104,052 Btu/h. The total is negative because heating energy is reduced more than the compressor input energy. A higher percentage of the energy is electric, however, so the economics depend on local energy costs. The economics also depend greatly on the hours of operation and percentage of zones served that have high minimum ventilation requirements (HV10).

Periodic maintenance is important with economizers, as dysfunctional economizers can cause substantial excess energy use.

HV20   ***System-Level Control Strategies*** **(Climate Zones: all)**

Control strategies can be designed to help reduce energy. Having a setback temperature for unoccupied periods during the heating season or a setup temperature during the cooling season can help to save energy. Programmable thermostats allow each zone to vary the temperature setpoint based on time of day and day of the week. But they also allow occupants to override these setpoints or ignore the schedule altogether (by using the "hold" feature), which thwarts any potential for energy savings. Another approach is to equip each zone with a zone temperature sensor and then use a BAS to coordinate the operation of all components of the system. The BAS contains time-of-day schedules that define when different areas of the building are expected to be unoccupied. During these times, the system is shut off and the temperature is allowed to drift away from the occupied setpoint. As previously discussed, grouping "like" zones together enhances the simplicity and possible savings since groups of zones can be controlled together.

Optimal start uses a system-level controller to determine the length of time required to bring each zone from the current temperature to the occupied setpoint temperature. Then, the controller waits as long as possible before starting the system, so that the temperature in each zone reaches occupied setpoint just in time for occupancy. This strategy reduces the number of hours that the system needs to operate, and saves energy by avoiding the need to maintain the indoor temperature at occupied setpoint even though the building is unoccupied.

A preoccupancy ventilation period can help purge the building of contaminants that build up overnight from the off-gassing of furnishings or materials. When it is cool at night, it can also help precool the building. In climates with humid seasons, however, care should be taken to avoid bringing in humid OA during unoccupied periods.

In a VAV system, SAT reset should be implemented to minimize overall system energy use. This requires considering the trade off between compressor, heat, and fan energy, as well as the impact on space humidity levels. If SAT reset is used in a climate with humid seasons, include one or more zone humidity sensors to disable reset if the humidity level in the space exceeds a desired upper limit.

While a dedicated OA unit (see HV9) should deliver the conditioned OA at a cool temperature whenever possible, there are times when the discharge air temperature should be reset upward to minimize overall system energy use or avoid discomfort (Murphy 2006). Some possible strategies include resetting based on the temperature in the coldest zone (to avoid activating the boiler in a fan-coil system), resetting based on the temperature in the water loop (for a GSHP system), resetting based on the position of the furthest-closed VAV damper (in a VAV system), or resetting based on the outdoor temperature.

HV21   Reducing Air-Handling Unit Face Velocity (Pressure Drop) (Climate Zones: all)

The requirements of ASHRAE/IES Standard 90.1 are difficult to comply with in healthcare facilities. The goal of this Guide is to exceed those requirements substantially. To do this it is necessary to reduce system pressure losses and select high-efficiency fans. This tip deals with reducing system pressure losses.

In hospital air-handling systems in general, 50% of the pressure drop is in the duct system and 50% is in the air-handling unit. Reducing duct system pressure drop (HV22) requires either using low-pressure drop fittings, which often require long radiuses that may not fit in the available space, or using larger ducts to reduce velocities, which requires more building volume and increases sheet metal costs. It is usually more economical to reduce system fan power use by reducing air-handling unit pressure drop than by reducing duct system pressure drop. With that said, the opportunity to reduce both should not be overlooked.

The most basic strategy to reduce air-handler pressure drop is to lower the velocity through the air-handling unit. Traditional design uses velocities around 500 fpm (2.5 m/s). life-cycle cost analysis often shows that the optimum velocity is much lower, perhaps between 250 and 350 fpm (1.27 to 1.78 m/s). Not all components inside of air-handling units follow the basic fan laws, but most are at least close enough for this analysis. According to the fan laws, reducing the velocity across air-handling unit components by 50% reduces the total pressure drop to 25%. If half of the total system pressure drop were in the air-handling unit, the total system pressure would drop by 37.5%. Since some components may have laminar flow or incomplete turbulent flow, a more realistic estimate is 30%. For other options to reduce air-handling unit pressure drop, refer to HV43 under "Additional Bonus Savings."

HV22   Ductwork Design and Construction (Climate Zones: all)

Good duct design practices result in lower energy use. Low pressure loss and low air leakage in duct systems are critical to lowering the overall fan energy. Lowering the pressure needed to overcome dynamic pressure and friction losses decreases the fan motor size and the needed fan energy. Refer to the current *ASHRAE Handbook—Fundamentals* ("Duct Design" chapter) (ASHRAE 2009a) for detailed data and practices.

Duct system layout is critical to reduce required pressures. The mechanical, architectural, and construction teams must work together to allow straight runs of ductwork whenever possible. Special care should be taken in mechanical spaces to avoid high-velocity fittings and minimize system effect.

Dynamic losses result from flow disturbances, including changes in direction, duct-mounted equipment, and duct fittings or transitions. Designers should reevaluate fitting selection practices using the ASHRAE Duct Fitting Database (ASHRAE 2011a), a program that contains more than 220 fittings. For example, using a round, smooth radius elbow instead of a mitered elbow with turning vanes can often significantly lower the pressure loss. Elbows should not be placed directly at the outlet of the fan. To achieve low loss coefficients from fittings, the flow needs to be fully developed, which is not the case at the outlet of a fan. To minimize the system effect, straight duct should be placed between the fan outlet and the elbow.

Be sure to specify 45° entry branch tees for both supply and return/exhaust junctions. The total angle of a reduction transition is recommended to be no more 45°. The total angle of an expansion transition is recommended to be 20° or less.

Poor fan performance is most commonly caused by improper outlet connections, nonuniform inlet flow, and/or swirl at the fan inlet. Look for ways to minimize the fan/duct system interface losses, referred to as the system-effect losses. Be sure the fan outlet fittings and transitions follow good duct design and low pressure loss practices. Project teams must address space requirements for good, low-pressure duct design in the early programming and schematic design phases. Allow enough space for low-pressure drop fittings and locate air-handling units that result in short, straight duct layouts. Avoid the use of close-coupled fittings.

The use of flexible duct should be limited, because these ducts use more fan energy than a metal duct system. Recent research shows that flexible duct must be installed with less than 4% compression to achieve less than two times the pressure loss of equivalent-sized metal ductwork (Abushakra et al. 2004; Culp and Cantrill 2009). If the compression is more than 30%, the pressure loss can exceed nine times the pressure loss of metal ductwork. In addition, Lawrence Berkeley National Laboratory (LBNL) has shown that the loss coefficients for bends in flexible ductwork have a high variability from condition to condition, with no uniform trends (Abushakra et al. 2002). Loss coefficients ranged from a low of 0.87 to a high of 3.3 (for comparison purposes, a die-stamped elbow has a loss coefficient of 0.11). If a project team decides to use flexible duct, the following is advised:

- Limit the use of flexible duct to connections between duct branches and diffusers or VAV terminal units.
- Flexible sections should not exceed 5 ft in length (fully stretched).
- Install the flexible duct without any radial compression (kinks).
- Do not use flexible duct in lieu of fittings.

Where permissible, consider using plenum return systems with lower pressure loss. Whenever using a plenum return system, design and construct the exterior walls to prevent uncontrolled infiltration of humid air from outdoors (Harriman et al. 2001).

HV23   Duct Insulation (Climate Zones: all)

The following ductwork should be insulated:

- All supply air ductwork
- All outdoor air ductwork
- All exhaust and relief air ductwork between the motor-operated damper and penetration of the building exterior
- All ductwork located in unconditioned spaces or outside the building envelope
- All ductwork located in attics, whether ventilated or unventilated
- All ductwork buried either outside the building or below floors

In addition, all airstream surfaces should be resistant to mold growth and resist erosion, according to the requirements of ASHRAE 62.1.

While return and exhaust ductwork above a top-floor ceiling (with a roof above) or in an unventilated attic may seem like it doesn't need insulation, there is a real possibility that air removed from the space can have moisture condensation if the duct is located in a cold space. This condensation could cause physical damage and be a source of mold growth.

HV24 ***Duct Sealing and Leakage Testing* (Climate Zones: all)**

The ductwork should be sealed in accordance with ASHRAE/IES Standard 90.1. All duct joints should be inspected to ensure they are properly sealed, and the ductwork should be leak tested at the rated pressure. The leakage should not exceed the allowable cfm/100 ft^2 of duct area for the seal and leakage class of the system's air quantity apportioned to each section tested.

HV25 ***Testing, Adjusting, and Balancing* (Climate Zones: all)**

After the system has been installed, cleaned, and placed in operation, the system should be tested, adjusted, and balanced (TAB) in accordance with ASHRAE Standard 111 (ASHRAE 2008b) or SMACNA's Testing, Adjusting and Balancing manual (SMACNA 2002).

This will help to ensure that the correctly sized diffusers, registers, and grilles have been installed; that each space receives the required airflow; and that the fans meet the intended performance. The balancing subcontractor should certify that the instruments used in the measurement have been calibrated within 12 months before use. A written report should be submitted for inclusion in the operations and maintenance (O&M) manuals.

Energy savings resulting from ongoing balancing as opposed to one-time balancing are a secondary condition in large hospitals. Maintaining patient, visitor, and staff safety and comfort drive this requirement.

HV26 ***Filtration* (Climate Zones: all)**

Particulate air filters are typically included as part of the factory-assembled HVAC equipment and should be at least MERV 8 for areas covered by ASHRAE/ASHE Standard 170 and MERV 7 for other areas, both based on ASHRAE Standard 52.2, *Method of Testing General Ventilation Air-Cleaning Devices for Removal Efficiency by Particle Size* (2007). Use a filter differential pressure gauge to monitor the pressure loss across the filters and send an alarm if the predetermined pressure loss is exceeded. The differential pressure (monitored using the BAS) at which filters are to be replaced should not always be the maximum rated pressure loss of the filter. In many if not most cases, economics favor lower pressure loss filter change-out pressures based on weighing fan power against filter replacement cost. Designers should consider choosing a differential pressure setpoint that is lower than the maximum for the specified filter based on calculations of when the combination of fan energy cost and filter replacement cost provide the lowest life-cycle cost. Regardless of the pressure reading, the gauge should be checked and the filter should be visually inspected at least once each year.

ASHRAE/ASHE Standard 170 requires many healthcare occupancies to employ at least two filter banks in series. In those occupancies, Standard 170 requires MERV 14 or 17 filters for the downstream bank. It is common to use three filter banks in series with high-efficiency particulate air (HEPA) filters serving a portion of the flow from an air-handling unit. This practice wastes energy because the supply fan must supply enough pressure to satisfy the zones that are served by three filter layers and because the fan must overcome pressure loss for three sets of dirty filters. If HEPA filters are required for some areas served by an air-handling unit, a booster fan should be provided for that branch of the duct system. If high-efficiency (MERV 14 or HEPA) filters are to be used, consider using lower-efficiency (MERV 8 to 13) filters during the construction period. When construction is complete, all filters should be replaced before the building is occupied. Systems designed with particle filters should not be operated without the filters in place.

Fan energy accounts for 15%–20% of the total energy use in conventional VAV reheat hospitals. Any filtration system that reduces pressure loss while complying with the applicable ASHRAE Standard 52.2 MERV rating will reduce building energy use substantially. Designers should consider the average pressure loss of each filter system, including the clean pressure

Filter Change Costs

Filter change frequency can be performed on a periodic routine maintenance schedule, or can be done in response to filter loading (indicated by pressure drop across the filter). Consider evaluating the energy cost of operating the filter, along with the material cost of the filter and the labor to change it.

In this example, a 24 x 24 x 6 MERV 13 filter is operating at 400 fpm face velocity. It has an initial (clean) pressure drop of 0.4 in. wc, with a recommended maximum pressure drop (dirty) of 1.5 in. wc, and operates for 2190 h before reaching that pressure loss. The material cost of the filter is $4 and costs $5 in labor to replace. The electricity cost (at $0.10/kWh) of moving air through that filter is $60 during that 2190 h. The annual cost to own and operate that filter is $276 (4 filter changes per year).

If that filter is changed monthly (730 h, with a final pressure drop of 0.77 in. wc), the energy cost during that month is $12. The annual cost is $252.

The energy cost calculation is based on 1600 cfm through the filter and 65% motor/fan efficiency.

HP = (CFM × average (DP initial, DP final))/(6356 × EFF)

kWh = Hours × HP × 0.7457

For this particular set of assumptions, the minimum annual cost occurs at 1100 h (roughly 6 weeks), $243

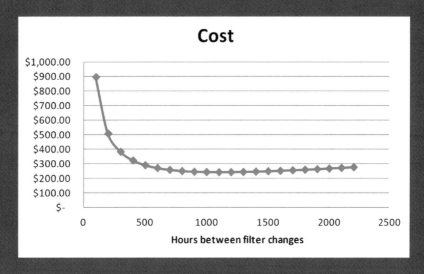

Graphical Representation of Cost Comparison

loss, final pressure loss, and dirt-holding capacity. For example, it is often economically justified to use 4 in. pleated MERV 8 prefilters in lieu of 2 in. filters because the average pressure loss over the life of the filters and the labor cost of replacements is lower.

Compliance with the fan power limitations of some versions of ASHRAE/IES Standard 90.1 can be very difficult for healthcare facilities with multiple filters in series and/or with HEPA filters. ASHRAE/IES Standard 90.1 includes adjustment to the allowable fan power based on the efficiency of each filter bank. Multiple adjustments can be made for multiple filter banks in series.

HV27   *Air-Cleaning Devices* (Climate Zones: all)

Several air-cleaner options are currently being used in hospitals, including electronic air cleaners and ultraviolet light.

Electronic air cleaners can very efficiently remove particulate matter, including dust or pollen. These cleaners are beneficial because they can provide contaminant removal at a lower pressure drop and, therefore, energy rate than using media filters alone. Using these devices may require approval from your local authority having jurisdiction (AHJ) if they are being used in lieu of filters required by ASHRAE/ASHE Standard 170.

Ultraviolet germicidal irradiation (UVGI) with ultraviolet (UV) lamps is also used to "disinfect" surfaces. It has been successfully employed in various configurations, including in room, in duct, and within air handlers. When used in air handlers, UVGI reduces microbial growth on wet surfaces, including drain pans and cooling coils, thus reducing odors and improving heat transfer efficiency of the coils to some degree. Room and, to a lesser extent, duct applications of UVGI have been shown to reduce the level of mold spores and viruses in the air, including tuberculosis. UV light can quickly degrade organic polymeric materials, such as rubber and plastic, and direct human exposure can result in damage to the eyes and skin. It is imperative to ensure that materials are compatible with or shielded from direct exposure to UVC light and that proper safeguards, including warning labeling and door electrical interlock switches, are provided to assure that people are not inadvertently exposed to UV energy both during normal operation or when performing service and maintenance activities.

For further details and descriptions of air cleaners, consult the 2008 *ASHRAE Handbook— HVAC Systems and Equipment* (2008a) and *Indoor Air Quality Guide: Best Practices for Design, Construction and Commissioning* (2009b).

HV28   *Relief vs. Return Fans* (Climate Zones: all)

Relief (rather than return) fans should be used when possible to maintain building pressurization during economizer operation. Relief fans reduce overall fan energy use in most cases, as long as return dampers are sized correctly. However, if return duct static pressure drop exceeds 1.0 in. of water, return fans may be needed.

HV29   *Space Setpoints* (Climate Zones: all)

Nothing can make a well-designed and well-constructed building perform more poorly from both an occupant comfort and energy consumption perspective than improper correction of occupant temperature complaints. Even buildings that were not formally commissioned have a testing and balancing requirement as part of acceptance. Too often, well-intentioned maintenance technicians overwrite setpoints instead of correcting underlying issues when responding to complaints. These technicians typically lack the necessary system diagnostic information, training in proper corrective maintenance techniques, or available time to properly research and correct the issue.

BAS contain a wealth of system diagnostic information as long as they are properly maintained. Humidistats and thermostats that no longer work, are no longer calibrated, or are poorly located can be the underlying cause of performance complaints and can make it extremely difficult for technicians to correct the issue. More advanced systems can be linked together in order to provide space heat maps (see Figure 5-34) that allow the technician to better understand what is actually occurring in the space and to more quickly and accurately find and correct the underlying issue.

With appropriate support systems and training, technicians can find and eliminate areas of simultaneous heating and cooling and other inefficient practices that degrade performance and lead to poor occupant comfort. This proactive approach eliminates a great many temperature complaints and quickly pays for itself in improved employee and patient experience.

HV30   *Zone Temperature Control* (Climate Zones: all)

The number of spaces in a zone and the location of the temperature sensor (thermostat) will affect the control of temperature in the various spaces of a zone. Locating the thermostat in one room of a zone with multiple spaces provides feedback based only on the conditions in that room. Locating a single thermostat in a large open area may provide a better response to the

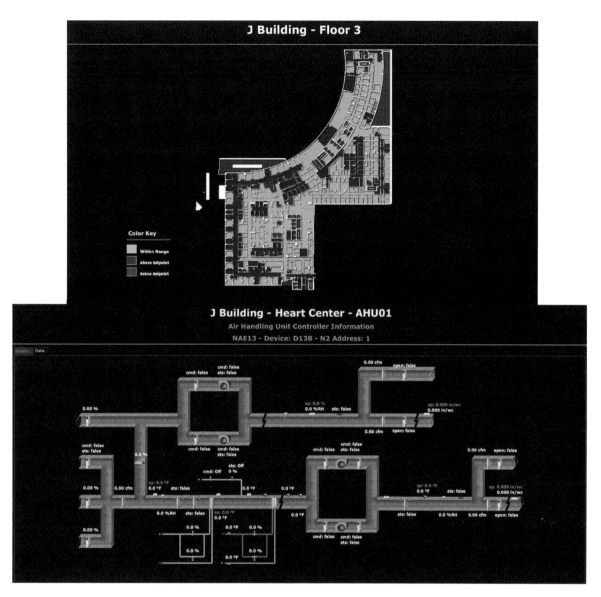

Figure 5-34 Example Space Heat Map
Image reproduced by permission of Cleveland Clinic

conditions of the zone with multiple spaces. Selecting the room or space that will best represent the thermal characteristics of the space due to both external and internal loads will provide the greatest comfort level.

Resetting the room control setpoint is an extremely effective energy saving strategy, especially for rooms that are not occupied. Spaces with tight comfort conditions when occupied, such as operating rooms, are especially good candidates for reset.

To prevent misreading of the space temperature, zone thermostats should not be mounted on an exterior wall. Where this is unavoidable, use an insulated subbase for the thermostat.

HV31   *Zone Airflow Control and Setback* (Climate Zones: all)

For each healthcare space in which ASHRAE/ASHE Standard 170 requires a minimum air change rate, the VAV terminal unit in the supply duct modulates supply airflow to maintain space temperature but not below the minimum air change rate required. This minimum air change rate can be reduced during unoccupied periods, but required space-to-space pressure

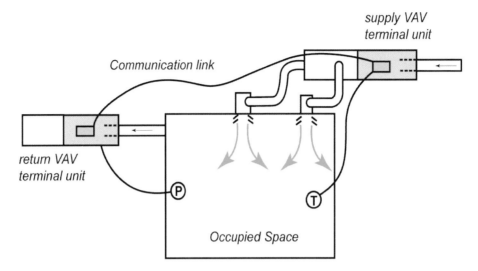

Figure 5-35 (HV31) Supply and Return VAV Terminals for Space Pressure Control

relationships must still be maintained. Note that if the minimum air change rate required for a zone is higher than the design airflow needed for cooling or heating, the supply airflow to that zone will be constant during occupied periods.

For each healthcare space in which ASHRAE/ASHE Standard 170 requires either positive or negative pressure with respect to adjacent spaces, a motorized damper or VAV terminal unit is also included in the return duct from that space (Figure 5-35). As the VAV terminal unit in the supply duct modulates supply airflow, the VAV terminal unit in the return duct modulates to maintain either a positive or negative pressure in the space (through direct pressure measurement or by controlling to an airflow offset from supply airflow rate). Use caution when selecting return air VAV terminals to minimize air-side pressure drop.

HV32 Humidification System (Climate Zones: all)

ASHRAE/ASHE Standard 170 requires humidification to 30% rh in many healthcare spaces. Some states have higher minimum requirements for some spaces (e.g., Illinois requires 40% minimum rh for operating rooms). The traditional method of humidifying in healthcare systems is to provide either a direct steam injection humidifier (which may not comply with ASHRAE Standard 62.1) or a clean steam system using domestic water and powered by steam, fossil fuel, or electricity.

Humidification energy can be reduced by several methods:

- Systems can incorporate enthalpy recovery (see HV15).
- Systems can incorporate water economizers instead of air economizers (see HV19).
- Systems can employ a DOAS, which normally includes enthalpy recovery see (HV9).

Spray-type humidifiers might be considered in warm, dry climates. However, infection control staff and accreditation authorities should be consulted. These units should not be reservoir type or evaporative-pan type, neither of which is permitted by ASHRAE/ASHE Standard 170.

HV33 Elimination of Steam Boilers (Climate Zones: all)

Steam boilers have often been used in hospitals in the past. Uses included humidification, sterilizers, and preheating very cold OA without concern of freezing the preheat coil. Steam boilers and their systems have a number of disadvantages, including the following:

- Producing steam at high temperatures and then reducing the temperature at the load leads to inefficiency.
- The maintenance of steam systems, including traps, requires significant time and cost. Using hot-water systems can lead to maintenance cost reductions of up to 75%.

More recently, hospitals have used other methods of humidification, such as electricity, and have realized installed, operating, and maintenance savings.

HV34 *Noise Control* **(Climate Zones: all)**

Oral communication, especially speech intelligibility, is critical in healthcare occupancies. Poor acoustic conditions affect the performance of all staff members. *ASHRAE Handbook— HVAC Applications* (2011b) is a source for recommended background sound levels in healthcare spaces. Other sources include the *Interim Sound and Vibration Design Guidelines for Hospital and Healthcare Facilities* (ASA 2006) and the FGI *Guidelines for the Design and Construction of Healthcare Facilities* (AIA 2010).

Avoid installation of noisy HVAC equipment directly above occupied spaces. Consider locations above less critical spaces, such as storage areas, restrooms, and corridors, or in acoustically treated closets adjacent to critical spaces. Acoustic requirements may necessitate attenuation of the noise associated with the supply and return air or of the noise radiated from the HVAC equipment. Acoustic concerns may be particularly critical in short, direct runs of ductwork between fans and air inlets or outlets.

VAV noise can be especially problematic in healthcare facilities because the rating system for VAV boxes (AHRI Standard 885-2008 [AHRI 2008b]) assumes that the ducts downstream of VAV boxes are lined. This is seldom true in healthcare facilities, which can cause the ratings to underestimate room noise levels by 10 to 20 dB. Another concern related to VAV boxes is that the pressure loss across VAV box dampers near the air-handling unit may be very high in duct systems operating at high static pressures. The noise ratings for VAV boxes depend strongly on the pressure loss across them. Minimizing the pressure loss between the first and last VAV box in the duct systems is the best method of combating this problem, and it simultaneously helps reduce fan energy consumption.

Refer to *A Practical Guide to Noise and Vibration Control for HVAC Systems* (Schaeffer 2005) for specific guidance by system type and to *ASHRAE Handbook—HVAC Applications.*

HV35 *Chilled-Water System* **(Climate Zones: all)**

Chilled-water systems efficiently transport cooling energy throughout the building. They may be combined with thermal storage systems to achieve electrical demand charge savings through mitigation of the peak cooling loads in the building. Chilled-water systems should generally be designed for variable flow through the building.

Small systems (<100 tons) should be designed for variable flow if the chiller unit controls can tolerate expected flow rate changes. Chilled-water systems should use two-way valves with a pressure-controlling bypass set to maintain the minimum evaporator water flow required by the chiller.

Strongly consider variable primary flow chilled-water system configurations. By varying water flow through the chiller evaporator(s), both installed and operating costs can be reduced. See references for specific strategies when employing variable primary flow configurations.

Piping should be sized using the tables in ASHRAE/IES Standard 90.1 (ASHRAE 2010b). Select cooling coils for a design chilled-water ΔT of at least 15°F to reduce pump energy. Select cooling coils to minimize air pressure drop. Chilled-water temperature setpoints should be selected based on a life-cycle analysis of pump energy, fan energy, and desired air conditions leaving the coil.

On the condenser water side of the system, the *ASHRAE GreenGuide* (2010d) recommends beginning with a condenser water temperature difference of at least 14°F. This reduces the pump power and cooling tower fan motor size and/or power. Even though chiller energy may rise, these system design parameters result in lower system energy consumption.

HV36   ***Chiller Diversity* (Climate Zones: all)**

Chilled-water plants are often designed with a number of identical chillers. This is seldom optimal. Having different chiller sizes, types, and efficiencies in the same plant may require a higher level of chilled-water plant control sophistication, but in a hospital that operates many hours each year at different loads and outdoor conditions, there are significant benefits in diversifying the chiller-water plant.

Hospital chiller diversity opportunities include the following:

- In facilities with small cooling loads during the winter season, select a small chiller that satisfies the smaller load and operates efficiently at lower condenser temperature.
- When condenser heat recovery is employed (HV38), selecting the total capacity of the heat recovery chiller(s) is important. Maximum savings occur when simultaneous heating and cooling loads are concurrent and balanced. During operation if no heat is needed, cooling-only chillers use less energy. If no cooling is needed, heat recovery chillers may be more or less expensive to operate than condensing boilers, depending on utility rates. Accurate load profiles for both heating and cooling, coupled with economic analysis should be employed to determine the optimum total capacity of the heat recovery chillers.
- In facilities using combined heat and power (HV38) and absorption chillers using the recovered heat, consider putting the absorption chiller upstream and in series with an electric chiller. Compared to all chillers making the same chilled-water temperature, in this position, the absorption chiller is both more efficient and able to deliver more cooling.
- Chillers that operate at reduced or part load conditions may benefit from a variable-speed drive.
- Chillers that operate at design conditions, when the condenser temperatures are highest, should be selected for high full-load/full-lift efficiency. These premium efficiency chillers provide significant demand reduction.
- A comprehensive chilled-water plant analysis helps identify which chiller diversity options provide benefits for each specific application.

HV37   ***Cooling Towers* (Climate Zones: all)**

Cooling towers are a very efficient method of cooling. Cooling towers remove heat by evaporation and can cool close to the ambient wet-bulb temperature. The wet-bulb temperature is always lower than the dry-bulb; thus, water cooling allows more efficient condenser operation than air cooling. See HV45 in the "Additional Bonus Savings" section for areas that have water restrictions. Unless specifically addressed, in this document "cooling tower" refers to an open cooling tower.

The *ASHRAE GreenGuide* recommends a condenser water temperature difference of 12°F to 18°F. This results in a cooling tower that is more effective at exchanging energy, because the inlet water temperature to the tower is higher, thus increasing the driving heat transfer force.

ASHRAE/IES Standard 90.1-2010 requires speed control for cooling towers 7.5 hp and above for most applications. Crowther and Furlong (2004) showed that judicious tower fan speed control, while increasing chiller energy, results in reduced system energy. Therefore, rather than having the tower produce the coldest temperature water possible at a given point in time, consider using methods that optimize the sum of chiller plus tower energy use.

Make sure that the water flow across cooling tower cells is always above the minimum required by the tower provider to keep surfaces wetted. At a given a condenser water flow rate, operating the maximum number of tower cells possible at or above the minimum water loading with all tower fans at the same speed results in the most effective cooling tower heat transfer at the lowest operating fan hp.

HV38   *Condenser Water Heat Recovery* **(Climate Zones: all)**

The principle behind condenser water heat recovery is that HVAC systems should use heat rejected from cooling equipment before using new heating energy. Healthcare projects are an excellent application for condenser water heat recovery. This is because most HVAC systems use cooling to reduce humidity and most healthcare facilities require both large amounts of domestic hot water (service water heating; see WH1 through WH7) and high minimum air change rates. The systems recommended in this guide significantly reduce reheat energy, but condenser heat recovery may still be viable.

Several issues must be considered when designing condenser heat recovery systems:

- The heating and cooling loads must exist simultaneously and both must be large enough to make the system economical. In cold climates, there may be times in winter when there is no need for cooling, although energy recovery systems can overcome this limitation in all but the coldest climates.
- There must be a use for relatively low-temperature heat (usually below 150°F, and preferably lower). This requirement is easily met by preheating domestic water. To increase the energy savings greatly, heating coils can be selected to operate with inlet water temperatures of between 100°F and 140°F. At these temperatures, depending on utility rates, chillers may produce heat at lower cost than even condensing boilers, even when the cooling must be rejected outdoors. In these cases, the cooling can be thought of as a "free" by-product. Under different utility rates, these systems are only economical to operate when there is a simultaneous need for cooling.

Despite these limitations, condenser heat recovery systems often have simple payback periods of two to four years, depending on the fuel-to-electric cost ratio. When combined with air-side energy recovery, the payback periods can be immediate (no increase in first cost).

Service water preheating systems are more economical for chillers with low-pressure refrigerants than for chillers with high-pressure refrigerants because they may not require heat exchangers (depending on the applicable plumbing code) to separate the potable water from the refrigerant; heat recovery systems are common for both high- and low-pressure refrigerant chillers.

If a system is chosen that can produce hotter water for reheat coils, there is an opportunity to use the same chillers to heat service water to the final distribution temperature instead of only to 85°F or a similar preheat temperature.

One caveat with condenser heat recovery systems is that the designers must make accurate estimates of the simultaneous needs for heating and cooling. Otherwise, the owner may not realize the desired return on investment because the heat recovery chillers do not run a sufficient number of hours per year. Often, systems will incorporate either solar service water preheat or condenser water heat recovery, although for some applications it may be economical to use solar for service water preheating and condenser heat recovery only for reheat loads.

Figure 5-36 depicts the principle of condenser heat recovery. The left-hand schematic depicts a traditional all-air system with the chiller and cooling tower operating to satisfy the cooling and dehumidification needs and the boiler operating to satisfy the reheat needs. The right-hand schematic depicts the same system with a heat recovery chiller. Under most operating conditions, the heating and cooling loads are not equal, so either the boiler or the cooling tower will run at reduced load to bring the system into heat balance. The main saving is the boiler energy. The same concepts apply to service water heating.

Any process that has trouble complying with the simultaneous heating and cooling limitations of ASHRAE/IES Standard 90.1 is a good candidate for condenser heat recovery. The largest waste of energy in healthcare facilities that condenser heat recovery systems can help prevent is operation of chillers while also using reheat coils to prevent overcooling. This occurs in virtually all zones that have minimum air-change rate requirements. In zones without minimum air-change rate requirements, compliance with ASHRAE Standard 62.1 or the applicable ventilation code may also cause this to occur. A typical condenser heat recovery design for

Figure 5-36 (HV38) Principle of Condenser Heat Recovery

Condenser Water Heat Recovery

Aurora Medical Center in Grafton, WI, is a 526,000 ft^2 facility with 107 private patient rooms, 18 operating rooms, a data center, and a variety of diagnostic equipment. While comfortable with the VAV reheat systems used, the facility was also interested in improved energy efficiency. To address this need, an energy recovery chiller was added to their typical systems. The payback period for the system was approximately four years.

The energy recovery chiller transfers energy from the chilled-water loop to the heated-water loop instead of rejecting the heat outdoors through cooling towers. Domestic water, in turn, is preheated by the heating water via a double-wall heat exchanger.

To maximize energy savings the following strategies are used:

- Chilled-water fan-coil units are used for any energy-intensive spaces, such as the data center, imaging equipment rooms, and data/technology rooms.
- Chilled water coils added to the exhaust airstream harvest energy during the colder periods experienced in Wisconsin.
- The energy recovery chiller is sized for the maximum year-round cooling load produced.

Energy Recovery Chiller System
Photo courtesy of KJWW Engineering

chilled-water systems involves a mixture of high-efficiency chillers that operate with cooling towers during periods of peak cooling loads and heat recovery chillers that are less efficient but can generate hot water at a temperature that is warm enough for the desired use. Usually this is in the range of 100°F to 140°F for reheat systems. Some chillers can produce higher temperatures, but this must be weighed against the decrease in compressor efficiency.

DOAS largely avoid this waste of reheat energy (see HV9). However, DOAS normally do not avoid this entirely at the central dedicated OA unit. Where OA systems are used, and the discharge air must be reheated to prevent overcooling, the use of secondary energy recovery devices or condenser heat recovery is recommended.

HV39 *Heating Sources* (Climate Zones: all)

Many factors, including availability of service, utility costs, operator familiarity, and the impact of source energy use, contribute to the decision of whether to use gas or electricity for heating.

Forced-air electric resistance and gas-fired heaters require a minimum airflow rate to operate safely. These systems, whether stand alone or incorporated into an air-conditioning or heat-pump unit, should include factory-installed controls to shut down the heater when there is inadequate airflow that can result in high temperatures.

HV40 *Operating Room Setback* (Climate Zones: all)

There are several strategies to manage reduction in unoccupied times. Those strategies are described in an *Operating Room Setback Strategies* (ASHE 2011). These strategies include differential pressure and airflow offsets. Setbacks can be done using either a time clock to initiate the sequence or an occupancy sensor.

During new construction, consider leak testing the operating rooms to reduce the amount of room leakage to minimize supply and return differential needed to maintain differential pressure requirements. This is similar to practices used for constructing AII rooms.

REFERENCES AND RESOURCES

Abushakra, B., I.S. Walker, and M.H. Sherman. 2002. A study of pressure losses in residential air distribution systems. Proceedings of the ACEEE Summer Study 2002, American Council for an Energy Efficient Economy, Washington, D.C. Lawrence Berkeley National Laboratory Report 49700.

Abushakra, B., I.S. Walker, and M.H. Sherman. 2004. Compression effects on pressure loss in flexible HVAC ducts. *International Journal of HVAC&R Research* 10(3):275–89.

AHRI. 2007. ANSI/AHRI Standard 340/360-2007, *2007 Standard for Performance Rating of Commercial and Industrial Unitary Air-Conditioning and Heat Pump Equipment*. Arlington, VA: Air-Conditioning, Heating, and Refrigeration Institute.

AHRI. 2008a. ANSI/AHRI Standard 210/240, *2008 Standard for Performance Rating of Unitary Air-Conditioning and Air-Source Heat Pump Equipment*. Arlington, VA: Air-Conditioning, Heating, and Refrigeration Institute.

AHRI. 2008b. AHRI Standard 885-2008, *Procedure for Estimating Occupied Space Sound Levels in the Application of Air Terminals and Air Outlets*. Arlington, VA: Air-Conditioning, Heating, and Refrigeration Institute.

AIA. 2010. *Guidelines for the Design and Construction of Healthcare Facilities*. Dallas, TX: Facility Guidelines Institute.

ASA. 2006. Interim Sound and Vibration Design Guidelines for Hospital and Healthcare Facilities. Public Draft 1, November 1, 2006, WG44 Joint Subcommittee on Speech Privacy of the Acoustical Society fo America (ASA), the Insitute of Noise Control Engineering (INCE), and the National Council of Acoustical Consultants (NCAC).

ASHE. 2011. *Operating Room HVAC Setback Strategies*. Chicago: American Society for Healthcare Engineering.

ASHRAE. 1997. *Ground-Source Heat Pumps: Design of Geothermal Systems for Commercial and Institutional Buildings.* Atlanta: American Society of Heating, Refrigerating and Air-Conditioning Engineers.

ASHRAE. 2004. ANSI/ASHRAE/IESNA Standard 90.1-2004, *Energy Standard for Buildings Except Low-Rise Residential Buildings.* Atlanta: ASHRAE.

ASHRAE. 2005. ANSI/AHRI/ASHRAE ISO Standard 13256-1:1998, *Water-source heat pumps—testing and rating for performance—Part 1: Water-to-air and brine-to-air heat pumps.* Atlanta: ASHRAE.

ASHRAE. 2007. ASHRAE Standard 52.2-2007, *Method of Testing General Ventilation Air-Cleaning Devices for Removal Efficiency by Particle Size.* Atlanta: ASHRAE.

ASHRAE. 2008a. *ASHRAE Handbook—HVAC Systems and Equipment.* Atlanta: ASHRAE.

ASHRAE. 2008b. ANS/IASHRAE Standard 111-2008, *Practices for Measurement, Testing, Adjusting, and Balancing of Building, Heating, Ventilation, Air-Conditioning and Refrigeration Systems.* Atlanta: ASHRAE.

ASHRAE. 2008c. ANSI/ASHRAE/ASHE Standard 170-2008, Ventilation of Health Care Facilities. Atlanta: ASHRAE.

ASHRAE. 2008d. ANSI/ASHRAE/ACCA Standard 180-2008, *Standard Practice for Inspection and Maintenance of Commercial Building HVAC Systems.* Atlanta: ASHRAE.

ASHRAE. 2009a. *ASHRAE Handbook—Fundamentals.* Atlanta: ASHRAE.

ASHRAE. 2009b. *Indoor Air Quality Guide: Best Practices for Design, Construction and Commissioning.* Atlanta: ASHRAE.

ASHRAE. 2010a. ANSI/ASHRAE Standard 55-2010, *Thermal Environmental Conditions for Human Occupancy.* Atlanta: ASHRAE.

ASHRAE. 2010b. ANSI/ASHRAE Standard 62.1-2010, *Ventilation for Acceptable Indoor Air Quality.* Atlanta: ASHRAE.

ASHRAE. 2010c. ANSI/ASHRAE/IES Standard 90.1-2010, *Energy Standard for Buildings Except Low-Rise Residential Buildings.* Atlanta: ASHRAE.

ASHRAE. 2010d. *ASHRAE GreenGuide: The Design, Construction, and Operation of Sustainable Buildings*, 3d ed. Atlanta: ASHRAE.

ASHRAE. 2010e. *Standard 62.1 User's Manual.* Atlanta: ASHRAE.

ASHRAE. 2011a. ASHRAE Duct Fitting Database, v6.00.0. Atlanta: ASHRAE.

ASHRAE. 2011b. *ASHRAE Handbook—HVAC Applications.* Atlanta: ASHRAE.

Culp, C., and D. Cantrill. 2009. Pressure losses in 12", 14", and 16" non-metallic flexible ducts with compression and sag. *ASHRAE Transactions* 115(1).

Crowther, H., and J. Furlong. 2004. Optimizing chillers and towers. *ASHRAE Journal* April 2004.

Dieckmann, J., K. Roth, and J. Brodrick. 2003. Dedicated outdoor air systems. *ASHRAE Journal* 45(3):58–59.

EPA. 2008a. National Ambient Air Quality Standards. www.epa.gov/air/criteria.html. Washington, DC: U.S. Environmental Protection Agency.

EPA. 2008b. The Green Book Nonattainment Areas for Criteria Pollutants. www.epa.gov/air/oaqps/greenbk. Washington, DC: U.S. Environmental Protection Agency. Harriman, L., G. Brundett, and R. Kittler. 2001. *Humidity Control Design Guide for Commercial and Institutional Buildings.* Atlanta: American Society of Heating, Refrigerating and Air-Conditioning Engineers.

Harriman, L., G. Brundett, and R. Kittler. 2001. *Humidity Control Design Guide for Commercial and Institutional Buildings.* Atlanta: American Society of Heating, Refrigerating and Air-Conditioning Engineers, Inc.

Morris, W. 2003. The ABCs of DOAS: Dedicated outdoor air systems. *ASHRAE Journal* 45(5):24–29.

Mumma, S. 2001. Designing dedicated outdoor air systems. *ASHRAE Journal* 43(5):28–31.

Murphy, J. 2006. Smart dedicated outdoor air systems. *ASHRAE Journal* 48(7):30–37.

NEMA. 2006. NEMA Standards Publication MG 1-2006, *Motors and Generators.* Tables 12-12 and 12-13. Rosslyn, VA: National Electrical Manufacturers Association.

Schaffer, M. 2005. *A Practical Guide to Noise and Vibration Control for HVAC Systems* (I-P edition), 2d ed. Atlanta: American Society of Heating, Refrigerating and Air-Conditioning Engineers.

Shank, K., and S. Mumma. 2001. Selecting the supply air conditions for a dedicated outdoor air system working in parallel with distributed sensible cooling terminal equipment. *ASHRAE Transactions* 107(1):562–71.

SMACNA. 2002. *HVAC Systems—Testing, Adjusting and Balancing*, 3d ed. Chantilly, VA: Sheet Metal and Air Conditioning Contractors National Association.

Warden, D. 1996. Dual fan dual duct: Better performance at lower cost. *ASHRAE Journal* 38(1).

QUALITY ASSURANCE

Quality assurance, including commissioning, helps to ensure that a building functions in accordance with its design intent and thus meets the performance goals established for it. Quality assurance should be an integral part of the design and construction process as well as a part of the continued operation of the facility. General information on commissioning is included in Chapter 2.

COMMISSIONING

QA1 *Commissioning Overview* (Climate Zones: all)

With any renovation or new construction project, commissioning must be a fundamental aspect of the process. A well-managed and implemented commissioning program can ensure that the space functions as designed in order to support its intended use. In healthcare, where patient outcomes, safety, and experience are design imperatives, commissioning takes on added importance. Additional benefits of commissioning are that it can help improve building energy efficiency, assure proper system performance, and help the O&M staff develop knowledge of maintenance and troubleshooting techniques for new systems. Although commissioning has been historically limited to energy-consuming electrical and mechanical systems, consideration should be given to expanding the commissioning scope to include envelope, lighting and daylighting, fire, life safety, and emergency power systems, as each of these is a key contributor to the environment of care. The expanded scope can help improve performance during initial inspections by the numerous AHJs during early pre- and postoccupancy periods. By including a commissioning authority, designers, contractors, and owner representatives, the commissioning team can oversee the design through the occupancy period of the project and ensure that systems perform correctly. For a detailed look at these options, consider reviewing the *Health Facility Commissioning Guidelines* (Kenneday et al. 2010).

To be effective, commissioning should start early in the planning and design phases. Development of key components that should be included in the commissioning plan to ensure energy efficiency include the following:

- Owner performance requirements and Basis of Design (BoD) documents
- Energy performance targets, particularly important if pursuit of any sustainability awards are part of the project
- Schedules, including milestones, specific tasks, and responsibilities of all members of the commissioning team
- Process to evaluate value-engineering recommendations for impacts to operational performance
- Process to resolve issues and deficiencies identified throughout the project, including project close out and warranty management
- Occupancy and setback schedules based on intended use, system design, and code requirements

- Dashboards and trending that are critical to managing performance throughout the life of the building, particularly if the facility will employ an ongoing commissioning process
- Preventative maintenance tasks and schedules

QA2   *Defining Quality Assurance at Prebid* (Climate Zones: all)

The building industry has traditionally delivered buildings without using a verification process. Changes in traditional design and construction procedures and practices require education of the construction team that explains how the QA process will affect the various trades bidding the project. It is extremely important that the QA process be reviewed with the bidding contractors to facilitate understanding of and to help minimize fear associated with new practices. Teams who have participated in Cx typically appreciate the process because they are able to resolve problems while their manpower and materials are still on the project, significantly reducing delays, callbacks, and associated costs while enhancing their delivery capacity.

These requirements can be reviewed by the architect and engineer of record at the prebid meeting, as defined in the specifications.

QA3   *Verifying Building Envelope Construction* (Climate Zones: all)

The building envelope is a key element of an energy-efficient design. Compromises in assembly performance are common and are caused by a variety of factors that can easily be avoided. Improper placement of insulation, improper sealing or lack of sealing at air barriers, poorly selected or performing glazing and fenestration systems, incorrect placement of shading devices, misplacement of daylighting shelves, and misinterpretation of assembly details can significantly compromise the energy performance of the building (see "Cautions" sections throughout this chapter). The value of the Cx process is that it is an extension of the quality control processes of the designer and contractor as the team works together to produce quality energy-efficient projects.

QA4   *Verifying Lighting Construction* (Climate Zones: all)

Lighting plays a significant role in the energy consumption of the building. Lighting for all of the space types should be reviewed against anticipated schedule of use throughout the day.

QA5   *Verifying Electrical and HVAC Systems Construction* (Climate Zones: all)

Performance of electrical and HVAC systems are key elements of this Guide. How systems are designed and installed affects how efficiently they will perform. Collaboration between the entire design team is needed to optimize the energy efficiency of the facility. Natural daylight and artificial lighting impacts the heating and cooling loads with respect to both capacity and operation mode. The design reviews should pay close attention to the fact that proper installation is just as important as proper design. Making sure the installing contractor's foremen understand the owner's goals, the QA process, and the installation details is key to system performance success. A significant part of this process is a careful and thorough review of product submittals to ensure compliance with the design. It is in everyone's best interest to install the components correctly and completely the first time. Trying to inspect quality into a project is time consuming, costly, and usually doesn't result in quality. It's much better to ensure all team members are aligned with the QA process and goals. Certainly, observations and inspections during construction are necessary. The timing is critical to ensure that problems are identified at the beginning of each system installation. That minimizes the number of changes (time and cost) and leaves time for corrections.

QA6   *Performance Testing* (Climate Zones: all)

Performance testing of systems is essential to ensure that commissioned systems are functioning properly in all modes of operation; after all, regardless how effective a given design strategy may be, potential performance can only be realized through proper implementation. Unlike most appliances, none of the mechanical/electrical systems in a new facility are plug and play. If the team has executed the Cx plan and is aligned with the QA goals, the performance testing will occur quickly and only minor issues will need to be resolved. Owners with O&M personnel can use the functional testing process as a training tool to educate their staff on how the systems operate and for system orientation prior to training.

QA7   *Substantial Completion* (Climate Zones: all)

Substantial completion has been achieved when life safety systems have been implemented and verified and the facility is ready to be occupied. All of the systems should be operating as intended. Expected performance can only be accomplished when all systems operate interactively to provide desired results. As contractors finish their work, they will identify and resolve many performance problems. The CxA/QA provider verifies that the contractor maintained a quality-control process by directing and witnessing testing and then helps to resolve remaining issues.

QA8   *Final Acceptance* (Climate Zones: all)

Final acceptance generally occurs after the Cx/QA issues in the issues log have been resolved, except for minor issues the owner is comfortable resolving during the warranty period.

OPERATIONS AND MAINTENANCE

QA9   *Operation and Maintenance* (Climate Zones: all)

O&M is a critical consideration and will likely have a large impact on a facilities' energy use over its life. Designers should consider O&M from the onset of any building project to help ensure that energy savings are realized year after year. Designers need to take some responsibility for making the building owner aware of the following:

- Proper means of operation of mechanical systems
- Scope of an appropriate maintenance program
- Estimation of the annual operating and maintenance budget
- Any special skills needed to maintain equipment

In too many circumstances, owners are sold on investing in new, high-tech systems with promises of energy savings and quick paybacks. Too often, the savings are never realized because of improper installation, operation, or maintenance. In a recent study, with 85 existing facilities reporting over 3500 deficiencies, approximately 80% of the recommended retrocommissioning measures were O&M issues, while only 20% were design, installation, or replacement issues (Mills et al. 2004). In many of these cases, owners have no way of knowing that their energy systems are underperforming. Avoid this pitfall by commissioning the systems and by planning and implementing appropriate (simple) verification and maintenance programs.

System selection evaluations must include O&M. Providing only the energy savings of an alternate system is incomplete and misleading. O&M items to consider include the following:

- Evaluate existing maintenance staff capacity and skill level
- Include staff additions and/or training
- Maintenance self-performed or by a service contractor
- Estimate preventative and unexpected failure maintenance
- Consider O&M in economic evaluations
- Determine if adequate measurement and verification (M&V) strategies can be developed

As an example, informative Annex A of ASHRAE/ASHE Standard 170 states that heat pumps and fan coils should be maintained each month. Selection of such systems in patient care areas must address maintenance procedures.

Some facilities have limited maintenance staff and rely completely on service contractors. Some facility owners should consider negotiating premiums for service contractor "quick response," such as in the case of a hospital or outpatient surgery or imaging facility. Facility owners may want to have some spare parts on site or at the service contractor's storage facility to minimize downtime. The facility's O&M staff capacity and capability need to align with the level of complexity of the mechanical and electrical systems. If there is misalignment, then different tactics (e.g., staff education, outsourcing, or contract maintenance) need to be developed. This evaluation should take place during the programming phase.

Consider assisting the building owner in developing an energy verification program. It should include data collection, analysis, and recommendations. After time, the data becomes a benchmark that is useful for identifying changes and potential problems. Verification programs can use some of the procedures from the Cx functional or performance testing (See QA6 and QA12-15).

Make use of the BAS. Take advantage of the data trending, alarm, and preventative maintenance features. Consider installing electrical submeters at key circuits. Be sure that this is a coordinated effort with the electrical designer and the proposed circuiting design. As with the maintenance programs, the verification program needs to align with the complexity of the systems. It can be as simple as a monthly examination of the utility bills and ensuring the systems are operating on the right schedule. The person in charge of reviewing the data needs to be familiar with the systems and data to recognize deficiencies and unacceptable levels. Ask local utilities if they have any real-time metering options on their tariffs.

Designers need to understand that healthcare facility owners provide their services to patients, visitors, and staff in these facilities. Designers also need to consider that healthcare staff recruitment and retention is a top priority throughout the industry. If systems underperform or fail, the results will likely include lower patient and staff satisfaction levels, lost revenue, and tarnished market image. Designers need to provide reliable systems that an owner is capable of operating properly and maintaining year after year.

QA10   *Maintenance Tasks* (Climate Zones: all)

An important step in maintaining optimal energy performance is to make sure that scheduled maintenance tasks are implemented that include steps that will focus on energy consumption. The following is a sample plan for a building:

- Daily Tasks
  - Review electric, steam, and chilled-water consumption profiles and compare to target
  - Review BAS change logs to identify any critical setpoint changes
  - Review alarm list for issues
  - Review BAS information to assure all points are functional
  - Review setpoint versus actual in morning and afternoon to identify poor performing spaces (temperature >3° from setpoint)
- Weekly Tasks
  - Review weekly trends on air handlers, hot-water valve performance, supply and exhaust air trends, box-count trends (boxes that exceed 90% heating or cooling loop-out)
- Monthly Tasks
  - Coordinate and assist on any critical point calibrations
  - Tour off hours for unoccupied performance of lights and equipment
  - Provide staff education on an energy saving topic
- Semiannual
  - Calibrate hot- and chilled-water temperature sensors
  - Calibrate and check economizer sensors and damper operations
- Annual
  - Calibrate large air-handler discharge temperature sensors if used for control
  - Steam trap maintenance

- As needed
  - Assist in controls replacements
  - Quality control preventive maintenance on critical equipment

Developing an energy preventive maintenance program can be included in routine maintenance. This approach provides a regular opportunity to review performance and ensure that major energy-consuming equipment is well maintained.

Regular staff education is an important aspect of the program. Staff engagement and performance is critical to program success. Training provides staff knowledge to make the right changes to achieve the desired result. Most importantly, technicians have to be taught to solve underlying issues rather than making changes to setpoints every time a complaint arises. Systems are placed into service fully balanced and should be rebalanced periodically or whenever space-use changes warrant. Too many setpoint changes cause unintended consequences and make it very difficult to maintain either user comfort or energy efficiency.

QA11   *Heat-Pump Maintenance* (Climate Zones: all)

Installation of a heat-pump system (see HV2) in a hospital needs to be carefully planned. Heat pumps present additional challenges in the patient care environment that may not be apparent.

Heat pumps require maintenance semiannually or quarterly depending on manufacturer. Typical maintenance includes filter change, inspection of condensate pans to make sure they are clean and that there is no microbial growth occurring in these systems, and condensate trap prime check. The heat exchanger must also be kept as dust free as possible in order to maintain efficiency. The location must be carefully selected to minimize interruption to clinical operations. Options for locations include above ceiling locations in either the room or zone served or in the corridor. Other organizations have placed these units in service closets that allow access outside of the room served.

While heat-pump maintenance tasks are not technically challenging, technicians do need to receive training that differs from systems traditionally found in the large hospital environment. Because heat pumps function at point of service, there are more of them, and it takes longer to maintain them than it does a central system. Hospitals need to plan their maintenance staffing accordingly. Additionally, maintenance technicians need to be more aware of infection control procedures than they are for central systems, because the area where the maintenance is performed is closer to the patient population.

Many heat-pump failures require replacement of the unit. The room or zone served by the unit may not be usable until the unit is replaced. It is strongly recommended that the hospital have several spare units for each installed size to maintain full room and space use. Review with suppliers the typical lead time for replacement units. When servicing units above ceiling, use of control cubes is required to limit infection exposures to patients and staff.

Care must be taken to make sure that heat pumps are operating in ranges that minimize condensing at the unit. Even with drain pans, if the systems routinely condense, the likelihood of microbial growth exists.

MEASUREMENT AND VERIFICATION

QA12   *Monitor Postoccupancy Performance* (Climate Zones: all)

Established measurement and verification procedures for actual building performance after commissioning can help identify when corrective action and/or repair is required to maintain energy performance. Utility consumption and related factors should be monitored and recorded to establish building performance during the first year of operation.

Variations in utility use can be justified based on changes in conditions that affect energy consumption, such as weather, occupancy, operational schedule, maintenance procedures, and equipment operations required by these conditions. While most buildings covered in this Guide will not use a formal measurement and verification process, tracking the specific parameters listed above does allow owners to quickly review utility bills and changes in conditions. Poor performance is generally obvious to the reviewer when comparing the various parameters. CxA/QA providers can help owners understand when operational tolerances are exceeded and can provide assistance in defining what actions may be required to return the building to peak performance.

Another purpose of the postoccupancy evaluation (POE) is to determine actual energy performance of low-energy buildings to verify design goals and document real world energy savings. Additionally, the POE provides lessons learned regarding design, technologies, operation, and analysis techniques to ensure current and future buildings operate at a high level of performance over time. For details and some case studies and lessons learned, refer to NREL's published report (Torcellini et al. 2006).

QA13 Measurement and Verification Electrical Panel Guidance (Climate Zones: all)

Designing the electrical distribution system to be submetered reduces complexity, minimizes the number of meters, shortens installation time, and minimizes rewiring. Disaggregate your electrical panels (put lights together on one panel, HVAC on another, miscellaneous loads on a third, etc.), and repeat for emergency circuits. Meter as much as possible at the main distribution panel and repeat for emergency circuits to minimize installation and wiring costs. Consider using electrical panels with integral submeters to reduce capital costs. Integrate testing of the meters into your commissioning plan to ensure that the submetering system is operating correctly.

QA14 Measurement and Verification Data Management and Access (Climate Zones: all)

Detailed M&V systems can results in an overwhelming amount of data. The success of an M&V system depends on proper management of this data. Collect submetered data at resolutions appropriate for the intended use. For example, save one-minute data for one day to aid equipment troubleshooting and identifying failures, save data at five-minute intervals for one week to help analyze the building schedules, and save 15-minute data for at least one year to help with benchmarking, to determine annual energy performance, to compare to the original energy model (weather variance removed), and to compare end-use benchmarks. In general, make sure you have sufficient data resolution to determine electricity demand information and equipment failures.

To ensure ease of interoperability and consistency with other submetering efforts in your district, comply with your district's metering standard. If one does not exist, consider developing a metering standard that documents interoperability and accessibility requirements. In addition, allow for external consultants and design team members to easily access the metered data remotely.

QA15 Measurement and Verification Benchmarking (Climate Zones: all)

An owner should benchmark utility bills and submetered data to ensure that energy performance targets are met and should be prepared to repeat this exercise monthly. CxA and quality assurance providers can typically help owners understand when operational tolerances are exceeded and can help determine actions to return the building to peak performance. By benchmarking your facility, poor performance can be identified in multiple ways. Submetered data can be benchmarked against previous trends, energy models, or other facilities with submetered data. Monthly energy performance should be benchmarked against historic performance and other facilities in the district. Annual energy performance should be benchmarked using ENERGYSTAR Portfolio Manager and the energy targets provided in this Guide (see Chapter 4).

REFERENCES AND RESOURCES

ASHRAE. 2002. ASHRAE Guideline 14, *Measurement of Energy and Demand Savings.* Atlanta: ASHRAE.

ASHRAE. 2005. ASHRAE Guideline 0-2005, *The Commissioning Process*. Atlanta: ASHRAE.

ASHRAE. 2007. ASHRAE Guideline 1.1-2007, *HVAC&R Technical Requirements for The Commissioning Process*. Atlanta: ASHRAE.

DOE. 2011. Federal Energy Management Program. Energy Savings Performance Contracts. U.S. Department of Energy, Washington, DC. http://www1.eere.energy.gov/femp/financing/espcs.html.

EPA. 2011. ENERGY STAR. Portfolio Manager Overview. U.S. Environmental Protection Agency, U.S. Department of Energy, Washington, DC. http://www.energystar.gov/index.cfm?c=evaluate_performance.bus_portfoliomanager.

DOE. 2002. International Performance Measurement & Verification Protocol: Concepts and Options for Determining Energy and Water Savings—Volume I. Washington, DC: U.S. Department of Energy. DOE/GO-102002-1554. http://www.nrel.gov/docs/fy02osti/31505.pdf.

Kenneday, M., R. Ross, C. Seekman, and E. Tinsley. 2010. *Health Facility Commissioning Guidelines*. Chicago: American Society for Healthcare Engineering.

Mills, E., H. Friedman, T. Power, N. Bourassa, D. Claridge, T. Haasl, and M.A. Porter. 2004. The Cost-Effectiveness of Commercial Building Commissioning: A Meta-Analysis of Energy and Non-Energy Impacts in Existing Buildings and New Construction in the United States. LBNL Report No. 56637, Lawrence Berkeley National Laboratory, Berkley, CA.

Nexant. 2008. M&V Guidelines: Measurement and Verification for Federal Energy Projects: Version 3.0. Prepared for the U.S. Department of Energy Federal Energy Management Program. Boulder, CO: Nexant, Inc. http://www1.eere.energy.gov/femp/pdfs/mv_guidelines.pdf.

Torcellini et al. 2006. *Lessons Learned from Case Studies of Six High-Performance Buildings*. National Renewable National Laboratory. NRETL/TP-55-037542. 2006. Golden, Colorado.

ADDITIONAL BONUS SAVINGS

OTHER HVAC STRATEGIES

HV41   *Radiant Heating and Cooling with Displacement Ventilation* (Climate Zones: B Climates Only)

In this system, a high-efficiency chilled-water system distributes water to radiant cooling panels or to tubing imbedded in floor slabs in each thermal zone to provide local cooling. Ventilation air is provided by a DOAS. The energy efficiency of this system derives from the following characteristics:

- The surface area of the systems allows heating and cooling loads to be met with very low temperature hot water and relatively high-temperature chilled water. Chilled water is typically supplied to the system at a minimum temperature of 60°F, while heating loads can usually be met with a maximum hot-water temperature of 95°F.
- Heating or cooling energy is transferred to the space with no energy expenditure for moving air. Heat transfer is entirely by natural convection and radiant means.
- Using radiant heating/cooling allows reduction of patient room airflow to either
    a. four total air changes per hour based on the entire room volume or
    b. six total air changes per hour based on the volume from the finished floor to 6 ft. above the floor, when using Group D (displacement ventilation [DV]) diffusers.
- Use of displacement ventilation is limited to patient rooms and rooms that do not need to comply with ASHRAE/ASHE Standard 170.

Radiant heating and cooling systems may be implemented through the use of ceiling-mounted radiant panels that affix water tubing to a ceiling tile. This tubing is served by water piping above the ceiling. Automatic valves control water flow to sections of the ceiling to provide temperature control in the space. If the ceiling radiant system is used for both heating and cooling, the ceiling may be divided into interior and perimeter zones with four pipes (hot and chilled water) to the perimeter zones.

Design of radiant systems that incorporate cooling is a specialized task that should only be undertaken with experienced engineering input. Issues of temperature control, load response, condensation avoidance, etc., are likely to be peculiar to each project and may require custom solutions.

Design recommendations for implementing radiant heating/cooling with DV in patient rooms include the following:

- The cooling capacity of a DV system is limited by the minimum allowable supply air temperature required to maintain thermal comfort.
- Room thermal gains and losses must be controlled if the performance of the DV system is to be maintained:
  a. Façades should be designed to minimize the thermal gains and losses to prevent warm and cold surfaces, especially with respect to glazing. The warm surfaces could affect the DV airflow.
  b. Manual or automatic solar shading devices should be installed to minimize/eliminate direct solar gains. Field tests showed that floor surfaces warmed by direct solar gains can act as a thermal hot spot, creating localized thermal chimneys and causing most of the displacement supply air to short circuit the breathing level.
  c. Lighting and medical equipment loads should be minimized.
- DV should not be used for space heating:
  a. Providing supply air from the low sidewall displacement diffuser at a higher temperature than the room's temperature results in decreased performance of the DV system.
  b. When using a supplemental heating method, such as radiant or convective baseboard heating, the performance of the DV can be maintained if not improved.
- The placement of the supply air diffuser is not critical but should be coordinated with the room design. The diffuser should be located at low level in a location that will not be blocked with solid furniture such as a storage cabinet.
- The toilet transfer grille should be located at high level. Experience has shown that the DV effect/pluming/high-level removal of airborne particles can be seriously affected if the supply air is allowed to short circuit at low level directly into the toilet room.

Another form of the radiant heating and cooling system uses polymer tubing imbedded in concrete floor slabs. This approach has been applied to radiant heating for a number of years but recently has also been extended to space cooling. The primary issue for floor-slab radiant heating and cooling is changeover between the two modes of operation. Control systems must be designed with a significant deadband so that rapid changeover (with time-lagged system "fighting" in the slab) can be avoided. Typically, radiant heating and cooling floor-slab systems should not be controlled directly by air thermostats, because transient conditions may result in frequent changeover. Use room thermostats to reset slab temperatures within a range, but be aware that rapid changeover is still a problem to overcome. Well-designed systems take advantage of the thermal capacitance of the floor slab to mitigate transient loads and provide consistent interior comfort conditions.

Radiant ceilings are less effective for space heating than are radiant floors, while radiant floors are less effective for space cooling, except for offsetting cooling loads from direct solar gain on the cooling floor. Radiant floor slabs over a ceiling plenum can transfer as much heat to that plenum as to the space above the radiant slab. Radiant ceilings are more often seen in patient rooms, operating rooms, and office spaces, while radiant floors are often seen in spaces at grade level, such as lobbies, atriums, and some circulation spaces.

The radiant system, however, provides only sensible heating and cooling. All humidity control (both dehumidification and humidification) must be provided by a DOAS. In some cases, the required dew-point temperature of the incoming ventilation air may be lower than common practice in order to achieve the necessary dehumidification. For radiant cooling systems, especially in humid climates, avoidance of condensation on the cooling surfaces is the most important design consideration. Mechanisms for avoiding condensation include the following:

- Control of entering dew-point temperature of ventilation air to meet maximum interior air dew-point temperature limits
- Design of radiant cooling systems to meet sensible cooling loads with elevated (>60°F) chilled-water temperatures
- Monitoring of space dew-point temperature with radiant system shutdown upon detection of elevated space dew-point temperature
- Design of building envelope systems to minimize infiltration and construction-phase quality control of envelope systems to meet infiltration specifications (refer to section on building envelope pressure testing)
- Omission of radiant cooling elements from areas immediately surrounding exterior doors
- Provision of excess dehumidified ventilation air adjacent to likely sources of exterior air infiltration
- Condensation detection on chilled-water supply pipes connecting to radiant panels

Passive chilled beams behave similarly to radiant chilled ceilings. The same issues of condensation avoidance and control apply. Passive chilled beams are also relatively ineffective for space heating.

HV42   *Combined Heat and Power* (Climate Zones: all)

Combined heating and power (CHP) is particularly suited for applications involving distributed power generation. Buildings requiring their own power generation must also satisfy various thermal loads. A conventional fossil-fuel-fired boiler and/or electric chiller can be displaced to some extent, if not entirely, by a heat recovery device and/or an absorption chiller driven by the waste heat from the power generator. Since the source of heating and/or cooling is waste heat that would ordinarily have been rejected to the surroundings, the operating cost of meeting the thermal demand of the building is significantly mitigated if not eliminated.

Economic analyses suggest that CHP systems are ideally suited for base-loaded distributed power generation and steady thermal (heating and/or cooling) loading. The thermal and power generation "loads" should coincide for the recovered energy to be economically viable. In addition, emissions from the power generating equipment, as well as acoustics, should be addressed early in the project planning process, since codes may impose limits on each. Additionally, the system will need to interact with the local utility and may be affected by utility regulations.

Once it is clear that codes, site, and utility are addressed, relative local fuel costs should be used to determine the return on investment of the CHP system.

HV43   *Fan Arrays* (Climate Zones: all)

Fan choices affect both healthcare HVAC system energy use and asepsis. From a thermodynamic standpoint, there are advantages to systems with blow-through cooling coils. The disadvantage is that, when the final filters that are required for many healthcare systems are exposed to 100% rh air, the filters become wet, which may result in increased pressure drop and wet filters that may become moldy.

Two viable alternatives are desiccant systems (refer to HV18) and systems that use draw-through coil arrangements. These add the fan heat to the air prior to it passing through the filters so that it is not 100% saturated.

Even with draw-through systems, air entering a filter bank leads to a second problem related to pressure drop. When a conventional centrifugal fan discharges through a plenum with a filter bank downstream (ASHRAE/ASHE Standard 170 requires that the second filter bank be downstream of the fan), the air must be distributed evenly across the filters. Distributing this air evenly usually involves two pressure drops. The first is the fan discharging into the plenum. (For a backward-inclined airfoil (BIAF) centrifugal fan, this is a loss of velocity pressure.) The second is for a baffle plate or other air-distribution device to distribute air evenly over the filters.

One way to avoid these pressure drops is to use fan arrays—two or more plenum fans enclosed in acoustic baffle assemblies. Plenum fans normally have similar static efficiencies as BIAF fans, so there is no efficiency difference between the two in that respect, but plenum fans have the advantage that no airstream baffle is needed to evenly distribute the air. Also, the acoustic baffles usually eliminate the need for the pressure drop of silencers downstream of the fan, and there is redundancy due to the use of multiple fans.

HV44   *Evaporative Condensing* (Climate Zones: all)

Some air-conditioning equipment (most commonly packaged DX equipment) can be equipped with evaporative condensers. Hot refrigerant vapor flows through tubes and outdoor air is drawn or blown over the tubes by a fan. Water is sprayed on the outer surfaces of the tubes and, as air passes over the tubes, a small portion of the water evaporates. This evaporation process absorbs heat, causing the refrigerant vapor inside the tubes to condense into a liquid. The remaining water then falls into a sump, where a pump recirculates it to be used again. The water that evaporates in this process must continuously be replaced with fresh water.

In a conventional air-cooled condenser, the refrigerant condensing temperature is dependent on the dry-bulb temperature of the ambient air. In an evaporative condenser, the condensing temperature is dependent on the wet-bulb temperature. This lowers the condensing temperature (pressure), which reduces the energy used by the compressor.

Evaporative condensers require more maintenance than air-cooled condensers and are typically more expensive and heavier. In addition, in subfreezing climates, they require freeze protection.

HV45   *Water-Restricted Locations* (Climate Zones: all)

Some locations lack water. Due to their critical nature hospitals often require the capability to operate up to 96 hours without any outside services or utilities being available. For water-cooled systems, a critical utility is make-up water for cooling towers.

In such locations, a substitution of air-cooled chillers may be made, but this choice may increase the energy use of these systems. Water-cooled systems are more efficient at design conditions, since the chiller condensing pressure in a water-cooled system (dependent on outdoor wet-bulb temperature) is considerably lower than in an air-cooled system (dependent on outdoor dry-bulb temperature). In locations where the diurnal dry-bulb temperature drops more than the wet-bulb temperature, this energy difference is reduced at night.

In water-restricted locations, water costs are generally high. This coupled with air-cooled chillers requiring no water treatment can help can offset some of the cost issues related to increased energy use.

RENEWABLE ENERGY

RE1   *Photovoltaic (PV) Systems* (Climate Zones: all)

Photovoltaic (PV) systems have become an increasingly popular option for on-site electric energy production. These systems require very little maintenance and generally have long lives.

Options for installing PV systems include rooftop mounted (including collectors integrated with the roofing membrane), ground mounted, or as the top of a covered parking system, or PV integrated in sunshades, in fenestration or on spandrels. The systems may be fixed mounted or tracking. Each installation method offers different combinations of advantages and disadvantages.

RE2 *Solar Hot-Water Systems* (Climate Zones: all)

Simple solar systems are most efficient when they generate heat at low temperatures. Service water preheating offers an excellent opportunity in healthcare facilities. Because of the relatively high SWH demands in many healthcare facilities, solar hot-water systems often provide economically justifiable energy savings. Combined space heating and domestic hot-water systems may also be beneficial.

General suggestions for solar domestic hot-water heating systems include the following:

- It is typically not economical to design solar systems to satisfy the full annual load.
- Systems are typically most economical if they furnish 50%–80% of the annual load.
- Properly sized systems will meet the full load on the best solar day of the year.
- Approximately 1–2 gal of storage should be provided per square foot of collector.
- 1 ft^2 of collector heats about 1 gal per day of service water at 44° latitude.
- Glazed flat plate systems often cost in the range of $100 to $150 per square foot of collector.
- Collectors do not have to face due south. They receive 94% of the maximum annual solar energy if they are 45° east or west of due south.
- The optimal collector tilt for service water applications is approximately equal to the latitude where the building is located; however, variations of ±20° only reduce the total energy collected about 5%. This is one reason that many collector installations are flat to a pitched roof instead of supported on stands.
- The optimal collector tilt for building heating (not domestic water heating) systems is approximately the latitude of the building plus 15°.

Collectors can still function on cloudy days to varying degrees depending on the design, but they perform better in direct sunlight; collectors should not be placed in areas that are frequently shaded.

Solar systems in most climates require freeze protection. The two common types of freeze protection are systems that contain antifreeze and drainback systems.

Drainback solar hot-water systems are often selected in small applications where the piping can be sloped back toward a collection tank. By draining the collection loop, freeze protection is accomplished when the pump shuts down, either intentionally or unintentionally. This avoids the heat transfer penalties of antifreeze solutions.

Closed-loop, freeze-resistant solar systems should be used when piping layouts make drainback systems impractical.

In both systems, a pump circulates water or antifreeze solution through the collection loop when there is adequate solar radiation and a need for service water heat.

Solar collectors for service water applications are usually flat plate or evacuated tube type. Flat plate units are typically less expensive. Evacuated tube designs can produce higher temperatures because they have less standby loss but also can pack with snow and, if fluid flow stops, are more likely to reach temperatures that can degrade antifreeze solutions.

Annual savings can be estimated using performance data from the Solar Rating and Certification Corporation Web site (www.solarrating.org/ratings/rating.htm). A free downloadable program called RETScreen from Natural Resources Canada (www.retscreen.net) can assist with economic feasibility analysis, and many utility rebate programs use it in calculating rebates or determining eligibility. The first cost of the system must be estimated.

RE3 *Wind Turbine Power* (Climate Zones: all)

Wind energy is one of the lowest-priced renewable energy technologies available today, costing between 5 to 11 cents per kilowatt-hour, depending on the wind resource and financing of the particular project. Small- to medium-size wind turbines are typically considered for hospitals.

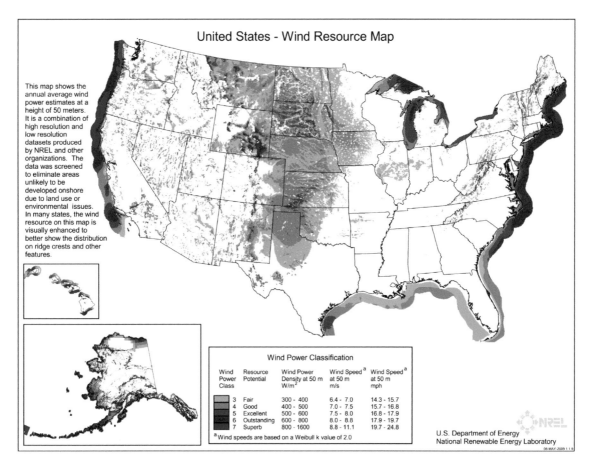

Figure 5-37 (RE3) Average annual wind power estimates.
Source: National Renewable Energy Laboratory (NREL), U.S. Department of Energy (DOE), Wind Powering America
(www.windpoweringamerica.gov/wind_maps.asp)

These turbines range from 4 to 200 kW and are typically mounted on towers from 50 to 100 ft and connected to the utility grid through the building's electrical distribution system.

One of the first steps to developing a wind energy project is to assess the area's wind resources and estimate the available energy. From wind resource maps, one can determine if an area of interest should be further explored. Note that the wind resource at a microlevel can vary significantly; therefore, one should obtain professional evaluation of a specific area of interest.

The map in Figure 5-37 shows the annual average wind power estimates at 50 m above ground. It combines high- and low-resolution datasets that have been screened to eliminate land-based areas unlikely to be developed due to land use or environmental issues. In many states, the wind resource has been visually enhanced to better show the distribution on ridge crests and other features. Estimates of the wind resource are expressed in wind power classes ranging from Class 1 (lowest) to Class 7 (highest), with each class representing a range of mean wind power density or equivalent mean speed at specified heights above the ground. This map does not show Classes 1 and 2, as Class 2 areas are marginal and Class 1 areas are unsuitable for wind energy development. In general, at 50 m, wind power Class 4 or higher can be useful for generating wind power. More detailed state wind maps are available at www.windpoweringamerica.gov/wind_maps.asp.

Although the wind turbines themselves do not take up a significant amount of space, they need to be installed an adequate distance from the nearest building for several reasons, including turbulence reduction (which affects efficiency), noise control, and safety. It is essential that coordination occurs between the owner, design team, and site planner to establish the optimal wind turbine location relative to the other facilities on the site.

The three largest complaints about wind turbines are noise, the killing of birds, and aesthetics. Most of these problems have been resolved or greatly reduced through technological development or by properly siting wind turbines. Most small wind turbines today have an excellent safety record. An important factor is to consider how the wind turbine controls itself and shuts itself down. Can operators shut it off and stop the turbine when they want or need to do so? This is extremely important, and unfortunately there are very few small turbines that have reliable means to stop the rotor on command. The few that do may require you to do so from the base of the tower—not exactly where you want to be if the turbine is out of control in a wind storm. Look for a system that offers one or more means to shut down and preferably stop the rotor remotely.

Using energy modeling, the electric energy consumption of the building can be modeled. Using this data in conjunction with the financial details of the project, including rebates, the owner and designer must choose the correct size of turbine to meet their needs. Note that the closer the match of the turbine energy output to the demand, the more cost effective the system will be. Make sure that all costs are listed to give a total cost of ownership for the wind turbine. This includes the wind turbine, tower, electrical interconnection, controls, installation, maintenance, concrete footings, guy wires, and cabling.

In addition to evaluating the initial cost of the turbine, it is extremely important to consider the federal and state policies and incentive programs that are available. The database for state incentives for renewables and efficiency (www.dsireusa.org) provides a list of available incentives, grants, and rebates. Also critical to the financial success of a wind turbine project is a favorable net metering agreement with the utility.

RE4 *Power Purchase Agreements* (Climate Zones: all)

A primary barrier to the use of various on-site renewable energy strategies is the high initial capital investment cost. One way to finance and thus implement such a strategy is the power purchase agreement. This arrangement involves a third party who designs, installs, owns, operates, and maintains the power generation asset. The healthcare facility then contracts to purchase the energy produced by the generation system, usually for a long period of time. This arrangement not only allows the facility to avoid the high first cost, it also keeps the balance sheet clear of obligation and locks in an energy price, thus hedging the cost of energy over time from fluctuations in the prices of other energy sources. These agreements are especially attractive to nonprofit organizations who cannot access tax-based incentives that help to offset the cost of renewable systems. These agreements are complicated, with many considerations, and require negotiation by people familiar with the complexities, both from an engineering as well as from legal and financial perspectives.

ELECTRICAL DISTRIBUTION SYSTEMS

ED1 *Transformer Efficiency* (Climate Zones: all)

The use of energy-efficient transformers can provide additional energy savings. The Energy Policy Act of 2005 (U.S. Congress 2005) established minimum energy-efficiency standards for low-voltage, dry-type distribution transformers and specifies that any such transformer manufactured after January 1, 2007, "shall be the Class I Efficiency Levels for distribution transformers specified in Table 4-2 of the *Guide for Determining Energy Efficiency for Distribution Transformers* (NEMA 2002). These specifications are referred to by DOE as "TP-1" and are the lowest efficiency available today (DOE 2004).

Energy-efficient transformers that are roughly 30% more efficient than the minimum TP-1 were classified by DOE as Candidate Standard Level 3 (CSL-3). It is recommended that all low-voltage, dry-type distribution transformers (single phase or three phase) used in small hospital and healthcare facility construction meet the CSL-3 efficiency specifications.

The use of the CSL-3 efficiency classification will improve the energy efficiency of distribution transformers. This efficiency classification recognizes the low loading and no-load losses with current transformer design. The classification includes details on the no-load losses for specific-size transformers and specific percent efficiencies at given loadings. For example, a CSL-3 75 KVA 277/480 to 120/208 V transformer maximum no load loss is 170 W/h versus the pre-2007 industry average of more than 850 W/h. This same transformer meets or exceeds 98.4% efficiency at one-sixth loading. The efficiency of the pre-2007 standard transformers specified at one-sixth loading is 80% to 85%.

Energy-efficient transformers should be specified using DOE's CSL-3 classification efficiencies as the basis. Specifications must include maximum no-load losses for specified transformer sizes and percent efficiencies at 16.7% loading. A statement should be included in the specifications that requires the bid submission to include test data for the transformers being provided.

ED2   *System Design* (Climate Zones: all)

Electrical distribution design can affect energy consumption, at least at the margins. Distribution systems can impact voltage drop across both transformers and conductors, and all such losses represent needless energy consumption. In general, a system consisting of shorter, larger conductors results in lower overall energy loss. On the other hand, sizing transformers larger than the load results in underloading and energy loss. Similarly, higher-voltage systems for a given load result in lower overall losses. The right balance between higher voltage distribution and transformer location, coupled with larger, shorter feeders and more closely tailored transformer sizing minimizes useless system energy losses.

ED3   *Metering* (Climate Zones: all)

Distribution systems can also facilitate or complicate the metering and submetering of energy within the building, thus making the building easier or more difficult to tune to optimal performance. Experience has shown that simply paying attention to energy consumption can change behaviors and help the building staff to improve and optimize the operation of the building, including achieving lowest energy consumption. And, the cost of metering systems coupled with advances in energy control systems make it easier and less expensive to provide more extensive metering systems. Project teams, using integrated design, should involve the building operating staff in helping to plan the distribution system so as to optimize the appropriate metering facilities to achieve optimal performance. Design the electrical distribution system to make submetering easier, rather than more difficult.

Provide submetering for the following electrical and mechanical systems (as applicable to the scope of the project): lighting systems, plant loads, air distribution systems, voice/data systems, emergency power systems, and large process loads (i.e., kitchen, imaging areas, etc.).

Appendix A— Envelope Thermal Performance Factors

Each recommendation table in Chapter 4 presents a prescriptive construction option for each opaque envelope measure. Table A-1 presents U-factors for above-grade components, C-factors for below-grade walls, and F-factors for slab-on-grade floors that correspond to each prescriptive construction option. Alternative constructions would be equivalent methods for meeting the recommendations of this Guide provided they are less than or equal to the thermal performance factors listed in Table A-1.

Table A-1   Opaque Construction Options

Roof Assemblies	
R	U
Insulation Above Deck	
20	0.048
25	0.039
30	0.032
35	0.028

Slabs	
R - in.	F
Unheated	
10 - 24	0.54
20 - 24	0.51
Heated	
7.5 - 12	1.02
10 - 24	0.90
15 - 24	0.86
20 - 24	0.843
20 - 48	0.688
25 - 48	0.671
20 full slab	0.373

Walls, Above Grade	
R	U
Mass Walls	
5.7	0.151
7.6	0.123
11.4	0.090
13.3	0.080
19.5	0.062
Steel Framed	
13 + 7.5 c.i.	0.064
13 + 15.6 c.i.	0.042
13 + 18.8 c.i.	0.037

Walls, Below Grade	
R	C
7.5 c.i.	0.119
10.0 c.i.	0.092
15.0 c.i.	0.067

Floors	
R	C
Mass	
4.2 c.i.	0.137
10.4 c.i.	0.074
12.5 c.i.	0.064
14.6 c.i.	0.056
16.7 c.i.	0.051
20.9 c.i.	0.042
23.0 c.i.	0.038
Steel Framed	
19	0.052
30	0.038
38	0.032
49	0.027
60	0.024

C = thermal conductance, Btu/h·ft^2·°F
c.i. = continuous insulation
F = slab edge heat loss coefficient per foot of perimeter, Btu/h·ft·°F
FC = filled cavity
Ls = liner system
R = thermal resistance, h·ft^2·°F/Btu
R - in. = R-value followed by the depth of insulation in inches
U = thermal transmittance, Btu/h·ft^2·°F

Appendix B— International Climatic Zone Definitions

Table B-1 shows the climate zone definitions that are applicable to any location. The information is from ASHRAE/IESNA Standard 90.1-2007, Normative Appendix B, Table B-4 (ASHRAE 2007). Climate zone information for specific cities in Canada, Mexico, and other international cities can be found in the same appendix and is also available on the AEDG Web page (www.ashrae.org/aedg) in the "Additional Information" section. Weather data is needed in order to use the climate zone definitions for a particular city. Weather data by city is available for a large number of international cities in 2009 *ASHRAE Handbook—Fundamentals* (ASHRAE 2009).

Table B-1   International Climatic Zone Definitions

Climate Zone Number	Name	Thermal Criteria*
1A and 1B	Very Hot–Humid (1A) Dry (1B)	$9000 < CDD50°F$
2A and 2B	Hot–Humid (2A) Dry (2B)	$6300 < CDD50°F \leq 9000$
3A and 3B	Warm–Humid (3A) Dry (3B)	$4500 < CDD50°F \leq 6300$
3C	Warm–Marine (3C)	$CDD50°F \leq 4500$ AND $HDD65°F \leq 3600$
4A and 4B	Mixed–Humid (4A) Dry (4B)	$CDD50°F \leq 4500$ AND $3600 < HDD65°F \leq 5400$
4C	Mixed–Marine (4C)	$3600 < HDD65°F \leq 5400$
5A, 5B, and 5C	Cool–Humid (5A) Dry (5B) Marine (5C)	$5400 < HDD65°F \leq 7200$
6A and 6B	Cold–Humid (6A) Dry (6B)	$7200 < HDD65°F \leq 9000$
7	Very Cold	$9000 < HDD65°F \leq 12600$
8	Subarctic	$12600 < HDD65°F$

*CDD = cooling degree day, HDD = heating degree-day.

DEFINITIONS

Marine (C) Definition—Locations meeting all four of the following criteria:

- Mean temperature of coldest month between 27°F and 65°F
- Warmest month mean < 72°F
- At least four months with mean temperatures over 50°F
- Dry season in summer. The month with the heaviest precipitation in the cold season has at least three times as much precipitation as the month with the least precipitation in the rest of the year. The cold season is October through March in the Northern Hemisphere and April through September in the Southern Hemisphere.

Dry (B) Definition—Locations meeting the following criterion:

- Not marine and $P < 0.44 \times (T - 19.5)$
  where
  P = annual precipitation, in.
  T = annual mean temperature, °F

Moist (A) Definition—Locations that are not marine and not dry.

REFERENCES

ASHRAE. 2007. ANSI/ASHRAE/IESNA Standard 90.1-2007, *Energy Standard for Buildings Except Low-Rise Residential Buildings*. Atlanta: American Society of Heating, Refrigerating and Air-Conditioning Engineers.

ASHRAE. 2009. *ASHRAE Handbook—Fundamentals*. Atlanta: American Society of Heating, Refrigerating and Air-Conditioning Engineers. [Available in print form and on CD-ROM.]